ENVIRONMENT, POPULATION AND DEVELOPMENT

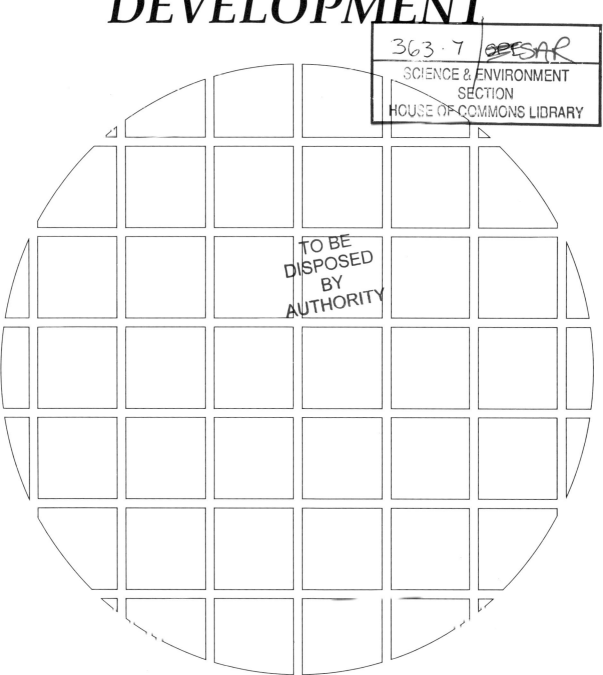

This book is the second in a series published by Hodder and Stoughton in association with The Open University.

Environment and Society
edited by Jonathan Silvertown and Philip Sarre

Environment, Population and Development
edited by Philip Sarre

Energy, Resources and Environment
edited by John Blunden and Alan Reddish

Global Environmental Issues
edited by Paul M. Smith and Kiki Warr

The final form of the text is the joint responsibility of chapter authors, book editors and course team commentators.

The books are one component of the Open University course U206 *Environment*. Details of the course are available from the Student Enquiries Office, The Open University, PO Box 71, Milton Keynes MK7 6AG.

ENVIRONMENT, POPULATION AND DEVELOPMENT

EDITED BY PHILIP SARRE
FOR AN OPEN UNIVERSITY COURSE TEAM

Hodder &
Stoughton

LONDON   SYDNEY   AUCKLAND   TORONTO

IN ASSOCIATION WITH

The Open
University

This book has been printed on non-chlorine bleached paper, produced in
Sweden from wood from continuously farmed forests. Independent tests by the
Swedish Environmental Research Group confirm that the paper mill concerned,
Papyrus Nymölla AB, is the first and so far the only pulp mill producing
bleached pulp in which dioxin contaminants do not occur.

British Library Cataloguing-in-Publication Data

Environment, population and development.
  – (Environment)
  I. Sarre, Dr Philip   II. Series
  333.7

  ISBN 0–340–53360–9

First published in the United Kingdom 1991

Designed by the Graphic Design Group of the Open University

Typeset by Keyset Composition, Colchester, Essex

Printed in the United Kingdom for Hodder and Stoughton Educational, a division
of Hodder and Stoughton Ltd., Mill Road, Dunton Green, Sevenoaks, Kent by
Butler & Tanner Ltd, Frome and London.

Contents

This book is the second in a series of four which presents an interdisciplinary and integrated explanation of environmental issues. Throughout it is stressed that environmental issues are complex and that to understand them one must combine scientific evidence and theory, analysis of social processes, knowledge of technological possibilities and awareness of underlying value positions. The series considers a range of environmental issues, some local, many transnational and some global. In doing so, it aims to widen readers' *awareness* of environmental issues, to deepen their ability to *analyse* them and to equip them to *evaluate* policies to influence them. It stresses that solutions to particular problems should be complementary with, and ideally contributory to, the solution of international and global problems, including global warming.

The first book, *Environment and Society*, explores three aspects of the context within which contemporary environmental issues occur, and teaches basic concepts and skills to be applied to understand environmental problems. The first aspect is the ecological analysis of life on Earth, stressing the role of living things in modifying the environment through geological time, the variety of life-forms and their mutual dependence. The second aspect is the impact of human societies on environments over millennia and the greatly augmented power, for good or ill, of technological society. The third aspect is that of values, considered both from a dispassionate philosophical viewpoint and through the passionate convictions of environmentalist pressure groups. The perspectives explored in the first book remain highly relevant, but later books in the series become more deeply involved in the detail of particular issues which the course team have recognised as of strategic importance in the interaction of society and environment.

This book focuses on population growth and economic development, which have both contributed to environmental change and affected each other. The book starts by considering the growth of the human population, which has doubled since 1950 to a current figure of just over 5 billion, and is likely to double again before it ceases to grow. This growth raises questions about both past and future: how has it been possible to achieve economic development in the past so that larger populations could be supported at higher standards of living and – perhaps more crucially – how might this be done in future without excessive damage to the environment? The book explores these questions in the case of agriculture and urbanisation. In so doing it establishes a paradoxical relationship: population growth has historically been stabilised only in countries which experienced economic and technological development, but development greatly increases the impacts of a given population on the environment.

The analyses in the chapters of the book suggest that the relationships between environment, population and development are rather more complex than they often seem in mass media discussions, particularly because of the paradoxical relationship between population growth and economic development. Chapter 1 confirms that population growth has only been controlled in societies which have experienced rapid economic development – but shows that this does not occur automatically, nor does development lead to more rational environmental management in all cases, as is spelled out for agriculture in Chapters 2, 3 and 4. Demand for food and raw materials has led to dramatic agricultural change, but rather than promoting environmentally friendly forms of intensification, the move has been towards capital-intensive mechanical and chemical inputs which have both over-produced certain commodities and created new problems of land degradation and water pollution. Analysis of agriculture suggests that world economic and political systems are compounding both population and environmental problems. Chapter 5 confirms that British and European agricultural policy has reflected political expediency rather than balancing agricultural output, environmental and wider social goals. However, the collapse of the argument for production at all costs leaves the British countryside open to a range of pressures from new non-agricultural uses, many of which threaten further impacts on the quality of life. The centrality of economic and political processes is confirmed by Chapter 6's analysis of the problems of nineteenth-century industrial cities and the present-day 'inner-city problem'. Chapter 7 examines third world cities, confirms that they face formidable environmental problems and that some aspects of economic and political policy hinder provision of a better environment and quality of life. However, the chapter comes full circle by identifying the rate of population growth and the difficulty of promoting economic development as two crucial obstacles to progress. At present, economic growth is given high priority but this seems to make it inevitable that pollution and resource problems will grow worse in future, with no guarantee that the development will be achieved which is expected to control population numbers and permit higher living standards.

The subsequent books in the series take up two sets of issues arising from this one. *Energy, Resources and Environment* analyses the materials and energy technologies which have been applied in past economic growth, with a critical look at the negative environmental impacts of current systems of supply and demand. Later parts of the book go on to evaluate technical and policy options which are now available, showing that there is room for improvement but that it is not being pursued very energetically. However, a case study of nuclear waste disposal suggests that environmental politics is progressing beyond minority reaction to become a force to be reckoned with. *Global Environmental Issues* uses new and emerging scientific knowledge of global issues, notably atmospheric change (both ozone depletion and greenhouse warming) and management of the oceans, to emphasise the need for the adoption of new policies. Finally, the concept and reality of sustainable development is examined to see whether more equitable and less environmentally damaging approaches to the future are possible.

If such a concept can be delivered, it will inevitably have a lot to say about agriculture, urbanisation and alternative forms of economic development. In effect this will mean coming back to the topics in this book, and in fact the book has been written to try to open up options for the future as well as to explain the present and past.

1 Introduction

Human population growth is not new: at a global level there has been a continuous increase since the late seventeenth and early eighteenth centuries. What is of recent concern is the sustained and accelerating high rates of growth which have been recorded in many countries of the so-called third world (see Box 1.1) during the twentieth century. In 1987 the world's population exceeded five billion (that is, 5000 million or 5×10^9) people and was increasing at about 2% per annum. But what do figures like these mean? In terms of the immensity of the numbers involved it is perhaps easier to think of there being an extra 100 million people to feed and shelter each year. This is a population about twice the size of that living in England in 1981. Population growth is not, however, simply an issue of quantities. Not all of the millions of babies born each year place the same demands on the Earth and its resources. In many respects the 80 million extra people added to the populations of the less developed countries result in a much smaller net impact on their environments than the 20 million extra people living in the wealthier nations. This is so simply because of the differentials in living standards and thus of consumption of the world's resources: ecologists, for example, have estimated that on average a North American baby is 50 times as demanding on the world's resources as an Indian child. Thus the question is whether there is a population problem, a resource problem or an allocation problem.

Some ecologists and conservationists (such as some members of the British Green Party) have argued that faced with a finite planet, a fragile physical environment and a limited resource base, human populations cannot be allowed to continue to grow but must stabilise or be reduced. By contrast some population specialists (demographers) have argued that certain population trends are unavoidable, that rates of world population growth have already peaked and that by the twenty-second century the world's population will once again have stabilised of its own accord, albeit at a much higher level than before. Clearly the debate is a critical one. What attitudes and actions should be adopted concerning the implications of population growth in relationship to environmental change?

This chapter examines these issues by answering three broad questions:

- What is the rate of population growth in different parts of the world?
- How can these differences be explained?
- To what extent are different economic systems and their attendant environments capable of sustaining current population trends?

Section 2 outlines the broad pattern of population growth in different parts of the world. Section 3 looks at several attempts to explain population change: are different rates of population change the result of environmental constraints or problems of food supply? More recent explanations stress the need to account for fertility and mortality independently, and these are the concern of Section 4. Section 5 brings together earlier analyses to argue that population change is closely linked to the nature and extent of economic development and that population policies must take account of economic and social factors if they are to slow current growth rates in a humane fashion.

Box 1.1   The third world: concept and reality

The concept of a third world emerged during the cold war period when many of the countries of the world were divided into two opposed blocs – the first world, consisting of the United States of America and its allies (the liberal-democratic or advanced capitalist countries), and the second world of the USSR and its allies in eastern Europe (the state socialist or command economies). In the early years *political non-alignment* was the characteristic emphasised as typical of the third world, but as time has passed emphasis has shifted to the relatively *low level of economic development* of this group, under such terms as 'developing', 'underdeveloped' or 'less developed' countries.

The very origin of the concept – as the 'leftovers' after the first and second worlds – suggests that this might not be a very clearly defined or homogeneous group. This is also probable given the number of countries involved and their varied histories and geographies. When the United Nations was founded, it had about thirty members which would now be regarded as members of the third world, but this number has quadrupled as former colonies have gained political independence. Today, even omitting China, the third world covers about half the land surface of the Earth and contains somewhat over half the world's population (over half of whom live in chronic poverty), but produces only about one-fifth of the world's goods and services.

In the 1980s it has become common to recognise the great variety of the third world countries by dividing it into sub-groups. For example, the *Encyclopaedia of the Third World* recognises four such groups:

(a) *Petroleum exporters*: following the rise in oil prices in the 1970s a number of third world countries rose rapidly in terms of income per capita; indeed countries with a sparse population like Kuwait, Libya and Saudi Arabia rose to levels associated with first world countries. However, falling oil prices in the 1980s have caused setbacks, especially in oil exporters with large populations, like Mexico, Indonesia and Nigeria.

(b) *Advanced developing countries*, otherwise known as newly industrialising countries: a small number of countries (notably Brazil, South Korea, Taiwan, Hong Kong, Singapore and more recently Thailand) achieved rapid rates of industrial and economic growth in the 1970s and have begun to close the income gap between themselves and the less dynamic economies of the first and second worlds.

(c) *Middle developing countries*: these are another residual category consisting of the third world countries (like Egypt or Peru) which have been neither strikingly successful nor strikingly unsuccessful, with average annual incomes per capita of around a thousand dollars.

(d) *Least developed countries*: sometimes referred to as the fourth world, these 35 countries contain over one third of the world's population (half being in India) but produce only 3% of its wealth. If China is included in spite of its regime, this group would comprise half the world's population. The average annual income of people in these countries is only a few hundred dollars. To make matters worse, members of this group often suffer serious environmental problems from desertification in countries of the Sahel, like Niger and Chad, to frequent and catastrophic flooding in Bangladesh.

Other more complex classifications exist, notably that of the World Bank, but enough has been said to emphasise that the concept of the third world covers a very complex and varied reality. However, that reality should not conceal the fact that most countries in Latin America, Africa and Asia have incomes per capita which are at best a quarter of that of even a relatively poor first world country like the UK. At worst the populations of these countries have hardly enough to maintain a bare subsistence.

Further information about the origins and variability of the third world can be obtained from B. Crow and A. Thomas *et al.* (eds) *The Third World Atlas* (Buckingham, The Open University Press; 1983).

2   The growth of the human population

For most of human history there have only been a few million people living
on the Earth. This is not really surprising since they had to depend on
hunting and gathering activities to meet their food needs. As human beings
gradually developed more advanced methods of meeting their basic needs
for food, clothing and shelter, population numbers began to rise. At first this
seems to have happened in a rather uncertain fashion with the general trend
being upwards, but with crises such as wars, plagues and famines
periodically leading to geographically selective reductions in population
numbers. Two thousand years ago there were perhaps 300 million people on
Earth. It took at least the next 1500 years for the population to double. This
relatively slow rate of growth contrasts starkly with what was to follow. By
the late eighteenth and early nineteenth centuries some parts of the globe
were being introduced to innovative technologies, new economic systems
were being adopted and a radically different social order was emerging. In
parallel with the changes in the structure and organisation of society came
changes in demographic regimes. The result was that between 1750 and
1900 world population size doubled to reach 1.7 billion. Temporal extension
and geographical expansion of forces promoting population increase meant
that, by the twentieth century, population growth rates had accelerated still
further to the point that within the thirty-year period, 1950 to 1980, world
population nearly doubled again to 4.8 billion. Projection of these very rapid
post-war population growth rates produces alarming results, since the
inevitable consequences of the world's population doubling every 30 to 35
years are not only a mushrooming of the numbers of people but an explosion
in the human demands placed upon the global ecosystem. Long-term
extrapolations suggesting, for example, that in 600 years' time there will be
standing room only on the Earth are never likely to be matched by real
population trends, but they do emphasise the finite capacity of the world.
Fortunately projections of this kind are based on statistical extrapolation
without adequate reference to the demographic processes that underpin
population change.

Activity 1

Draw a graph of the growth of world population over time using the
information above. You can check yours against the one at the end of
the chapter.

2.1   Geographical variation in growth rates

Even the most superficial examination of population growth rates for
different parts of the world shows that there are very significant
geographical variations in the rate and character of population change,
illustrating the need to base statements about population trends upon a
more detailed understanding of the processes which account for population
change.

Start by considering Figure 1.1 which maps national population growth rates for the period 1980–1988. It shows that across Europe, the USSR and Canada population increased at less than 1.0% per annum in the 1980s. By contrast in Africa and the Middle East all countries grew at over 2.2% and the majority at over 3.0% per annum. It would be easy to examine Figure 1.1 and to be satisfied with arriving at the generalisation that the more developed countries have very low growth rates and that the developing countries have very high growth rates. The pattern evident in Figure 1.1 indicates, however, that there is great diversity between the developing countries and that they do not share a common **demographic regime** (that is, similar birth and death rates: this will be explained further below). Latin America has much slower population growth rates than Africa while, as Figure 1.1 shows, China grew at only 1.2% per annum between 1980 and 1988. This meant that China's population growth rate was only slightly more than that of the United States during the same period (at 1.0% per annum) and it was lower than Australia's at 1.4% per annum.

Sometimes the impact of population growth rates is illustrated by considering how long it will take a population to double its present size: doubling times are shown in Table 1.1. This shows that the future size of a nation's population is critically determined by its population growth rate rather than by its absolute size. For example, although India's current (1988)

Table 1.1

Annual growth rate (%)	Doubling time (years)
1.0	70
2.0	35
3.0	24
4.0	17

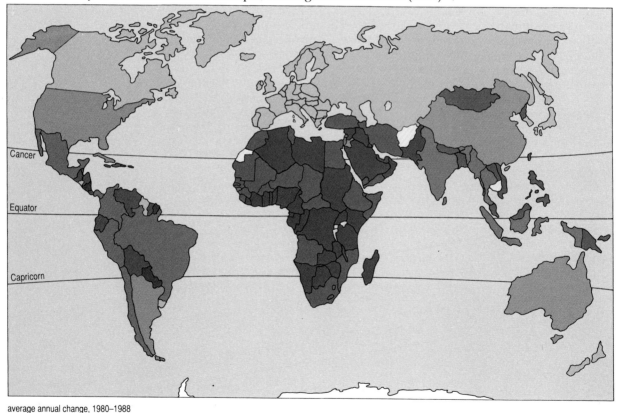

average annual change, 1980–1988

over 3.0%	1.0–1.4%
2.2–3.0%	under 1%
1.5–2.1%	no data

▲   *Figure 1.1   Average population growth, 1980–1988.*

population is 814 million to China's 1.084 billion, it has been estimated that by the year 2050 India will reach the staggering total of 1.68 billion (while China will be 1.45 billion), because of India's higher growth rate of 2.1% per annum.

Why do population growth rates vary so greatly between countries? There are, of course, economic, social, cultural and political forces which interact with demographic processes to produce the variations evident in Figure 1.1, but a more immediate answer to the question is that there exist very substantial geographical variations in mortality and **fertility rates** between nations and in particular between different regions sharing similar cultures. Table 1.2 presents some data on regional fertility patterns for the early 1980s. It is necessary to consider in more detail how fertility is measured before evaluating the patterns which the table reveals.

The **crude birth rate (CBR)** is the simplest measure of fertility, measuring the number of births in a year per thousand persons of the mid-year population of a region or country. Since not all members of a population (males, children, older females) have the potential for child-bearing and since these elements of a population may vary in their numerical importance between one place and another and through time, the CBR is only of value in comparing fertility levels. More useful are **age-specific birth rates** which compare the number of births in a given year

Table 1.2   Fertility rates by world region for the early 1980s

	Total population (millions)	Crude birth rate (per 000)	Total fertility rate	GNP per capita (US$)
North Africa	124	41	5.9	1 240
West Africa	161	49	6.8	660
East Africa	150	47	6.6	330
Middle Africa	60	45	6.2	420
Southern Africa	36	36	5.2	2 490
South-west Asia	110	37	5.5	4 110
Middle South Asia	1036	37	5.3	260
South-east Asia	393	33	4.5	720
East Asia	1243	20	2.6	1 360
Middle America	102	34	4.9	1 970
Caribbean	31	26	3.4	–
Tropical South America	220	32	4.3	2 120
Temperate South America	44	24	2.7	2 440
North America	262	15	1.8	13 000
North and west Europe	236	12	1.7	11 500
Eastern and southern Europe	253	15	2.0	5 270[1]
USSR	274	20	2.5	5 940
Oceania[2]	24	21	2.5	8 700

Notes: [1]Southern Europe only.

[2]Australasia, Polynesia, Micronesia and Melanesia.

Source: Coward, J. (1986) 'Fertility patterns in the modern world', in Pacione, M. (ed.) *Population Geography: progress and prospects*, London, Croom Helm, p. 63.

to the number of women in specific age cohorts. A particularly sensitive measure which population geographers and demographers like to use in making comparisons of fertility is the **total fertility rate (TFR)**. This measures the average number of children that would be born to a woman passing through the child-bearing cohorts. Although its calculation is more complex than the CBR, its analysis is more useful since variations in the TFR do not reflect the demographic composition of a population, but rather they mirror more fundamental patterns influencing fertility: these include knowledge of and prevailing attitudes towards contraception, and attitudes relating to family size, structure and formation. Some of these determining influences on fertility are discussed later in the chapter, but more immediately it is important to become aware of the variations in fertility levels which exist across the globe.

Activity 2

Compare the CBR, TFR, and GNP per capita measures shown in Table 1.2 and describe the geographical associations which you perceive to exist. Then read the following discussion.

Table 1.2 suggests a similar pattern to that already described for world population growth – a dichotomy between the more and less developed countries. North America and northern Europe have CBRs at or below 15 per thousand and TFRs which indicate that women have on average less than two children during their lifetime; in Africa CBRs of over 40 per thousand are recorded and TFRs suggest that on average women have six or more children.

Given such stark contrasts it is difficult not to jump to the conclusion that economic environments and demographic behaviour are closely linked, but closer examination of the table shows that wide variations do exist in fertility patterns both in the richer and the poorer countries of the world. For example, south-west Asia – which includes many of the oil-rich states – boasts quite high per capita incomes but also sustains high TFRs. Conversely the regions described in Table 1.2 as east Asia and temperate South America have only modest levels of GNP per capita, but have fertility levels only slightly higher than those of the most developed countries. Low fertility rates have emerged not only in some of the newly industrialising countries of the less developed world, but also in socialist states. Thus, for example, Singapore, Hong Kong and Cuba all now have TFRs of less than two. Demographers place particular significance on the TFR threshold of 2.1 since below this value a population is failing to replace itself by natural processes. This is to say, there will be more deaths than births in the long run, and population decrease rather than population growth can be anticipated.

In summary, Table 1.2 does confirm that major differences in fertility levels underpin the geographical divide observed in national population growth rates. There are also major variations in fertility rates between developing countries which suggests that social, political and cultural factors as well as economic ones have a role in influencing population change.

Consider the following illustrations of demographic change in both developed and less developed countries. The 1981 population census of Britain recorded the presence of 54 million persons, a figure only 0.57%

greater than the comparable statistic for the 1971 census. By contrast the figures for population change between the 1961 and 1971 censuses indicated a 5.25% change. Even this level of growth was low compared with that achieved in the nineteenth century when rates of 10 to 18% were recorded between censuses. Most of the prosperous industrial societies of western Europe and North America are currently experiencing very low levels of population growth, and in some cases numbers have actually been in decline. Denmark is currently ranked as the eighth wealthiest country in the world in terms of income per head of population, yet its population is expected to fall by 3.9% by the year 2000. Social and demographic forces have already produced substantial reductions in household size from 2.96 persons in 1960 to 2.39 in 1980. In 1983 only 27.3% of Danish households were families comprising a married couple and children, while 30.5% were single persons living alone.

Q   From the material presented in the preceding paragraph, what conclusions would you reach about the relationships between population trends and economic growth in western Europe?

A   It is difficult and misleading to make direct causal statements. Nevertheless, indirect relationships are clearly important. In western Europe demographic change occurred during a period of economic growth and social reorganisation. Only in the wealthiest European countries has the social structure evolved to the point where stable demographic structures have also emerged.

In stark contrast with the examples discussed above, which have been selected from the more developed countries, the countries of Africa south of the Sahara had an average population growth rate of over 3% in the 1980s compared with a rate of only 2.6% between 1961 and 1973. In this part of the world population growth is therefore high and accelerating. At current growth rates of 3.3% per annum the 500 million people of these countries will double their numbers by the year 2010. An extreme case is the state of Kenya whose population growth rate is expected to rise to 4.4% per annum during the 1990s, requiring that the country's economy achieve an incredible pace of expansion even to maintain the current living standards of the population. In many countries wealth simply cannot be produced fast enough to keep pace with demographic growth. In the 1980s the per capita

▲   *Contrasting conditions for child care: organised day care in Denmark, and a family in Mathare Valley shanty town near Nairobi, Kenya. Third world families face more difficult conditions even where family size is small.*

incomes of sub-Saharan countries fell by over 2% per annum taking the standard of living back to that of over thirty years ago.

It would be very easy to conclude that rapid population growth has caused underdevelopment and human suffering, but in practice there is much evidence to show once again that direct causal statements should be avoided. For example, while the level of maternal mortality in sub-Saharan Africa was tragically high at more than 500 maternal deaths per 100 000 live births, China (with a larger population and with a not dissimilar average income per head) had a comparable figure of only 44 deaths per 100 000 births. Contrasts like these make it difficult to provide simple explanations for population change, as will be shown in Section 3.

2.2   Summary

It would appear that population growth as a phenomenon is not new, but the accelerating and very rapid rates of population increase in the least developed countries of the world in the latter part of the twentieth century have been a cause for concern. The uneven patterns of economic and demographic growth are also highlighted by the trend in many of the wealthiest nations towards stable or gently declining populations. Examination of the data would refute both the view that slow population growth causes rapid economic growth and the common misconception that rapid population growth causes underdevelopment. This is not to say, however, that economic and demographic processes are not affected by the common underlying influences of social organisation and structure.

3   Explanation of population change

Given the importance of population growth, many theorists have attempted to explain what causes or prevents it. However, some of the difficulties of providing a simple explanation have already been referred to in interpreting Figure 1.1 and Table 1.2. This section assesses a range of explanations which have been proposed, moving from those which emphasise environmental constraints, through those which relate population to food supply to one which emphasises the role of industrialisation.

3.1   Environmental constraints and demographic trends

Human populations are, of course, part of the global ecosystem. Like other species the size of the human population is affected by the forces which determine birth, death and migration rates. The physical environment presents society with a series of opportunities and constraints which have affected whether, at any time or place, births have exceeded deaths and in-migration exceeded out-migration. Human interaction with the environment has been very strongly affected, particularly in the twentieth century, by technological and sociological factors.

There has, however, in some quarters been a tendency to over-emphasise the human ability to mould the environment and to forget how inseparable people are from the environment and how complex are the energy and material flows which link them to the global ecosystem. Environmental limits on human populations are imposed by the distribution of weather regimes, soil types, land forms and other physical features. As human geographers have frequently pointed out, most limits are specific to technological circumstances and cultural perceptions prevailing at specific points in time. It is important to ask, however, whether there are certain physical elements which have a common or universal effect on all human beings. Figure 1.2, for example, suggests that there are absolute limits to human endurance of certain climatic conditions. Examinations of a world population map readily shows the significance of environmental limits of this kind, with very little human settlement in those parts of the globe with very low temperatures such as the Antarctic or extreme aridity such as the Rub al Khali. Technological advance may have made it technically possible for people to survive under severe conditions over limited time-periods, but the fundamental constraints remain. Figure 1.2 also shows that there are considerable margins around what may be defined as the **human comfort zone** where human beings can exist.

An awareness of climatology makes one realise that weather conditions at any particular place on the Earth's surface are highly variable through time, with temperature and humidity levels changing on a daily and seasonal basis as well as being different from one year to the next. The

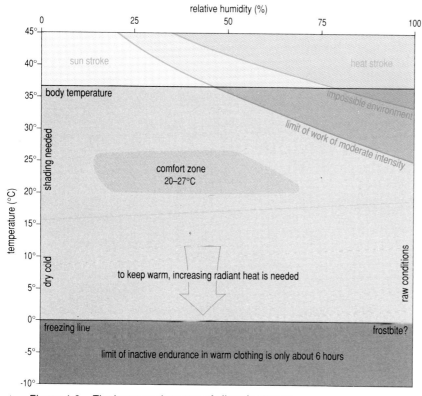

▲ Figure 1.2   The human relevance of climatic ranges.

resulting uncertainty produces geographical patterns which do not usually reflect absolute spatial limits to specific conditions but highly variable spatial weather patterns which often take people unawares in the form of so-called 'natural hazards'. These, regrettably, are still frequent contributory causes of human deaths through circumstances such as famine or floods (discussed in *Smith** in Silvertown and Sarre (eds) (1990)).

People are affected not only by the climate of a particular environment, but are widely dependent on the capacity of the physical environment to produce the nutrients they need to support human life and to absorb the waste products resulting from human activities. For most of the course of human history food supply to human populations has occurred on a very local scale. The potential of an area to supply the critical food needs of its human population (like its animal populations) was an important influence on population size. Where there was too little food for all the individuals in a population, starvation would result in more deaths than normal thus leading to a reduction in population size to a level closer to sustainable levels in terms of the food supply. Of course, the relationships within this self-regulating system are much more complex than have been described here. For example, it has been established from research on the effects of twentieth-century famines such as the great Chinese famine of 1960–61, that poor nutrition levels reduce human fertility even before they lead to increased mortality. Thus failures in the food supply not only reduce future food demands through increased deaths, but also through reduced numbers of births (see Figure 1.3). As will be discussed later, the causes of famine are not merely environmental ones, but, whatever the causes, the consequences in circumstances of limited human planning and organisation are starvation and population decline.

*An author's name in italics indicates another book or a chapter in another book in this series.

Q   Describe the absolute level of crude birth and death rates shown in Figure 1.3 and attempt to relate changes in the birth and death rates to trends in the total population size.

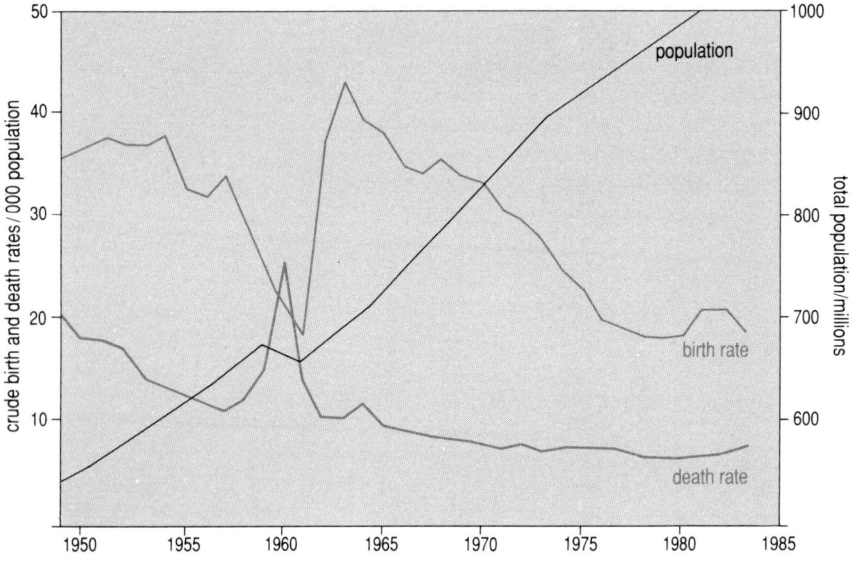

▲   *Figure 1.3   Demographic trends in China.*

A   Crude death rates in China fell from around 20 per 1000 in the late 1940s to below 10 per 1000 in the mid 1960s. This general trend was interrupted by the crisis years of 1959, 1960 and 1961 when drought and famine greatly increased the death rate. In the same years the adverse circumstances caused the crude birth rate to drop below 20 per 1000, compared with a norm of 35 to 38 per 1000 in the early 1950s. The other very marked feature of the figure is the dramatic and sustained decline of crude birth rates in the 1970s to a level of around 20 births per 1000 persons. The effect of the considerable excess of births over deaths is evident in the rapid growth in the total population during the 1950s and 1960s. As the vital rates begin to converge in the 1970s, so too the rate of population growth slackens, resulting in a slower rate of increase in the size of the total population.

It has been suggested above that the physical environment may impose certain constraints on humans' use of the Earth. The world distribution of population density (the number of people living in a specified unit of land) is shown in Figure 1.4 (over). Consider the spatial inequalities which exist in population distribution: China and India account for less than 9% of the Earth's land surface, yet together they are home to more than 36% of humankind. They, along with much of western Europe, Japan, Java, the Nile delta and the north-eastern United States, have population densities of over 100 persons per square kilometre over much of their land area. By contrast Figure 1.5 plots the world distribution of biological productivity (which is expressed in terms of the potential number of grams of carbon which could be produced by a square metre of land in a year; this can be taken as an indicator of the ecological resource potential of different parts of the Earth). Comparison of the patterns of Figures 1.4 and 1.5 makes it evident that there is little association between areas of high population concentration and high potential ecological productivity.

Q   How is it possible that the distributions of population and biological productivity are so dissimilar?

A   Society has developed the capacity through technology and through social and economic organisation to relax some of the constraints imposed by the physical environment. As a result the parts of the world yielding the highest output of cereals and livestock are not necessarily the same as the areas with the highest potential biological productivity. (The next three chapters look at this subject.) In addition it should be remembered that human settlement patterns also relate to non-food production activities.

A wider investigation of the development of the human use of the Earth would show that as economic systems have become larger in scale and as social structures have become more complex, so also the potential for altering the natural environment has grown, as has the potential for destroying it. It has not simply been technological advances which have increased the environmental impact of human society, but also the more powerful and more subtle influences of expanding economic systems, in forms such as the economic imperialism of western nations with regard to the less developed countries, which have had profound effects on the context of subsequent economic, demographic and environmental trends.

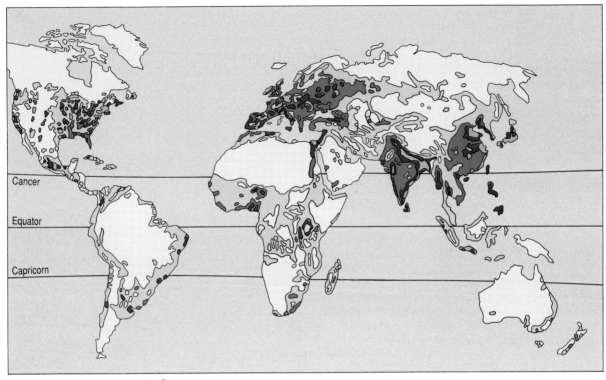

density of population / persons per km^2

■ over 200	▫ 3–25
■ 100–200	□ 0–3
■ 25–100	

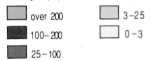 *Figure 1.4   Population density.*

3.2   *Population and food resources*

Having recognised the complexity of relationships between society and environment, it is now useful to examine some of the basic ideas which have been suggested to explain how population change affects the environment and vice versa. First of all it is interesting to consider the relationships which might exist between population density and food production systems within subsistence agriculture. Table 1.3 attempts to relate the intensity of agricultural production to population densities in 29 tropical communities.

Q   What conclusions would you draw from examining the survey results?

A   The evidence of the table would seem to suggest a positive correlation between population density and the intensity of land use in certain types of tropical food production. In the cases chosen for study by the researchers, forest fallow production was to be found mainly at population densities of under four persons per square kilometre. Indeed no other system was recorded amongst the communities studied in the most sparsely populated areas. Inversely, at population densities of over 64 persons per square kilometre short fallow or annual cropping was the norm.

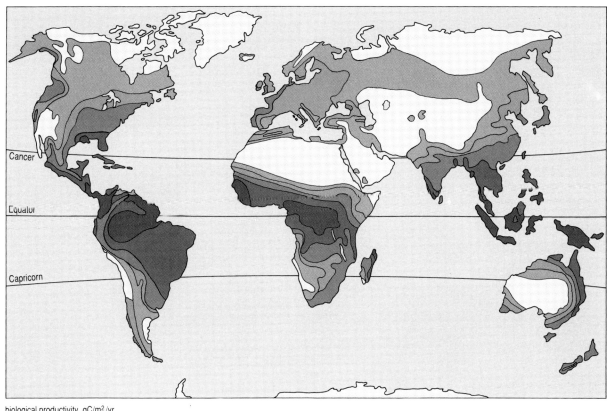

biological productivity, gC/m²/yr

■ over 800	■ 200–399
■ 600–799	■ 100–199
■ 400–599	□ 0–99

▲ *Figure 1.5   World distribution of biological productivity (expressed in grams of carbon).*

Table 1.3   *Population density and agricultural intensity: evidence from 29 tropical agricultural communities*

Population density (persons per square km)	System of supply for vegetable food			
	Forest fallow (FF)	Bush fallow (BF)	Short fallow (SF)	Annual cropping (AC)
less than 4	3	0	0	0
4–16	1	4	1	0
16–64	1	8	0	0
over 64	0	2	6	3

Notes: following Boserup the following definitions are used:

FF: one or two crops followed by 15–25 years fallow

BF: two or more crops followed by 8–10 years fallow

SF: one or two crops followed by one or two years fallow

AC: one crop each year with only a few months fallow.

Source: Turner, B. L., Hanham, R. Q. and Portararo, A. V. (1977) 'Population pressure and agricultural intensity', *Annals of the Association of American Geographers*, Vol. 67, pp. 386–7.

Some writers such as Boserup (1980) have taken this evidence to argue that rising population densities may actually act as a spur to innovation and development. This argument is implausible, however, in the contemporary world since relatively few communities operate closed systems producing food only to meet their own requirements. As soon as one moves from predominantly subsistence agriculture to food production systems governed by other methods of production, the society–land–food relationships become very complex, and the link between population density and agricultural productivity becomes obscure. More important become the social and economic forces which control access to markets and to means of production.

In the world today most people cannot freely organise either their own labour or the land which they work to meet the food and non-food needs of themselves and their immediate geographical community. For example, much of the world's cultivable land is concentrated into large landholdings so rural labourers in areas of high population densities do not have access to land and are not free to organise production methods simply to meet their own food needs. A United Nations study of land use in Central America showed that 10% of land-owners controlled 80% of all farmland. Those farmers who had four hectares or less cultivated 72% of their land, while farmers with over 35 hectares cultivated only 14%. In other words, those with the greatest potential for making improvements had the least incentive to do so, while those in the greatest need were least well positioned for reasons of capital and land shortages to increase production. An ever-increasing proportion of the world's agricultural labour force is employed in producing food for other people and in particular for multinational corporations who sell this production to the world's richest countries. For example, the United Nations estimates that multinational companies control production of approximately 90% of forest products, 90% of coffee, 85% of world cocoa, 85% of tea and 60% of sugar. Agricultural labour is therefore caught up increasingly in patterns of world crop production and the technologies which they use are not linked to local population densities or local food needs.

Even where subsistence agricultural systems persist, conditions of inadequate food production are much more likely in the short run to give rise to migration than to agricultural innovation. Boserup (1980) herself admits that rapid changes in population–resource ratios can lead to the adoption of agricultural technologies which may have environmentally harmful effects. She also recognises that in certain physical environments continual intensification of production may not be possible with rising population pressures. The semi-arid areas of Africa which experienced prolonged droughts in the 1970s and early 1980s would seem to be one example of an environment where population–land relationships have not been able to evolve in the way that might be expected given the relationship implied in Table 1.3, that is, local agricultural production has not been able to reorganise rapidly in response to population demands. See Box 1.2 (on pp. 18–19).

Unfortunately Ethiopia is not an isolated example. Rapid population growth and inadequate agricultural development led no less than 27 of the 39 countries of sub-Saharan Africa to face chronic food shortages in the 1970s and 1980s. Broadening the analysis to the world scale there were 70 countries out of a total of 126 in which food production did not keep pace with population growth between 1970 and 1980. Table 1.4 shows that although global rates of food output grew at 2.3% per annum or above between 1960 and 1980, when population growth is allowed for, per capita

Table 1.4   Growth rates of food output by world region, 1960–80 (average annual percentage change)

Region or country group	Total		Per capita	
	1960–70	1970–80	1960–70	1970–80
Developing countries	2.9	2.8	0.4	0.4
Low-income	2.6	2.2	0.2	−0.3
Middle-income	3.2	3.3	0.7	0.9
Africa	2.6	1.6	0.1	−1.1
Middle East	2.6	2.9	0.1	0.2
South-east Asia	2.8	3.8	0.3	1.4
South Asia	2.6	2.2	0.1	0.0
Latin America	3.6	3.3	0.1	0.6
Southern Europe	3.2	3.5	1.8	1.9
Industrial market economies	2.3	2.0	1.3	1.1
Non-market industrial economies	3.2	1.7	2.2	0.9
World	2.7	2.3	0.8	0.5

Source: World Bank (1985) *Population Change and Economic Development*, London, Oxford University Press, p. 50.

growth was only of the order of 0.5%. Even at this lower rate of growth there should have been enough food for the world's people, but, as Table 1.4 indicates, trends were geographically uneven. In low-income countries per capita food production declined between 1970 and 1980 by 0.3% per annum and in Africa the drop was even more serious being on average 1.1% each year. Given statistics such as these, and the frequent reporting of famine conditions in many parts of the third world, it is easy to see why some commentators have returned to considering the ideas of Thomas Malthus, an English demographer of the eighteenth century.

Malthus wrote two influential essays, in 1798 and 1803, in which he laid out his basic argument that the capacity of human populations for natural growth was geometric (as you showed in the graph you drew for Activity 1), while the potential for expanding food production was highly constrained and ultimately was limited by the amount of cultivable land. As a result population growth would always seem in the long run to outpace food production. When this happened Malthus suggested population increase would be brought to a halt by what have come to be termed **Malthusian checks**, namely war, vice and human misery as in the case of famine. In a capitalist society, in which labour is sold as a factor of production, uncontrolled population growth may lead to rising food costs (due to growing demand) and falling wage levels (as the labour supply expands). Ensuing conditions of poverty and malnutrition ultimately lead to population growth being halted by rising mortality levels. Some writers thinking in a neo-Malthusian way have extended the argument to apply to physical resources other than food in the face of the rising demands for fuel and minerals in the twentieth century. In the nineteenth century Malthus' predictions were not confirmed, despite very rapid population growth in what are now termed the more developed countries. Economic development associated with the emergence of industrial capitalism made a rise in living standards possible without facing a Malthusian check, while colonial expansion made it possible for the industrial countries to draw on food and other physical resources from the less developed countries. At the same time, and for reasons which are discussed later, fertility levels dropped substantially.

Ethiopia had an estimated population of 42 million people in 1988. Of these, five million were at risk from famine. One in five children die before their fifth birthday and life expectancy for the population as a whole remains amongst the lowest in the world at 45 years. The population is spatially concentrated in the highlands (i.e. above 1500 m) which dominate the centre of the country and in which varied farming systems have been practised. (See Plate 1.) Surrounding the highlands are lower areas which, although they account for almost 50% of the area, support only about 18% of the population. Population densities are particularly high in the central part of the Northern Highlands (including parts of the provinces of Wollo and Tigre) where densities are over 150 persons per square kilometre and where the cultivable area falls below 0.2 hectares per person: see Figure 1.6. Rising population pressures have led to more frequent cultivation of the land, but in this fragile environment, and given limited capital and technological assistance, this has led to serious damage to the soil structure and to soil erosion and land degradation. Unfavourable ratios of people to cultivable land led to spontaneous resettlement away from the most densely settled areas of the highlands (Wood, 1985). This involved the movement of hundreds of thousands of people in the period since 1950, but these movements also caused ecological problems with resettlement often leading to poor land-use practices or attempts at cultivation on unsuitable slopes. During the 1970s the continued rapid growth of population, combined with the very low average income per head of less than £60 per annum, contributed to a variety of resource crises including inadequate access to sufficient firewood. Large numbers of trees were cut down in many environmentally fragile areas, despite the devastating consequences in terms of the topsoil being blown or washed away. In the 1970s the price of wood in the capital city, Addis Ababa, rose tenfold and cost the average household about 20% of its income.

Rainfall in Ethiopia, as in other countries in this semi-arid region, is of very great importance in sustaining food production since agriculture depends on precipitation rather than either on wells tapping groundwater resources or on irrigation distributing water from rivers. Almost everyone in the region eats non-irrigated drought-resistant crops such as millet and sorghum. Wollo and Tigre provinces in particular have had a long history of being affected by drought, but the succession of drought years which lasted over more than a decade from the early 1970s to the mid 1980s produced extreme crisis conditions in these areas, most notably in 1984 and 1985. The death of tens of thousands of people from starvation as a result of the Ethiopian famine could as a result easily be interpreted as evidence that in any given area, the ecosystem can only support a limited number of people, and that when this limit is exceeded famine results, leading to a 'Malthusian' check on population growth.

While the drought conditions of the Ethiopian crisis were unavoidable, it is far from clear that widespread famine was inevitable. The current Ethiopian government came to power in 1975, having overthrown the previous Imperial Regime primarily because it failed to pay attention to the plight of the rural poor. For example, there was widespread discontent that the famine victims of the droughts of the early 1970s had been forced to sell their lands to buy food and that pastoralists had been evicted to make way for commercial agriculture. Having a socialist orientation, the revolutionary government was not well received by western governments. It also found itself faced with two civil wars in Eritrea and Tigre and chose to devote a high proportion of its very limited resources to military expenditure. As a result it continued to look to socialist countries for technical and military assistance. Attention to agricultural production was certainly inadequate, with food production per head of the population actually dropping by about 5% in the six years preceding the famine. At the same time the country's main commodity export to the world market, coffee, faced falling prices thus adding to the country's trade deficit and worsening its international debt. In the mid 1980s approximately one third of the country's annual budget was used on debt repayments. Faced with these extremely adverse circumstances it is perhaps less difficult to understand why the Ethiopian government was slow to seek international assistance, not doing so until 1982. There was only a minimal response to these initial requests from western nations. For example, in 1984 Ethiopia received only £7 million of relief assistance from the British government, a figure which compares unfavourably with the £37 million given to Kenya. Some have suggested that since the famine was most severe in the very areas in which the population was actively at war with the government, it was not in the Ethiopian government's interests to seek famine relief for these regions. The distribution of blame for the tragedy is, however, hard to allocate. It nevertheless remains a cruel irony that at the same time as famine was resulting in acute starvation for the people of Ethiopia, the US government was paying farmers billions of dollars to take vast tracts of arable land out of production.

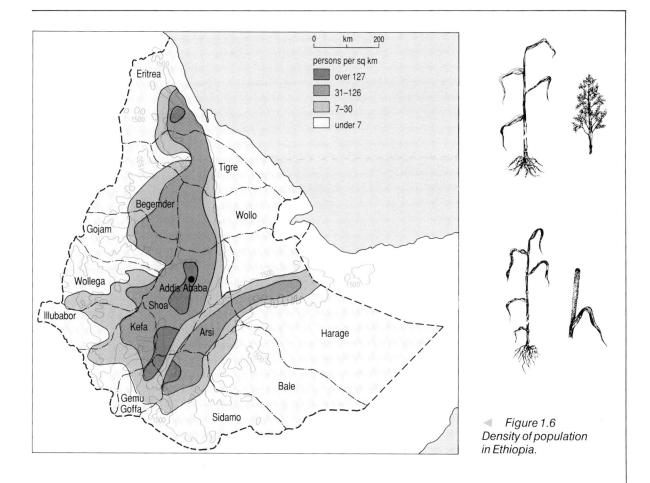

Figure 1.6
Density of population
in Ethiopia.

Migrants in Tigre. Drought leading to crop failures in 1984 and 1985 resulted in mass migrations.

Q If Malthus was wrong about population and food resources in the
   western world, why have some people returned to Malthusian views in
   the face of rapid population growth in less developed countries in the
   twentieth century?

A This trend in thinking would seem to have been encouraged on the one
   hand by the very high population growth rates recorded in some third
   world countries, and on the other hand by recurrent problems of famine
   in these countries.

The advent of recurrent famine in many developing countries is not,
however, adequate proof of neo-Malthusian trends. As has been shown
earlier in Table 1.4, world food production has increased more rapidly than
population, and organisations such as the United Nations Food and
Agricultural Organisation (FAO) predict that at a global level there should
be no problem in expanding production further to meet the needs of the 6.1
billion people who are expected to be alive in the year 2000. Table 1.4
identified the fact that if there is a population resource problem in terms of
food provision, then it is a regionally specific problem. Let us examine this
distribution aspect in more detail by considering the different types of food
in world trade.

     No part of the world grows every type of crop in adequate quantities.
Furthermore an ever smaller proportion of world food is grown by
subsistence cultivators and as a result an ever increasing proportion of the
world's population buys the food it needs, rather than growing it for
themselves. The result is a growth in the exchange of food between
producers and consumers and between one country and another. It has
been estimated that 10% of all grain crosses international boundaries
between the time of harvesting and consumption. Table 1.5 shows the scale
of world trade in grains, meats and milk. A negative sign indicates that a

Table 1.5   World trade in grains, meat and milk, by world region, 1980–82 (one-year average, million metric tons)

	Grains	Meat	Milk
North Africa/Middle East	−29.2	−1.18	−7.9
Sub-Saharan Africa	−5.8	−0.08	−1.3
South Asia	−1.6	0.05	−0.6
East Asia	−28.8	−0.82	−1.9
Asian Centrally Planned Economies	−18.6	0.23	−0.1
Latin America	−7.6	0.56	−2.2
North America	132.8	0.18	−1.1
European Community	4.3	0.12	11.3
Other western Europe	−11.0	−0.03	1.0
Eastern Europe	−11.4	0.49	0.3
USSR	−36.5	−0.80	−4.3
Oceania[1]	15.6	1.47	5.6
World total[2]	*152.7*	*3.10*	*18.2*

Notes: Negative amounts are imports. Positive amounts are exports.
[1] Australia, Polynesia, Micronesia and Melanesia.
[2] Exports only.

Source: World Resources Institute (1986) *World Resources*, 1986, p. 51.

region needs to make net imports of a particular food type. It shows for example that the Middle East and North Africa bought large quantities of grain, meat and milk, while at the other extreme North America made major exports of grain, but needed to import small quantities of milk. Only the EC countries and the Oceania region, according to this table, had no need to make net imports of any of these commodities.

Q   If the countries of sub-Saharan Africa are the ones in which food shortages are the most acute, why were food imports to these countries not greater?

A   The pattern of the world food trade is determined not by the absolute need for particular produce, but by the ability of consumers to pay the price demanded for the products they require. Many of the countries with the most chronic food shortages cannot afford to buy the food their populations need. The oil-producing countries of the Middle East were by and large able to purchase the foods which their populations needed and which could not be grown domestically, given the ecological and other constraints on their agricultural systems. The oil-producing countries, in particular, had no difficulty in making the necessary purchases of grain, meat and milk because of the exchange value of their natural fuel resources. The countries of sub-Saharan Africa were not, however, in this fortunate position. In the twentieth century the key question of population–food relationships was, therefore, whether the populations of countries with food deficits could afford to buy the food they needed. The continued occurrence of famine was not so much a population/resources problem as a poverty problem. This is not to say that population crises are any the less real or that population factors are not intertwined with patterns of poverty.

Summary

Malthus attempted to analyse the relation between population growth and resources in a highly selective fashion. The arguments which he presented were to a certain extent internally consistent and consequently his conclusions include certain elements of truth. However, the limiting assumptions of his work mean that his conclusions are not universally applicable. In particular he failed to pay sufficient attention to the spatially interdependent nature of economies and societies and to the rules governing interaction and exchange within and between societies.

3.3   Industrialisation and the demographic transition

By the time Malthus wrote his essays a process was under way which was both to prove him wrong (for a period at least) and to provide another 'grand theory' of population. The industrial revolution which transformed the British economy and society in the nineteenth century also had an unprecedented effect on the British population.

This change in the population, subsequently known as the **demographic transition**, is simplified in Figure 1.7(a). In stage 1 both fertility and mortality are high, so population growth is slow. One indirect effect of British industrialisation and economic growth was a reduction in mortality

PUNCHLINE
by **CHRISTIAN**

GUESS WHAT LITTLE PEASANT?! WE'VE DISCOVERED THAT BECAUSE OF THE "GREEN REVOLUTION"...

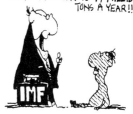

WHEAT PRODUCTION HERE IN INDIA IN JUST 20 YEARS HAS SOARED FROM 11 MILLION TO 47 MILLION TONS A YEAR!!

AND NOW YOU NEED NOT GO HUNGRY BECAUSE OF PROBLEMS OF FOOD PRODUCTION!!

BUT SIR, MY FAMILY AND I ARE **STILL** SUFFERING FROM MALNUTRITION!!

ER, YES...UNFORTUNATELY THAT'S A PROBLEM OF **DISTRIBUTION**...

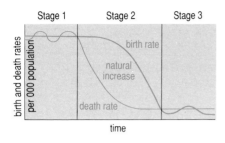

as a result of better nutrition, sanitation and medicine. The wide gap between high fertility and low mortality in the early part of stage 2 implies a rapid growth in the population. The crucial and unprecedented event occurred in the latter part of stage 2 with the reduction of fertility. This produced slower population growth and ultimately led to the re-establishment of a balance between crude birth rates and death rates in stage 3. Initially these critical changes were attributed to industrialisation producing better living standards and lower levels of infant mortality, which it was believed had a direct influence on the reproductive behaviour of married couples. More recently it has been suggested that the timing of fertility decline in England and Wales was associated with a substantial change in public opinion in favour of the limitation of family size, aided by the advent of mass education and only later influenced by a growing awareness of the reductions in infant mortality.

The earlier interpretation of fertility decline led to the expectation by some that industrialisation would produce falling death rates and later falling birth rates in other countries and in particular in the less developed world, as so-called 'modernisation' spread to new geographic areas. In practice, not only did knowledge and fruitful application of the medical advances which had increased life expectancies in western Europe diffuse very rapidly to other parts of the world, but they did so independently from the spread of industrialisation. As a result the transition model as initially formulated was demoted by some to no more than a descriptive model with no explanatory power (since the demographic experience of many countries as defined by the model did not relate to phases of so-called 'modernisation'), while others sought alternative explanatory frameworks. For example, it was suggested that the demographic transition was internally triggered, with fertility not falling until mortality had fallen, and with couples gradually altering their perceptions of desired family size once infant mortality levels had fallen to a sufficiently low level to ensure a reasonable chance of their children surviving into adulthood. Empirical evidence certainly shows that in no society has fertility declined prior to a sustained decline in mortality. There are, however, many examples from less developed and indeed from the Arab oil-rich states to show that neither rising income levels nor increased life expectancy necessarily stimulate a downturn in fertility. In some less developed countries advances in hygiene and medical care have now reduced crude death rates to levels as low as or lower than in the more developed countries, yet crude birth rates remain much higher. Population experts have therefore moved in the direction of seeking separate explanatory models of mortality and fertility trends, with the term **fertility transition** increasingly being used. This recognises that a radical change in fertility regimes has been experienced in many countries, which in descriptive terms resembles the trends outlined in the demographic transition model, but which in explanatory terms rests on a very different basis. Woods (1982) has therefore proposed a variable model

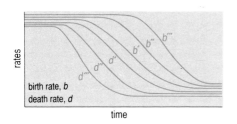

rates

birth rate, b
death rate, d

time

◀   *Figure 1.7(b)   A variable model of the demographic transition.
In the variable model of the demographic transition, trends in death
rates are not necessarily accompanied by any specific trends in
birth rates. Thus, for example, a country on trajectory d''' could have
b''' or b'' or b'. Thus not only are death and birth rates variable
between countries, but so also are rates of population growth.*

of the demographic transition (shown in Figure 1.7b), with different
determinants producing a reduction in death rates from those producing
fertility decline.

3.4   Summary

This section has argued that certain demographic features such as infant
mortality trends are closely related to levels of eonomic development (as
distinct from economic growth) and to patterns of poverty. Attempts to
explain all demographic processes as direct responses to economic stimuli
would, however, be simplistic and misleading. Models such as the
demographic transition are helpful descriptive generalisations but they
often lack an adequate explanatory basis. Economic growth was
undoubtedly vital in western Europe in the achievement of the so-called
demographic transition, but only because economic change produced new
social conditions favourable to lower fertility levels.

4   Fertility, mortality and migration

The previous section has shown that attempts to identify single explanations
or 'grand theories' of population change have been unsuccessful. They do
show that many factors are at work and suggest that more detailed analyses
of fertility and mortality are needed. This section follows up this suggestion,
providing more detailed information on variations of fertility and mortality
and seeking more evidence on the factors which influence them. It also looks
in more detail at the third component of population change – migration. As
well as helping to clarify what influences fertility and mortality, migration is
closely linked, through urbanisation, to economic development, which has
been identified as a major, though complex, influence on population
change.

4.1   Infant mortality

One demographic indicator which is often used to measure the ability of a
particular environment (in physical, economic and political terms), to
adequately provide for its population, is the proportion of babies surviving
their first year of life. It remains a statistical fact that the chances of death are
higher during the first year of life than in any other specific year. The reasons
for this are in one sense obvious, in so far as infants are totally incapable of

looking after themselves, and depend on the abilities of their parents, set within a specific social environment, to care for them. In other words the social environment (in the broadest sense of this term) into which a baby is born is of critical importance. Where this environment for one reason or other is unable to provide adequate support, the lives of the youngest members of society become very vulnerable.

Infant mortality rates are measured in terms of the number of deaths in a year of children under the age of one year per thousand live births. In Figure 1.8 the map of the world is transformed to show countries in terms of the average number of children born in each state in each year between 1975 and 1980. This makes India and China easily the biggest countries. The shading shows how likely babies were to die during their first year of life in the different social and economic environments of the contemporary world. Clearly life chances are much greater in some places than others with some environments much more able to sustain the most vulnerable members of society. The map shows that in North America and western Europe there were relatively few children being born, but that they had an excellent chance of surviving. Conversely, infant mortality was very high in Africa and southern Asia, which were also the continents with the largest numbers of children. Note that all the countries in which infant mortality rates exceed 150 per thousand are concentrated in these two continents, and that in Africa few countries could offer their infants more than a nine in ten chance of surviving their first year. Why?

The survival of infants depends on a wide range of factors. A particularly strong relationship has been found to exist between the educational status of mothers and the life prospects of their children. This immediate relationship should not however be allowed to cloud the broader environmental circumstances affecting infant mortality rates. These include

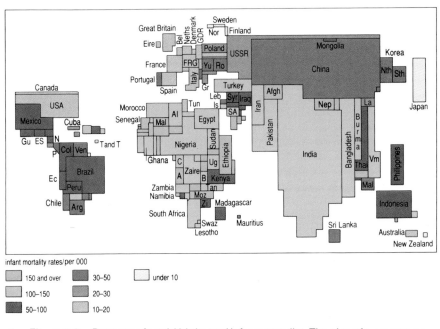

infant mortality rates/per 000

150 and over   30–50   under 10

100–150   20–30

50–100   10–20

▲   *Figure 1.8   Patterns of world births and infant mortality. The size of a country on this map is determined by the average number of babies born in it each year between 1975 and 1980. The shading shows how likely those babies are to die in their first year of life.*

provision of adequate medical care for mothers and children in an accessible
form before and after childbirth, the nutritional status of the mother and
child, adequate shelter and fuel for the immediate environment in which the
child will live, the provision of clean water and in most cases the relative
stability of household income necessary for the achievement of many of the
other conditions. Most demographers agree that population increase in
itself is not a cause of infant mortality, and indeed if there is a causal
relationship that it runs in the opposite direction. Factors associated with the
distribution of wealth and poverty play a much more important role in
providing ultimate explanations for the uneven world patterns of infant
mortality.

   Spatial analysis of infant mortality patterns carried out at different scales
shows surprisingly constant associations between high infant mortality and
areas of low income. The world map shown in Figure 1.8 confirmed this
pattern at an international scale. A recent cross-national study of the
socio-economic factors affecting child and infant mortality, by the
demographer John Hobcraft, stressed the importance of both mothers' and
fathers' educational and occupational status. These factors are likely to
influence household income. Hobcraft *et al.*'s (1984) work is of special
interest since it shows that the spatial variations which exist between
countries are also found *within* countries, with for example stark contrasts
between the health of children belonging to wealthy urban families from
those of the rural poor. For child mortality the former social group was
twenty times less at risk than the children of the rural poor. Studies even
within cities have shown stark contrasts in infant child mortality rates
between social groups and consequently between the urban environments
in which different social groups live.

   As with agricultural technology with regard to food production, so also
with medical knowledge, the twentieth century has been a period of
remarkable advances. This has permitted **life expectancies** in the more
developed countries to rise rapidly. Iceland, for example, has now attained a
life expectancy of 78 years. It was anticipated that the much lower life
expectancies of the less developed countries would catch up rapidly with

▲   *A clinic held weekly for Fulani women and children near Dori, and collecting water for domestic use in
Ofrey village, both in Burkina Faso. Provision of health care facilities and clean water are two significant factors
in reducing infant mortality rates.*

those of the more developed states, as medical knowledge and health-care facilities diffused to lower-income countries. Although there has been significant progress, life expectancies have not, however, risen as rapidly as anticipated. Initial progress occurred largely through the introduction of public health campaigns such as spraying against malarial infection and vaccination against diseases such as smallpox. Medical advances could not, however, remove poverty-related diseases. Diarrhoea-related illnesses and malnutrition have kept child and infant mortality rates high in a great many developing countries and have as a result also kept life expectancies lower than was originally predicted by demographers. The very slow rate of improvement in infant mortality rates has been a cause of particular concern, emphasising the inability of parents in the fragile social and economic environments of many developing countries to be able to earn an adequate living to provide for themselves and their children.

4.2   Fertility

As with mortality trends, so also with fertility, it was anticipated incorrectly that the western experience would transfer to less developed countries. The expected decline in fertility levels in developing countries has not occurred as soon or as quickly as population experts initially predicted. To understand some of the reasons why these expectations were formulated and why they have not been well founded, it is necessary to return to considering the demographic transition as it occurred in western Europe.

What explanations have been offered for declining fertility levels? The central pivot of early demographic transition theory was that all aspects of demographic regimes were fundamentally influenced by industrialisation and modernisation, yet this fits uncomfortably with the empirical data for western Europe. Demographers suggest that it was France rather than the then more industrialised nation of England which was first to experience fertility decline. In a similar vein, most regions of western Europe, despite their diverse economic circumstances, had experienced some reduction in fertility between 1890 and 1920. Figure 1.9 shows that in Germany a

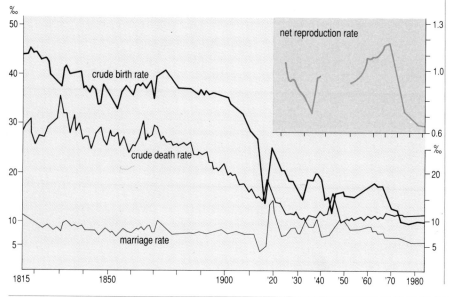

◀   Figure 1.9
Natural population change
in the Federal Republic of
Germany, 1815–1983.

sustained fall in fertility was evident from 1890. The diagram also shows that, despite the inevitable impacts of two major wars on both the crude birth and death rates of Germany, fertility in the long run has continued to fall until very recently, when it stabilised at a level slightly below mortality. In Germany, as in other west European countries, some of the reduction in fertility levels can be explained by the changing age of marriage, the increased involvement of women in the waged labour force, increased knowledge of and changing attitudes to contraception and new attitudes to family size, structure and formation. All of these factors are undoubtedly important, but the key issue is what determines these attitudes, with a continuing academic debate about the relative importance of cultural influences relative to the role of socio-economic structures and political contexts. Similar piecemeal explanations have been offered for the continuing high levels of fertility in many of the less developed countries.

Q   What socio-economic circumstances might encourage couples in the third world to have large families?

A   In the absence of adequate state welfare schemes to care for the elderly, one way to reduce the hardships of old age is perceived to be having many children who can provide for you. In the short term children may be seen to be potential wage-earners. This is particularly the case where parents do not have to support children throughout an extended education system and where agriculture depends on labour-intensive techniques. In urban situations in countries such as Brazil, India and Thailand, children are often significant wage-earners for the household. This situation occurs because of the difficulties of adults finding waged employment by comparison with the many jobs open to children in sweat-shops.

◄   *Children often have to contribute to the family income by working – as here in the rice harvest in the barrio of Lower Rugak, Agusan del Sur, Mindanao in the Philippines.*

An interesting extension of these ideas which can only be mentioned very briefly here is the work of the Australian demographer, J. Caldwell. In defending the view that it is economically rational for people in third world countries to have large families, he has proposed a theory of fertility change linked to the net direction of inter-generational wealth flows within the household. Where the economic context of a household results in a net transfer of wealth from children to parents because of the factors listed above and others, then it is entirely rational for parents to seek to have large families, while, as Caldwell (1982) points out, the increasing costs of having and supporting children in more developed countries has led to a reversal of the net wealth flows from older to younger generations. This is turn, he argues, has produced a progressive reduction in family sizes.

Caldwell's ideas remain to be fully tested, but they are interesting because unlike other work they focus the explanation neither on the individual decision-maker, nor on economistic arguments about the state, but rather on the fundamental demographic unit of the family. They lead naturally to an investigation of the relative significance of culture and economy in determining the roles of persons within the household and of the relations between production and reproduction within the household.

4.3 *Migration*

The relationship between household behaviour and the economic and cultural context is also explored by students of migration. Workers have often not been able to make an adequate living in agriculture and have transferred their labour to other sectors of the economy. To do this has usually also involved spatial relocation from a rural to an urban environment where there was the possibility of employment in industrial or service activities. Industrial developments in the more developed countries in the eighteenth and nineteenth centuries encouraged rural to urban migration during the historical phase where these countries were experiencing rapid population growth, although there was, of course, also massive migration of surplus population to settle in the 'New World'. Although in developing countries today massive population redistribution away from rural areas has been recorded, the character of urban growth has been rather different from that in western Europe and North America. In the discussion which follows, treatment of the labour migration process in contributing to urban growth is therefore separated into its effects in more developed and less developed countries. It should also be noted that although human migration from one environment to another happens for many different reasons (for example, marriage migration, residential relocation to find better accommodation) and at many different scales, what follows concerns only the category of movement known as **labour migration**.

The industrial revolution which occurred in Britain and in other countries in western Europe in the eighteenth and nineteenth centuries resulted in a redistribution of labour from agricultural to industrial activities. There was associated with this a geographical redistribution of population to the new centres of industrial activity, as labour was drawn into the industrial process. The rapid physical expansion of towns and cities was, according to A. Weber writing at the turn of the century, 'the most remarkable social phenomenon of the century'. The concentration of capital in production in urban areas required a parallel growth of the urban labour force. Industrial production favoured the increased division of labour with specialisation of economic functions, and this process accelerated as the scale of production rose from regional to national and then international levels. The famous Glasgow economist, Adam Smith, whose analysis of the nature of the division of labour was to earn him international renown, was also well aware of the consequences of industrial capitalism. Indeed he predicted that the workers needed to sustain the industrial process would also be 'brutalised' by urban living.

The pace of the industrialisation process was such that accommodation for the migrant workers had to be constructed very quickly. The exact form of the housing solutions provided for the rapidly growing industrial cities of western nations varied greatly from one city to another, creating geographical variety in the forms of 'problem' housing which these cities would have to deal with in the twentieth century. As the case study on Glasgow in Box 1.3 shows, the newly built housing stock for the city's Scottish migrant populations were mainly one- and two-room tenements, which were to make the city notorious in the early twentieth century as having one of the most overcrowded housing stocks in western Europe. Ironically in the eighteenth century the tenement housing stock was far from the worst available and Irish immigrants, because of their relative poverty and desire for accommodation close to the city's casual labour market, showed a 'strong predilection for the densely packed warrens of cheap housing in the central districts' (Gibb, 1988, p. 18).

Insanitary conditions in Glasgow and other industrial agglomerations clearly arose from a complex web of forces associated with the low incomes of the new industrial force and the inadequate physical environment in which they were expected to live. Figure 1.10 shows that Glasgow was not alone, and in some respects was much better than other comparable British cities, in terms of the high levels of infant mortality recorded as a result of the unsatisfactory physical environment which it was able to offer its citizens in the nineteenth century. It is ironic that the history of society's occupation of the natural environment has been one of progressive conquest towards a position where the physical forces of nature present relatively little threat to health and well-being, while at the same time there are many examples which show that nineteenth- and twentieth-century built environments have often proved alien, dangerous or deadly to significant portions of society.

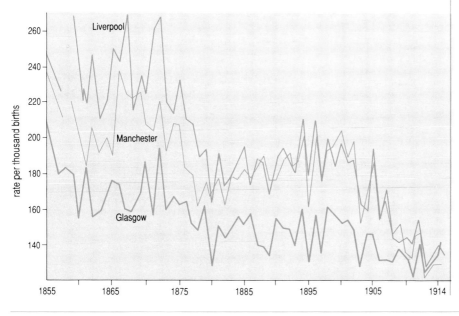

◀ Figure 1.10
Infant mortality in Glasgow, Liverpool and Manchester, 1855–1914.

Box 1.3   *Migration and the growth of industrial urban environments: the case of Glasgow*

The case of Glasgow, second city of the British empire in the nineteenth century, serves to illustrate these trends. Glasgow's early industrial and commercial growth was based on its trade in tobacco, linen and cotton textiles and sugar. By the second half of the nineteenth century, employment in shipbuilding and engineering began to rise in importance.*

In 1851, 56% of Glasgow's population were immigrants as defined by their place of birth. In addition to migrants from local labour sources, migrants also came from Ireland and by 1845 formed over a quarter of the city's population. Overall the city grew from having a mere 83 000 people in 1801 to a population of 761 000 a century later. Most of this growth, as in other industrial cities of western Europe, was due to the migration process.

The rate of growth was such that urban services were seldom able to keep pace with the demographic expansion which was taking place. Gibb (1988) notes that on the south side of Glasgow in 1831 there was only one doctor for the entire population. Similarly the urban environment was ill-equipped to house the immigrants. In the mid eighteenth century most working-class migrants lived either in unhealthy and overcrowded apartments in the 'backlands' around the city's central area or else in the city's infamous lodging houses. In the second half of the century purpose-built tenements were erected and to a certain extent delayed the city's housing crisis, since most of the new two-room tenement properties had to be designed to be affordable for the city's low-income population. Overcrowding and poverty provided an urban environment conducive to child neglect and was an obstacle to hygiene and the eradication of disease.

If Glasgow provided such a difficult, if not dangerous, environment in which to live, why did so many people move there during the nineteenth century? Part of the answer has already been given in terms of the rapid expansion of the industrial base of the city as a result of its favourable locus relative to Britain's growing economic role within the world economy. But population redistribution here as elsewhere was not only a function of the growth of labour demand in certain activities, but also a change in the requirements for labour in the areas from which the migrants were coming. In the case of Glasgow in the early nineteenth century three migrant streams can be seen to be sourced in areas where the capitalist mode of production was shifting its emphasis. Many migrants came from rural areas of Central Scotland where the enclosure movement was threatening to change their status from multiple

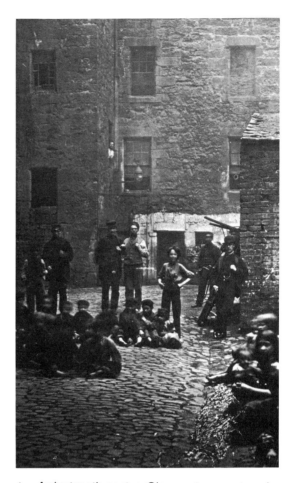

▲   *A nineteenth-century Glasgow tenement yard.*

tenancy farmers to hired labourers. A second stream came from the fragile and deteriorating economic environment of the Highlands which Gibb (1988, p.7) describes in neo-Malthusian terms as 'over-populated'. The final stream, already alluded to above, came from Ireland, which faced political unrest and industrial decline. The main waves of Irish came in the 1840s and 1850s during the country's appalling potato famines, paradoxically 'forced' to leave their homeland at the same time as Britain was shipping wheat in armed convoys to certain other parts of its empire.

*Details of how these and other industrial activities attracted migrants to Glasgow from all over Scotland have been documented by Gibb (1988) and it is based on his work that most of this case study is built.

If the industrial cities of western Europe in the eighteenth and nineteenth centuries provided precarious environments for human life and reproduction, the large cities of developing countries in the late twentieth century, as a result of very rapid rates of natural population increase and high levels of in-migration, have become the insecure living environments for an ever growing proportion of the world's population. It has been estimated that if current urban growth rates are sustained, then by the year 2000 there will be 25 cities in the world with more than 10 million inhabitants and of these 20 will be in the third world. By contrast in 1970 there were only four urban agglomerations of this size and three of them were in the more developed countries. If the projections are correct, then the world's largest centre in the year 2000 will be Mexico City with a staggering population of over 30 million. Migration has been the principal mechanism fuelling urban growth in many of the largest cities. 75% of the population increase of Lagos in the 1950s and 68% of the urban growth of São Paulo in the 1960s were due to migration. In the oil states even higher contributions have been made to urban growth both by rural–urban migration and international labour migration. For example, in the 1970s over 80% of the populations of the Saudi cities of Dammam, Jeddah, Riyadh and Taif were migrants. Most migrants to third world cities have concentrated in just one or two cities in each country. Usually these cities have been the former locus of colonial administration or major ports for the export of raw materials to the more developed countries.

Q   Can you think of any reasons why migration to third world cities in the twentieth century should be seen as a different phenomenon from migration to western cities in the nineteenth century?

▲   *The scale of international labour migration is demonstrated by these queues of refugees, waiting for food and water, in the Sha'laan 1 camp between Iraq and Jordan. Over 80 000 migrant workers from Bangladesh, India, Pakistan, Sri Lanka, Thailand and the Philippines from more than 2 million foreign nationals trapped in Iraq and Kuwait – engineers, sales executives, technicians etc. – were stranded in two camps in September 1990 after Iraq's annexation of Kuwait.*

◄ An example of work
in the informal sector –
pedalling a tricycle rickshaw
in India.

A   There are of course many differences of context, but one of the most
     important is that while rapid urbanisation in the west was related to
     a phase of concentration of capital in urban environments
     associated with the experience of industrialisation, in the third world
     many cities have little industrial base. Urban growth in the third world
     has not been closely associated with industrialisation, and, as a result,
     urban environments have developed in a very different way from in the
     west. For many migrants the third world city provides no secure waged
     employment in the so-called 'formal' sector, and instead they have been
     forced to seek a living in what have been termed 'survival' or 'informal
     sector' occupations. Such jobs might, for example, involve small-scale
     production of clothes, street vending of food or providing low-income
     transport systems such as rickshaws or tricyles. You will return to this
     subject in Chapter 7.

4.4   Summary

Population change is produced by a combination of fertility, mortality and
migration. The variation of each of these components is influenced at
household level by both cultural and economic factors. The highest rates of
population growth occur in the cities, whether in nineteenth-century
Europe or in the twentieth-century third world. The growth of these cities is
boosted by migration, which seems to reflect both urban–rural and
international differences in economic development.

5   Production, reproduction and population surplus

So far in this chapter attempts to explain population change have focused
mainly on the possible causal relationships between population change and
the physical and social environments. Economic arguments have been
introduced in looking at the demographic transition but it now becomes
pertinent to consider whether there might exist some wider link between
systems of economic production and patterns of demographic reproduction.

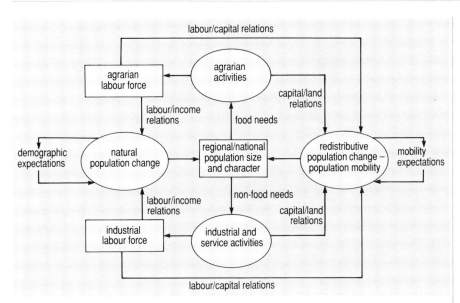

Figure 1.11 seeks to examine some of the ways in which the dynamics of
population change and economic development are interrelated. The
overall impression which it should give you is that ultimately the
demographic and economic systems interact in a circular and
interdependent fashion. The reasons why this is so will only become
apparent as you consider the individual linkages in the diagram.

Consider first the central box of the diagram relating to population size
and character. From this box flow two arrows indicating that a population
has certain food and non-food needs. Both Malthus and Boserup identified
this linkage between population and economy, but disagreed about how a
change in population size would impact on economic structure. Figure 1.11
suggests that the impact should be assessed in terms of at least three factors
– labour, capital and land. These three factors are sometimes taken, along
with enterprise, and described as the **factors of production**. Although an
abstract economic concept, what is meant by this is that these are the basic
building-blocks of economic activity. For example, population growth will
contribute to the labour force through increasing the number of potential
workers, and it will introduce new pressures on land availability through
the need to produce more food and non-food goods as well as through
increased need for residential, transport and recreational space.

Economic organisation in any one place or time may be differentiated
from that at another by the way that the factors of production are combined.
Both Malthus and Boserup investigated population change in relation to
some of the factors of production while holding other factors of production
constant. For example, Malthus writing at the beginning of the nineteenth
century could not conceive of the way in which human enterprise in the
form of the industrial revolution would transform the potential productivity
of the economy. As a result rising population and rising living standards no
longer proved self-checking in the way in which Malthus expected. Boserup
assumed that labour immobility in relation to finite land stocks would
produce new forms of human enterprise, while in practice, as has been
shown, population redistribution has often permitted labour to combine
with capital at new locations and within an industrial rather than

agricultural economic context. It becomes evident therefore that in terms of understanding the impact of population change on economic systems, greater thought is required about the ways in which the factors of production combine and in particular about the ways in which population growth results both in an increase in labour supply and in the demands placed on economic production through rising food and non-food needs.

The particular way in which a human society organises its productive activities is termed the **mode of production**. This involves not only the amount of labour, land or capital which is employed in a particular productive activity, but also the way that these factors of production are organised. Five major modes of production, or forms of economic organisation, are often identified: subsistence, slavery, feudalism, capitalism and socialism. These categories are themselves usually subdivided in more precise groupings to describe the ways in which the factors of production are combined. For the purposes of this discussion, however, what matters is that each of these modes of production has potentially different influences on patterns of demographic reproduction. Return again to Figure 1.11. Under the subsistence mode of production of the kind studied by Boserup in relation to, for example, shifting agriculture, agricultural labour is controlled by the cultivator who is working to produce for his or her own family's food needs. Production is controlled within the family with net wealth flows being from children to parents in the way proposed by Caldwell. High fertility may prove highly logical since more children may equate with more labour in the future and hence the potential for either cultivating a greater land area or of cultivating the land more intensively. Therefore under this mode of production and in the context of one particular agricultural environment – shifting cultivation – it becomes possible to see how organisation of the labour force may have implications for demographic circumstances, which in turn will have an influence on future population size and character.

Under capitalism the labourer owns none of the other factors of production but is free to sell his or her labour. Organisation of the labour force reflects the tension between those wishing to sell their labour for an adequate wage in order to be able to meet their food and non-food needs, and those controlling the other factors of production whose concern is to accumulate capital from the production process: this is achieved through the differential between the value of the work received from labour and the wages paid to labour, that is the 'surplus value'. Furthermore because labour is seldom producing food, industrial goods or services directly for its own needs, there may be a significant spatial separation between place of production and consumption allowing economic and geographical specialisation of production. Finally, this mode of production implies an exchange of 'value' between producers and consumers, and control of this exchange will be critical in determining whether a population's food and non-food needs are adequately met. (Consider again the previous discussion of population growth and famine in Ethiopia.)

A number of writers on population issues have recently begun to explore population–resource relationships from the perspective of their understanding of the forces underpinning the organisation of capitalist society. From this perspective the growth of population can be interpreted as having implications for society as a whole, and may be a trend which will either be encouraged or discouraged by those who mediate power within society. This search for a political-economy explanation has inevitably led to a consideration of the writings of Marx, who was first to recognise the need to understand how capitalism worked.

Marx was well aware of the writings of Malthus, but dismissed his work in a rather disparaging fashion. Marx's interest in population growth related to the fact that in his view it led to the creation of 'surplus population' as opposed to the Malthusian concept of 'overpopulation'. Surplus population created a potential expansion of the labour force.

> Surplus population . . . also becomes a condition for the existence of the capitalist mode of production. It forms a disposable industrial reserve army, which belongs to capital just as absolutely as if the latter had bred it at its own cost.   (Marx, 1976, p. 784)

The significance of **reserve armies of labour**, whether they be defined in terms of surplus population groups within a country or between different countries, is that they can be used to exert pressure on workers within the capitalist mode of production to keep wages low and to assure high levels of capital accumulation. From a Marxist perspective a fall in income per head does not arise simply because of population increase leading to a growth in labour supply relative to demand, but is sustained by economic and social structures operating to exploit tensions between owners of capital, employees and the unemployed. In the twentieth century the geographical control of most of the world's capital has been concentrated in the developed economies of North America, western Europe and Japan. The capitalist mode of production has, however, been 'exported', establishing production systems which operate on a world scale and which also involve the internationalisation of labour markets and finance. Each of these interrelated events can be argued to have had direct and indirect effects on the demographic circumstances of the less developed countries. For example, one phase in the emergence of international labour markets was the introduction of so-called 'guest workers' from less developed countries as a new 'reserve army' to be tapped by the industrial economies. In the 1980s there were estimated to be no less than 20 million international labour migrants mainly from the less developed countries working in either the more developed economies such as in the western European labour markets or in the oil-rich states of the Arab world.

Another example of the type of interrelationship which may exist between the changing scale of the capitalist mode of production and demographic patterns is the way in which the internationalisation of finance and unfavourable terms of trade with the more industrialised countries has led many developing countries into a situation of growing indebtedness. The combination of dropping oil prices and rising dollar interest rates in the early 1980s produced what has come to be termed the 'debt crisis'. A large number of developing countries (including Argentina, Brazil, Ivory Coast, Mexico, Morocco, Nigeria, Peru, the Philippines and Venezuela) had debts that in 1987 were, on average, valued at 60% of their Gross National Product. According to the World Bank, the third world's debt had risen still further by 1989 to record levels with the poorer states of the world being forced to use an increasing proportion of their limited incomes simply to service their debts. Since debt servicing can only be done in foreign currency, less developed nations can only meet their creditors demands by cutting back on much needed imports (such as food), by diverting goods produced on the home market into exports, or by replacing production for the home market by production for export (as for example in the replacement of domestic food production by cash crop production). The need to pay for their increasing debts has therefore forced many less developed countries to reduce production geared to meeting the needs of their own populations (hence reducing living standards) and to reorganise the production of their economies (and labour forces) in such a way as to be able to earn more foreign currency (consider again the links in Figure 1.11). The International Monetary Fund has estimated that output in the world's debtor nations rose by only 1.1% in 1989 while the populations of these countries rose by 2.0%. One consequence has therefore been a lowering of living standards in these nations and consequently a reinforcement of inequalities in life chances. This may be one factor sustaining the continued spatial unevenness in demographic patterns such as in the global pattern of life expectancies.

International differentials in life expectancies do not, of course, arise because of deliberate malevolent actions, and there is ample evidence to show that people living in western capitalist nations do not desire people in the less developed countries to have shorter lives. Rather, differentials exist because of 'the **core–periphery structure** of the world economy, whereby the life chances of the population of the periphery are subordinated to those of the population of the core' (Johnston, 1989, p. 222).

Differentials in life expectancy and other demographic indicators do, of course, arise from a whole range of intertwined forces and not only because of the outworkings of any one economic process, such as the international system of indebtedness discussed above. It does, however, seem plausible to suggest that the way economic systems are structured by the capitalist mode of production has had a significant influence on demographic processes. If this statement is true it would also seem logical to expect that states which have sought to follow rather different economic courses such as radical socialist economies would also have produced distinctive demographic conditions as a result. Before examining this through considering the case of China (in Box 1.4), it is important to balance the arguments which have been presented by stating that most students of development issues, while accepting the thesis that economic structures have an influence on demographic processes, also recognise that demographic processes are not determined solely by the economic environment in which they occur. As shown earlier in Figure 1.11, economic processes influence demographic factors, but these in turn affect economic organisation. Thus 'population has an absolute dimension which in turn has implications for accumulation and the distribution of capital' (Corbridge, 1986, p. 103).

5.1   Summary

This chapter has explored some of the relations which exist between population processes and environmental circumstances. It has been pointed out that selective conceptions of population environment and population–resource relationships posited by Malthus and others have only limited validity. Population issues seem increasingly to relate to the social and economic contexts of demographic processes, rather than to circumstances determined by physical or ecological forces. Conversely it is not so much population numbers as the technological and sociological bases by which specific population groups seek to meet their needs which determines the impact they have on their immediate physical environment, as well as on environments in other parts of the globe. Understanding the social and economic environments appears to be increasingly critical in exploring and explaining the associations which exist between economic production and demographic reproduction in both rural and urban areas.

Box 1.4   China's population policy

The absolute dimension to population was well recognised by the Chinese communist leader, Mao. His interpretation of the role of demographic reproduction relative to the economic functions of production within a socialist state experienced an interesting reversal through time. Mao moved from an early stance favouring high population growth rates to a Chinese population policy which later forcefully endorsed a strict birth control programme. This perhaps reflected a shift from a view of people as being equated to labour with productive value, to the perception of people as also being consumers requiring food and shelter which a socialist state should seek to provide and distribute in an equitable fashion. To achieve this goal was clearly going to be easier if China's population growth could be slowed, and if, as a result of having fewer children, women's energies could be engaged in the labour force. In the 1970s birth control became a national priority in China, if the country's very rapid population growth was not to exacerbate (as distinct from causing) the country's problems in producing sufficient food, housing and jobs for the 1 billion Chinese. The government established its policy in the early 1970s using the slogan *wan-xi-shao* (later, longer, fewer). This meant later marriage, a longer interval between children and few children per couple. Initially a two-child family was advocated in urban areas and three in rural areas, but in 1979 China instituted a 'one couple, one child' policy: see Plate 2.

    This policy has in fact encountered severe difficulties with more than 90% of rural families wanting two or more children and only about half the

urban population being willing to conform to the one-child norm (Jowett, 1989). Inevitably data on births in a country with a policy of this kind are difficult to interpret. The data which do exist suggest that in 1987 only 51.7% of births were in fact first births and that the remaining 48.3% were second, third or subsequent births. Enforcement of the one child policy via a series of incentives for those complying with government policy and a range of penalties for those couples failing to do so has therefore so far failed to achieve the target of the one-child family. The policy has faced the greatest difficulties in the rural areas of China and amongst ethnic minority groups. Despite this it must be acknowledged that China has succeeded in greatly reducing its fertility levels. During the 1970s the birth rate was halved and by the early 1980s China's TFR stood at 2.4, only slightly above the replacement level. By contrast developing countries with a similar level of GNP per capita to China had an average TFR of over 6.0. China therefore represents the case of a socialist regime which has as a result of its policies produced demographic changes out of character with those found in market economies at the same level of economic development (Jowett, 1989). These changes have, however, only been achieved at the expense of the loss of considerable personal freedom. It is also important to note that even in a radical socialist regime willing to impose its policies in a very forceful fashion, there would appear to be limits to the extent to which demographic change can be engineered by those in control of a particular socio-economic environment.

Answer to Activity

Activity 1

Your graph should look like this:

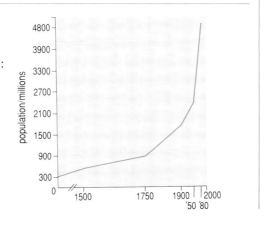

References

BOSERUP, E. (1980) *Population and Technology*, Oxford, Basil Blackwell.

CALDWELL, J. (1982) *Theory of Fertility Decline*, London, Academic Press.

CORBRIDGE, S. (1986) *Capitalist World Development*, London, Macmillan.

GIBB, A. (1988) 'The demographic consequences of rapid industrial growth', Occasional Papers, No. 24, Department of Geography, University of Glasgow.

HOBCRAFT, J., McDONALD, J. and RUTSTEIN, S. (1984) 'Socio-economic factors in infant and child mortality', *Population Studies*, Vol. 38, pp. 193–224.

JOHNSTON, R. (1989) 'The individual and the world economy', in Johnston, R. and Taylor, P. (eds) *The World in Crisis*, Oxford, Blackwell.

JOWETT, A. (1989) 'China's one child programme', *Applied Population Research Unit Discussion Papers* 89/3, Department of Geography, University of Glasgow.

MARX, K. (1976) *Capital*, Vol. 1, Harmondsworth, Penguin Books (*Das Kapital* written 1867–94).

SMITH, P. (1990) 'Natural hazards', Ch. 6 in Silvertown, J. and Sarre, P. (eds) *Environment and Society*, London, Hodder and Stoughton/The Open University (Book One of this series).

WOOD, A. (1985) 'Population redistribution and agricultural settlement schemes in Ethiopia', pp. 84–111, in Clarke, J. *et al.* (eds) *Population and Development Projects in Africa*, Cambridge, Cambridge University Press.

WOODS, R. (1982) *Theoretical Population Geography*, London, Longman.

Further reading

FINDLAY, A. and FINDLAY, A. (1987) *Population and Development in the Third World*, London, Routledge.

JONES, H. (1990) *Population Geography* (2nd edn), Ch. 7, London, Paul Chapman.

WOODS, R. (1989) 'Malthus, Marx and population crises', in Johnston, R. and Taylor, P. (eds) *A World in Crisis?*, Oxford, Blackwell, pp. 151–74.

1   Introduction

The previous chapter has shown that there has been progressively faster growth of the human population through history, with the fastest rate occurring over the last few decades. This increase has been made possible by equally rapid growth in the supply of food, largely as a result of transformations in agriculture. However, these developments raise a number of questions for environmentalists, of which this chapter considers three:

- How have agricultural systems adjusted to the variety of ecosystems, soils and climatic zones which exist in different parts of the world?
- Which systems have been and are the most productive?
- What problems have these agricultural systems created?

As so often happens, the questions are not as straightforward as they appear when one begins to attempt to answer them. It is certainly the case that environmental factors constrain what can be grown, but, as *Simmons* (in Silvertown and Sarre (eds), 1990) has shown, cultural differences and technology also play important roles: there are great differences between the products of subsistence farmers and of commercial producers even where environmental conditions are similar. These differences also arise when considering productivity, because productivity can be defined in a number of ways: by relating output per worker, or per hectare, by cost of inputs and so on. Finally, in considering problems brought about by agriculture, it turns out that not only do some highly productive systems generate serious problems like soil erosion, water pollution and poisoning of wildlife, but they are also dependent on high inputs of energy and materials which may not be sustainable in the long term. There may be problems for the future being stored up, especially in relation to feeding a growing world population.

    The structure of the chapter will be dictated by the three questions. Section 2 will show how the current variety of agricultural systems has resulted from a combination of environmental and social factors. Section 3 will explore the different kinds of productivity and Section 4 will consider how the concept of sustainability brings together the impacts of agriculture and problems of its dependence on energy and materials inputs.

2 The origins and diversity of agricultural systems

2.1 Introduction

From the array of flora and fauna particular to the world's biomes (that is, the natural major vegetation types) and the ecosystems which existed about 12 000 years ago, the first 'farmers' selected their crops and animals for domestication and began the first agriculture. The distribution of the world's biomes reflected the distribution of temperature, rainfall and solar radiation, resulting in the spread of vegetation types from equatorial forest to the tundra of the sub-Arctic and the high mountains (as described by *Silvertown* (1990a), Sections 2.2 and 3.2). This broad climatic framework is still the main influence on the pattern of agriculture, although it has been affected by vegetation change and human influence has changed the limits of growth of particular crops.

The section will look first at the origins of agriculture with the domestication of particular plants and animals, the global dispersal of selected plants and at the limitations imposed on this by these climatic features. Some of the ecological factors relevant to the development of agriculture are also outlined.

2.2 Agricultural beginnings

The first evidence of animal and plant domestication dates from about 10–12 000 BP.* Remarkably rapidly – in the context of human history – hunter-gatherers were displaced or became sedentary cultivators or pastoralists. By 2000 BP farming had penetrated to most parts of the globe and the hunter-gatherers were pushed into the areas least suitable for cultivators.

Although plants and animals were domesticated at a number of places on the Earth's surface, five areas are particularly important to the subsequent development of agriculture (see Figure 2.1). First is south-west Asia and the eastern Mediterranean where the first agricultural communities appeared in upland areas; cattle, sheep and goats were domesticated and wheat, barley and later lentils, peas, flax, olives, vines and figs were grown. These crops and animals were later adopted in the irrigated floodplains of the Tigris and Euphrates and the Nile. They were subsequently carried westwards along the shores of the Mediterranean, and wheat and barley were taken north of the Alps. Farming was first practised on the shores of the North Sea and the Baltic by about 6000 BP.

A second major area of plant domestication was in south-east Asia. Two types of agriculture appeared here: vegeculture, where parts of the growing plant were cut and planted, using the taro, the Asiatic yam, breadfruit, sago and bananas; second, and more important, was the domestication of rice, which spread into India, China and later Indonesia, where it has become the dominant type of farming in deltas and river valleys. Pigs, chickens, ducks and geese were domesticated in this area.

In China there was a third centre in the north where millet, soya beans and the mulberry were domesticated. Little is known of the early history of

*This book uses the convention of time 'before the present' (BP), by adding 2000 years to BC dates.

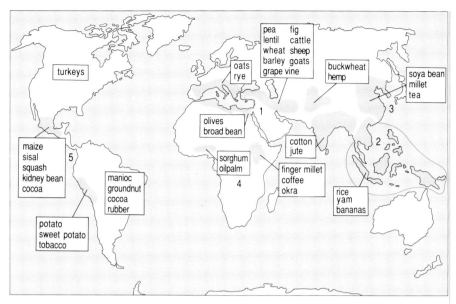

▲   Figure 2.1   Regions of plant domestication. The areas numbered 1–5 are the
earliest and most important. The other areas were later in time or involved fewer and
less important varieties.

agriculture in the fourth area – Africa – since evidence of early farming
systems (seeds etc.) are preserved better in semi-arid conditions, but African
yams and oilpalms were domesticated in West Africa by about three
thousand years ago, and some crops were domesticated in Ethiopia.

The Americas were the fifth area of early domestication and a quite
different set of plants and animals were domesticated there: maize, squash
and beans in Central America, manioc (or cassava) in the lowlands of the
Amazon basin, and potatoes in the Andes. Only the turkey was of much
importance as a domesticated animal.

Despite all the developments since, humankind is still basically
dependent on choices made by primitive peoples in particular climatic zones
thousands of years ago. There are still only about 20 major crops in
agricultural production in the United States and Europe, compared with an
estimate of 200 000 species of wild plants, animals and micro-organisms in
the US alone. Even now, six species of domestic animals predominate as
food sources and all were domesticated at least 4000 years ago.

2.3   Underlying ecological principles

Even from this brief description of the origins of agriculture, it is clear that
different centres of domestication involved very different combinations of
plants and animals, even though all societies had the same goal of providing
an adequate diet. In part, the need to select from local wild species explains
the differences, but the variety in various parts of the world historically
shows that many combinations of roots, cereals, animals and fruit can
provide the essential dietary components – carbohydrates, proteins, fats,
minerals and vitamins. In making these initial selections, early farmers were
influenced by a number of ecological principles.

● *It was necessary to strike a balance between staple crops that provide mainly carbohydrates and those foods which provide greater inputs of proteins, fats, vitamins and so on. Such decisions were influenced by the productivity of particular crops and the efficiency of substitution of foods 'higher up' the food chain.*

Plants use solar energy to synthesise simple carbohydrates (sugar, starch, cellulose etc.) from carbon dioxide and water; this is the process known as **photosynthesis** (see Section 2.3 of *Silvertown*, 1990b). Green plants are the only primary producers of foodstuffs; humans cannot photosynthesise atmospheric carbon compounds for themselves, so they are dependent on plants for all their food, either directly or indirectly.

The average energy requirement is about 10.4 MJ per capita per day, most coming from carbohydrates and fats (see Box 2.1). Crops vary in the amount of energy they supply but starch is the principal component of some very productive staple crops, especially in the wet tropics where bananas and root crops such as cassava, sago and yams mean that carbohydrates supply four-fifths or more of the total energy supply. These starchy crops are, however, low in protein (lower than cereals) and therefore need to be supplemented by a protein-rich food such as beans, fish or meat.

There is a second stage in the **food chain**. Grass, grains and root crops can be eaten by livestock, as herbivores, and the products of the animal – meat, eggs or dairy products – eaten by humans, who are omnivores. However, the energy available in meat is a very small proportion of the energy stored in plants. Thus the energy in meat from cattle fed on corn in the United States is one twentieth of the energy in the corn; on ranches in the western United States cattle feed upon a very sparse scrub, and the meat produced per square hectare is only one sixtieth of the energy in this plant cover. Consequently, growing crops is always a far more efficient way of producing food calories than raising livestock: there is always a loss of energy in conversion from plant to animal.

The difference between ruminants and non-ruminants is of great importance. Ruminants – sheep, goats and cattle – can digest cellulose and hence feed upon grass and much of the natural vegetation. They can consequently utilise land which is not climatically suitable for growing food crops and so produce food for human beings from inferior land. Single-stomached animals such as pigs and poultry, in contrast, cannot digest the cellulose in grass and feed mainly upon grain or scraps. In poor countries

Box 2.1   Measuring energy

You may be familiar with seeing the amount of energy that can be derived by oxidizing food given in kilocalories, for instance on food packaging. However, SI units are being increasingly used, so the joule (J) is being adopted as the unit of energy.

A joule is the amount of energy supplied by a watt acting for a second. The rate at which the body consumes energy varies according to what is being done: 70 W when resting in bed, 180 W when walking, 380 W for fast walking.

It is convenient for most purposes to use the total energy expended in 24 hours, that is the average wattage multiplied by 86 400 seconds. Because the

resulting number is large, it is usually expressed in megajoules (MJ = 10^6 J = 1 000 000 J): thus resting in bed expends 6.05 MJ and fast walking 32.83 MJ per day.

The same unit is used to measure the energy content of food. Someone doing manual labour requires about 12.5 MJ (or 3 000 kilocalories) per day, while an agricultural worker may need 15 MJ. Adults in well-fed societies consume about 14 MJ a day, or 31% above their probable requirement, while the average person in the third world may have only 8.9 MJ, well below their needs.

In Chapter 4, Figure 4.8 you will come across gigajoules (GJ):

1 GJ = 10^9 J = 1 000 000 000 J or 1 000 MJ

they are scavengers and are very useful in getting rid of such wastes, utilising ground unsuitable for anything else, and producing meat and eggs as well. When such animals are stall-fed on food which could have been used for human consumption or which was grown on land which could have been used to grow such food, then it is a very inefficient form of production: it takes about 8 kg of grain to produce 1 kg of pork. Intensive production of beef is even less efficient, taking 20 kg of grain for 1 kg of beef. Over 90% of the grain consumed per head of the US population is in the form of meat, poultry and dairy products; two-thirds of their daily protein intake is of animal origin, compared with a world average of 25%.

● *The second decision which had to be made was how to maintain soil fertility.*

For growth, crops need from the soil nitrogen, potassium and phosphorus compounds and traces of another thirteen elements. The most important nutrient is nitrogen, and an insufficiency of nitrogen in the soil is the factor most commonly limiting crop growth.

In a natural ecosystem, nitrogen is obtained from the atmosphere, which is 79% nitrogen, but in this gaseous form is not usable; it has to be formed into nitrogenous compounds – or fixed – by the action of bacteria in the soil. Some of these are free-living, and **fix nitrogen** at a low rate; others exist in a symbiotic relationship with leguminous plants and fix at a much higher rate: clover can fix 400 kg of nitrogen per hectare per annum.

Where a crop is eaten, by people or animals, on the ground where it was grown and when all the waste including their excretions are spread again on the ground, there is more or less a closed cycle: most of the elements are returned for use by the next crop. But when the crop is eaten elsewhere, the soil is steadily depleted of nitrogen, phosphorus, potassium and so on. In order to preserve the nitrogen content of soil and hence its fertility, farmers must find a means of returning to the soil the nutrients which have been taken out by the crop. This can be done in a number of ways:

● cropland is abandoned after growing crops for 2–3 years and the field colonised by the local vegetation (**shifting cultivation** with **bush fallowing**): thus a cycle between vegetation, organic litter and soil is re-established and after a long period (10–40 years) soil fertility is restored;

● crops can be grown alternately with grass which increases the soil's organic matter and improves soil structure (**fallowing**);

● leguminous crops can be grown alternately with other crops (**crop rotation**): these include peas, beans, lentils, soya beans and clover; they all aid fixation of nitrogen in the soil;

● the dung of livestock kept by the farmer can be deposited on land used for growing crops (*organic fertiliser*); dung contains nitrogen, potassium and phosphates;

● the cultivation of 'paddy' rice is a special case: it requires the crop to be grown partially submerged in water and blue-green bacteria thrive in these conditions and have the ability to fix nitrogen (this is discussed in detail in Chapter 3).

Farmers have always used a variety of fertilisers such as human excreta, marl, horse dung and crop residues. Bones were ground to provide phosphorus. Although traditional means of providing nitrogen are still used, the use of manufactured nitrogen fertilisers has had a great impact on farming and has increased dramatically in the developed countries in the last fifty years (see Section 3.3).

● *The third decision was how to deal with weeds and pests.*

Within a natural ecosystem a large number of plant species occupy the land. A natural ecosystem is always moving to equilibrium and it is this diversity of species which directly contributes to the stability of the system. In farming, in contrast, the aim is to simplify this system and to produce only one crop from each field, and often hectare after hectare of the same crop. Farmers therefore set out to reduce the number of species of plants, animals and micro-organisms: any that are not economically useful are eliminated. After such an alteration, 'successional change' begins and the ecosystem slowly accumulates additional species; under natural conditions, gradually a new complex and stable ecosystem would evolve. The improved conditions that are made available to the crop are attractive to other plants – that is, weeds – which will also colonise the field and use water and plant nutrients that could be used by the crop plants. Farmers thus spend much of their time trying to remove weeds. This is done by ploughing and hoeing in traditional farming systems and, in modern farming, by spraying with herbicides.

An equal problem for the farmer is that of pests, which include small animals like rabbits and birds, but more importantly insects and bacteria. In traditional agriculture, growing crops in rotation and alternating crops and grass partially reduce the level of plant disease; in the tropics **intercropping**, where several crops are grown on the same plot, does occur. However, where one crop predominates, and is grown year after year, there is obviously the danger that if a disease takes hold, the consequences are going to be much more serious, as it will attack the entire crop. It thus becomes increasingly vital to protect the crop from such risks and chemical pesticides have to be used on a habitual basis. Pesticides kill all 'pests', including any natural predators; even if the original pest is killed, this may leave an ecological niche into which another may move. Pesticides have thus removed farming from having to attempt to fit in to some kind of ecological balance; they can be crude weapons in a very complex system and thus always risk unforeseen consequences.

◀ *Subsistence agriculture in Rwanda, showing a farmer and her child hoeing their land. Crops grown on these steep hillsides include cassava intercropped with beans, bananas and, in some areas, tea.*

2.4   Farming methods

The earliest farmers in every region used the simplest tools – digging sticks, hoes and the sickle – with shifting cultivation methods. The first fundamental technical advance was the ox-drawn plough, developed in the Middle East 4–5000 years ago; it later spread into Europe, India and China, but not into tropical Africa until the twentieth century, where it is still less important than the hoe, and not into the Americas until after 1492.

After the invention of the plough, the most important changes were the wider growth of legume crops to fix nitrogen in the soil and the use of cattle dung. Implements were slowly improved: in northern Europe the mouldboard plough allowed the cutting of grass sods, more effective destruction of weeds and effective ploughing of heavy clay soils.

Plant dispersal

Until the nineteenth century perhaps the most important way of improving agriculture was by the exchange of plants. Crops domesticated in particular regions were slowly taken to other regions; thus by 2000 BP wheat, domesticated in the Near East 10–11 000 years ago, was grown in Europe, North Africa, northern India and northern China. The exchange of plants was greatly accelerated by the European voyages of discovery that began in the fifteenth century when the Portuguese reached China and Columbus the Americas. Farming was transformed by the crops that European settlers took with them together with the plough that was unknown to the Amerindians. More dramatic was the introduction of horses, cattle, pigs and chickens. But plants indigenous to the Americas had equally remarkable effects upon other parts of the world. The potato and maize increased the food output of Europe in the eighteenth and nineteenth centuries; in the nineteenth and twentieth centuries maize and cassava became staple crops in tropical Africa.

The exchange of crops did not greatly affect the staple food crops of Asia, although maize, peanuts, sweet potatoes and cassava became important supplementary food crops, but cash crops were introduced by Europeans which profoundly altered local economies. In the late nineteenth century rubber proliferated in Malaya and Indonesia; earlier in the century tea from China had been adopted in India and Ceylon, and groundnuts from the Americas became a major cash crop in West Africa, coffee was taken from Africa to Brazil and to Indonesia. The process has continued into the twentieth century: improved rice varieties bred in the Philippines have supplanted the indigenous varieties in much of the rest of Asia, and wheat of Mexican origin is now widely grown in northern India.

Q   Would this trade in plant varieties increase or decrease the variety of plants being grown?

A   While it would potentially increase the variety of useful plants which could be grown in any particular area, the overall effect has been to reduce variety in several ways. Of the huge numbers of naturally occurring plant species, only about a thousand have been domesticated and most of the area under cultivation is devoted to quite a small number, as shown in Table 2.1. Finally, the breeding of improved varieties means that increasingly large proportions of the areas devoted to each major crop are sown with a few types of seed (discussed in Section 3.3).

Table 2.1   *Areas under cultivation of the ten most widely grown crops, 1985*

	Million hectares	% of total arable area
Cereals	721.0	49.0
Oilseeds, nuts and kernels	149.0	10.0
Pulses	65.0	4.4
Roots and tubers	46.0	3.1
Cotton[1]	33.1	2.2
Sugar-cane and beet	24.6	1.7
Vegetables and fruit	23.5	1.6
Coffee	10.6	0.7
Cocoa	5.1	0.3
Tobacco	4.6	0.3
Total arable area	1475	
Total percentage		73.3

Note: [1]Data for 1971.

Source: FAO (1987) *Production Yearbook 1986*, Vol. 40, Rome.

The industrialisation of agriculture

As well as the dissemination of crops, there were other profound changes in agriculture from the middle of the nineteenth century as traditional methods were supplemented and then replaced by techniques which depended upon scientific advances and the industrial production of inputs.

First was the substitution of power based upon commercial energy for human and animal muscle. Threshing by steam power had largely replaced the flail in Britain by the 1860s, and steam was being applied, although not very successfully, to ploughing. In the 1890s the first tractors were produced in the United States, although it was not until after the Second World War that they finally replaced horses in North America and western Europe. Machinery began to replace labour, especially in harvesting grain: the reaper, which cut grain, was invented in the United States in the 1830s and slowly adopted in western Europe; later the reaper-binder cut and bound the grain in stooks, and finally the combine harvester both cut and threshed. The latter was first used in the 1880s in California, but it is only since 1950 that it has replaced the reaper-binder. Milking machines, cotton pickers, sugarbeet harvesters and a variety of other machines have greatly reduced labour needs, mainly since 1950.

The invention of the internal combustion engine made the machinery less bulky and easier to use. Tractors with their multitude of attachments have proliferated. Their increasing size and power have allowed vast areas to come under cultivation.

The use of chemical fertilisers dates from the 1840s, but the critical advance was the discovery in 1910 of a way to fix nitrogen. Similarly herbicides and pesticides were used in the late nineteenth century, but only since 1950 have they transformed farming in North America and western Europe. Breeding of improved varieties of crops began after 1900; advances in plant genetics have allowed breeders to produce crops immune from specific diseases and extremely responsive to fertilisers.

◁   A thresher powered by a steam engine. The portable steam engine was steadily improved through the 1850s and 1860s and gave great flexibility as a source of power on the farm.

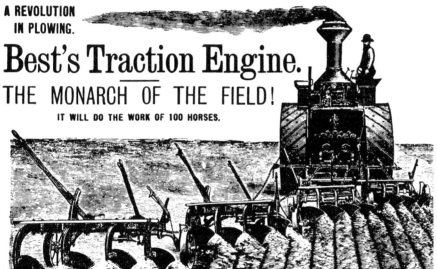

A REVOLUTION IN PLOWING.

Best's Traction Engine.

THE MONARCH OF THE FIELD!

IT WILL DO THE WORK OF 100 HORSES.

◁   An advertisement in Pacific Rural Press in 1890, when, it was claimed, twenty-two such engines were in operation.

◁   Lifting sugar beet at Sawston in Cambridgeshire: large-scale machinery has enabled more land to be brought into intensive cultivation while numbers of agricultural workers have declined.

◀   *A trailer full of grain at the 45 000 ton grain store in Wimblington, Cambridgeshire. Improvements in storage technology have been required to accommodate large surpluses.*

A critical contribution has been made by improvements in storage. Pre-industrial agriculture experienced massive losses of stored food through decomposition and attack by pests. Industrialisation allowed the development of structures more resistant to rodents and insects, drying, temperature and humidity control, freezing, pesticides and, most recently, irradiation. Better storage has allowed larger quantities of food from more varied sources to reach consumers in better condition, although there are still substantial post-harvest losses due to micro-organisms, insects and rodents, estimated to range from 9% in the United States to as much as 20% in some developing countries, especially those in the tropics. Recently, some storage technologies have themselves been questioned, but the net benefits have been great, with room for further improvement in the third world.

2.5   *Climate and crop distribution*

The movement of plants was in response to social, economic and scientific factors, but climatic factors remain a primary control of the particular location and the broad pattern of crop distribution. The two climatic factors of greatest importance in limiting the areas available for particular crops are rainfall and temperature.

Rainfall and crop growth

Rainfall provides the moisture in the soil that is essential for crop growth. Plants act as highly efficient pumping machines, taking water from the soil, incorporating some of it in their tissues and releasing the remainder into the atmosphere: this is **transpiration**. Every plant has a root system with an enormous total surface area to draw this water from the soil. Wheat takes only 350 to 500 kg of water to produce a kilogram of dry wheat plant, whereas the same amount of rice needs about 2200 kg; this is equivalent to about 1500 kg of water for one kilo of wheat grain, and 10 000 kg of water to produce a kilo of rice.

A sufficient amount of water is vital to plant growth: with too little water the plant wilts and dies. However, crop yields do not increase with every increase in water supply. For every crop there is an optimum amount, and with further increases yields begin to decline. The moisture requirements of individual crops vary greatly. Wheat and rye, for example, are grown mainly in areas where the annual rainfall is between 25.40 cm (10″) and 101.60 cm (70″). In contrast rubber needs over 178 cm and tea over 254 cm. Over half the Earth's land surface receives between 25.40 and 101.60 cm, so that wheat can be – and is – widely grown. But only 10% of the land has more than 178 cm, and only 5% over 254 cm, so that tea and rubber have a much more restricted distribution.

The amount of water available in the soil for the crop is not a function solely of rainfall since part of the rain is **evaporated**. The rate of evaporation increases with temperature, so that crops in the tropics need higher rainfall than those in the temperate zone (although even in Britain, from an annual rainfall of 90 cm, 38.10 cm evaporates before it can be used, and 46 cm flows back to the sea). Figure 2.2 was derived from the difference between mean annual rainfall and potential **evapotranspiration** (the loss from evaporation and transpiration). It shows where crop growth is impossible without

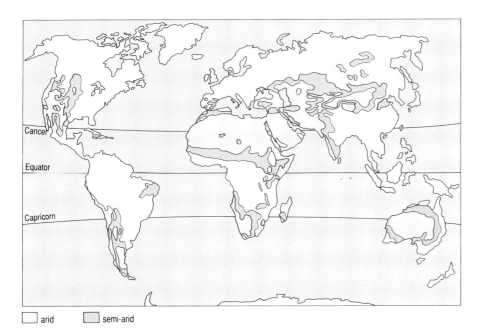

☐ arid   ▨ semi-arid

▲   *Figure 2.2   The distribution of arid and semi-arid climates.*

additional water – the arid zone – and where farming is possible without it
but difficult – the semi-arid zone.

The semi-arid zone presents particular problems. Farmers there can
only grow crops that are tolerant of low rainfall, such as millet, sorghum and
wheat. But rainfall in both the arid and semi-arid zones is much more variable
than in humid areas and consequently there is a higher probability that
rainfall will fall below the minimum requirements for the crop and it will fail,
or yields will be substantially reduced.

The total global supply of fresh water cannot be significantly added to,
but it is possible to increase the efficiency with which it is distributed and
thus to mitigate the effects of shortfalls or drought periods. This is done
through **irrigation**, either from groundwater, as in parts of the south-
western United States, or from rivers that rise in humid areas outside the
desert and then cross it to the sea; the Nile, Colorado, Indus, Tigris and
Euphrates are examples (see Box 2.2 below). With clear skies and high
temperatures these arid and semi-arid areas provide ideal conditions for
crop growth.

Temperatures

Temperature is an important determinant of the distribution of crops,
and they can be divided into two categories: those crops adapted to
the temperature conditions of the tropics, and those adapted to the lower
temperatures of the subtropics and temperate areas.

A number of crops grown only in the tropics are severely damaged if
temperatures fall below 0°C and frosts occur; others are even more
susceptible to cold and will die if temperatures fall below 10°C. For most
tropical crops growth is most rapid when temperatures are 31°–37°C.

Most crops grown in the subtropics and the temperate zone have both
poleward and equatorial limits. Polewards, the **growing season** – the period
between the last frost in winter and the first frost in autumn – diminishes
(see Figure 2.3) so that the number of crops that can be grown declines (see
Figure 2.4). North of the Arctic Circle only rye and oats have any significance.

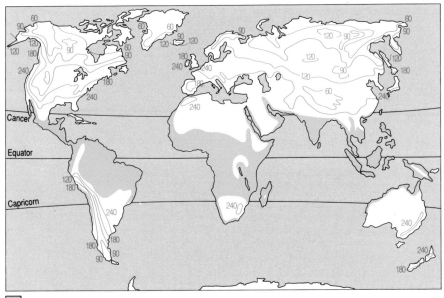

☐ areas without frost

◀ *Figure 2.3
Frost-free period in days.*

Many temperate and subtropical crops also have limits of cultivation towards the equator. Some of these crops require a cold period to trigger growth, a process called **vernalisation**, will not thrive in higher rainfall, and are susceptible to diseases found in the tropics. However, it will be seen from Figure 2.4 that potatoes and most of the cereals are in fact grown at or near the equator.

Q How can temperate crops be grown near the equator?

A The effect of altitude is to lower the average temperature. Because of this, temperate crops can be grown at higher altitudes.

Arable land is absent from the cold, dry and mountainous areas of the world; it is also uncommon in the humid tropics. Here the rate of net photosynthesis is surprisingly low. This is because cloud cover reduces the amount of solar radiation received; further, although gross photosynthesis rates are high, respiration is also high, because of the high temperatures at night, so that net photosynthesis is low, indeed lower than in middle latitudes. Although this does not preclude cultivation, it is compounded by difficulties with tropical soils, which are exposed to higher rainfall and temperatures than are soils in the temperate zone, and have made it difficult to use farming systems other than shifting cultivation, bush-fallowing and the growth of perennial crops.

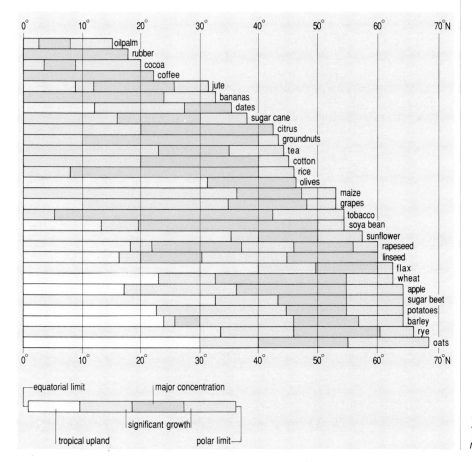

◀ Figure 2.4
The latitudinal spread of the major crops.

2.6   An overview of world agriculture

In spite of millennia of effort by subsistence farmers, several centuries of
world trade in agricultural products and a century of commercial farming
using machinery, chemicals and selective breeding, Figure 2.5 shows that
the present area of cultivation is rather limited. This area could be extended,
and perhaps doubled, though this would be extremely costly. However,
constraints of climate, slope, soil and pests will continue to limit arable uses
to a small minority of the land surface. Table 2.2 shows that much larger
areas are useable as pasture and forest, as well as showing variations
between continents. A third of the total land area is too cold and too dry to be
useable for the growth of food, fibre or fuel.

Farms differ from each other in a great number of ways. There are
variations in the crops that are grown, in the type of livestock kept, in the
relative importance of crops and livestock in the farmer's income, in the level
of technology, the amount of labour used per acre, and in the proportion of
the output retained upon the farm. Differences in farm size and the type of
land tenure are also important. It is thus exceedingly difficult to group farms
into types of agriculture even for a small region, and a satisfactory
classification of world agriculture has never been made. However, Derwent
Whittlesey's classification of the major types and distribution map
(Figure 2.6), made over fifty years ago, is still a useful guide.

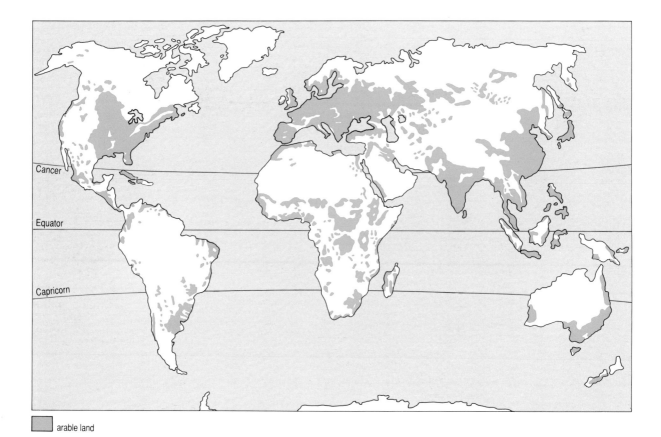

arable land

▲   *Figure 2.5   The world distribution of arable land.*

Q   Compare Figure 2.6 with Figures 2.2 and 2.3 and pick out at least two major climatic effects on agriculture.

Table 2.2   Patterns of world land use, 1985 (million hectares)

	Land area	%	Arable	%	Pasture	%	Forest	%	Other	%
North America	1838	100	236	12.8	272	14.8	591	32.2	738	40.2
Europe	472	100	139	29.4	84	17.8	155	32.8	94	20.2
Oceania	842	100	50	5.9	453	53.8	159	18.9	179	21.4
USSR	2227	100	232	10.4	374	16.8	935	42.0	687	30.8
Africa	2964	100	184	6.2	788	26.6	697	23.5	1295	43.7
Latin America	2054	100	180	8.8	553	27.0	984	47.9	337	16.3
Asia	2678	100	454	17.0	644	24.0	562	21.0	1018	38.0
World	13075	100	1475	11.3	3168	24.2	4083	31.2	4345	33.2

Source: FAO (1987) *Production Yearbook 1986*, Vol. 40, Rome.

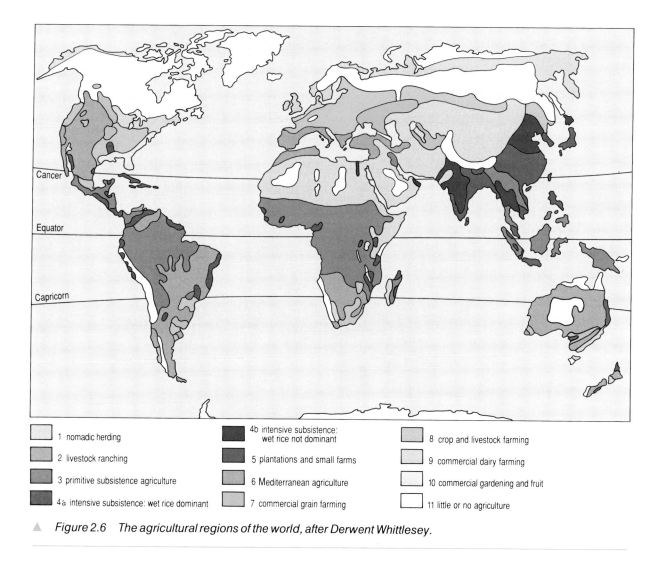

▲   *Figure 2.6   The agricultural regions of the world, after Derwent Whittlesey.*

A   The two most obvious limits are those of cold, especially in the belt from
     North America, Greenland and Norway to the Soviet Union, and
     aridity, especially from the Sahara through Arabia, Iran, Afghanistan
     and into Mongolia.

Q   Why are some arid areas characterised by nomadic herding and others
     by ranching?

A   The fact that ranching occurs in the western United States and Australia
     as well as South Africa and Latin America suggests that this is an effect
     of economic development. Both use extensive livestock as a response to
     aridity, but ranching is commercial and nomadism not.

Q   Is the distribution of primitive subsistence agriculture dictated by
     environmental problems or differences in development?

A   The fact that the major areas are the equatorial forests suggests that
     environmental problems play a strong role: it has been shown above
     that, even apart from problems of flooding and dense vegetation, soils
     tend to be poor and net photosynthesis low. However, the area of
     primitive subsistence agriculture in the highlands of south-east Asia in
     close proximity to areas of intensive subsistence agriculture in China,
     India, Bangladesh and Thailand suggests that there may be
     developmental or cultural processes at work which can overcome
     environmental constraints.

Q   How would you explain the belt of mixed crop and livestock farming in
     the eastern United States, western Europe and into the Soviet Union?

A   The other maps show that this is a major area with adequate rainfall and
     growing season plus good arable land, so both crops and livestock *can* be
     produced. But the fact that they *are* produced depends partly on history:
     these were areas where a mixed farming regime (using livestock manure
     to sustain fertility and produce a range of foods for fairly local
     consumption) developed before and during industrialisation. They are
     now areas with a high enough standard of living to afford animal
     products, unlike areas of intensive subsistence production in Asia. Since
     the map was drawn, many areas in Europe and the USA shown here as
     mixed farming or dairying have actually become more specialised
     producers of grain as mechanisation, fertilisers and price support made
     animals less necessary and desirable. Technical and economic change
     constantly shift what is agriculturally possible and preferable.

2.7   Summary

This section has explored the relationship between agricultural systems and
natural environments. It has considered the development of agriculture
over time, from natural biomes, through domestication of plants and
animals to the development of industrial societies and has stressed societies'
increasing capacity to modify natural processes to produce more agricultural
products, with concomitantly greater impacts on the environment, but still
subject to ecological and climatic limits. Finally, this section looked at an
attempt to classify the major types of agriculture around the world.

3   World agricultural production and productivity

3.1   Introduction

Although 45% of the world's workforce is engaged in agriculture, forestry and fisheries the value of agricultural output is dwarfed by the value of other goods – from the manufacturing and mining sectors – and services: see Table 2.3. The developed countries produce half the agricultural output by value although they have only a quarter of the world's population and 7% of the agricultural labour force.

Q   From what you learned in Section 2 above, how would you explain the relative performance of developed and less developed countries in agriculture?

A   Several factors contribute:

- the developed countries contain nearly half the good arable land

- their agricultural technology is more advanced, in the sense of using more energy, machinery and chemicals

- because their consumers are more affluent, they can produce higher value products as well as staples

- many developed countries subsidise agriculture to produce more than a free market would

- the figures for the developing world are an understatement because they do not include production for the farmers' own subsistence.

Table 2.3   Value of agricultural gross domestic product, 1981

	Agricultural GDP, US$ (millions)	Agricultural GDP as % of total GDP	Agricultural GDP as % of world agriculture GDP
All developed	427 027	4.5	49.3
Western Europe	127 348	4.0	14.7
USSR	97 165	15.0	11.2
North America	92 680	3.1	10.7
Eastern Europe	48 664	14.7	5.6
Japan	39 103	2.0	4.5
Australasia	15 166	8.1	1.8
All developing	439 466	18.1	50.7
Asian CPE[1]	99 734	33.5	11.5
Latin America	98 964	10.9	11.4
South Asia	75 656	38.5	8.7
Africa	56 278	21.1	6.5
Near East	51 074	10.6	5.9
South-east Asia	46 158	22.2	5.3
World	866 493	7.3	100.0

Note: [1]Asian CPE indicates Asian Centrally Planned Economies: China, Kampuchea, Vietnam, Mongolia, North Korea.

Source: Grigg, D. B. (1986) 'World patterns of agricultural output', Geography, Vol. 71, pp. 240–45.

Thus developed countries, although having few of their workforce engaged in agriculture, are the leading agricultural producers. Western Europe is first, closely followed by the Soviet Union and North America. It is also worth noting that agricultural output, even in the developing countries, accounts for a small proportion of their total Gross Domestic Product. It is most important in south and east Asia, where it accounts for one-third of the value of all output; in Latin America and the Near East it is only one-tenth.

Nevertheless, agricultural production is of prime importance to us all and, to many, the main criterion of 'successful' farming is that of increasing productivity. This section will look at ways of measuring productivity and thus of evaluating the success of various agricultural systems.

3.2   Measures of productivity

Measures of **productivity** should be a useful means of comparing different agricultural systems and evaluating their appropriateness in the global agricultural system. In practice there are difficulties as productivity is not easy to define in principle and comparable data are not always obtainable. This section will explore the various ways of measuring productivity which can either be a measure of output per area or of the efficiency of outputs in relation to inputs.

In ecological terms, biological productivity is measured in terms of annual **biomass** per hectare: 3.58×10^3 MJ of light energy (approximate amount fixed per hectare per crop season) produces about 3500 kg/ha of dry biomass: this ranges from 200 kg/ha for crops such as beans to 11 000 kg/ha for maize and sugar-cane; average agricultural (crop) ecosystems produce an annual biomass per hectare that is slightly greater than the average of natural ecosystems (but should do considering inputs from added moisture, fertiliser etc.). Crops in the US contribute slightly more than 20% of the total plant biomass produced annually (Pimentel and Pimentel, 1979).

Looking more specifically at agricultural outputs, an obvious starting-point is the weight of useful crops produced (i.e. grain rather than total crop plant including straw for example), that is the *yield by weight per hectare*. This is only appropriate when comparing similar crops, such as staple cereals, since it would make little sense to compare output weights of systems producing cereals, meat and lettuce. In these cases, and when comparing output of varied commercial systems, it makes more sense to compare the *value of output* rather than its weight. This too is not without problems, since value depends on effective demand and is influenced by the spending power of the customers as well as the effectiveness of producers, but is often preferable to yield. It may be more appropriate to measure **value added** by agriculture and so to allow for the fact that high outputs may be largely accounted for by manufactured inputs, like fuel, fertiliser and pesticides.

A similar point is made when contrasting intensive and extensive systems. In *intensive* farming systems, such as horticulture, the cost of inputs – labour, machinery, pesticides, seed and so forth – is high per hectare, but so is net income (the difference between sales and costs) per hectare. In contrast the cost of labour – and total costs – per hectare in extensive livestock farming systems is much lower, but so too is net income per hectare. Thus to have a satisfactory total income, farmers in these extensive agricultural systems have to have much larger farms. Such distinctions are to be found throughout the world; the sheep farms of Australia are extensive, the rice farms of Java intensive; the ranches of the western USA extensive, the corn farms of the Mid West relatively intensive.

In discussing intensiveness, inputs as well as outputs have been brought into the calculation. In economic terms the measure of productivity which best relates inputs to outputs is **total factor productivity**, since this relates the value of outputs to the value of land, labour and capital used in production. However, there are rarely statistics available on capital investment and these are certainly not available for international comparison. In practice, most measures of productivity relate output to only one input, either dividing total output by the land area used to give *land productivity* or dividing by the labour force to give *labour productivity*.

In the absence of any single ideal measure, the discussion below will consider and compare several measures of productivity, starting with yield per hectare, then relating value added per hectare to value added per capita. The source of data for international comparisons of agricultural productivity is the United Nations' Food and Agriculture Organisation (FAO).

3.3   Land productivity

Crop yields are the most obvious measures of **land productivity.** Each crop ought to be considered, but as cereals occupy a high proportion of the total area under cultivation in all but a few countries, they are a good guide to the general level of yields.

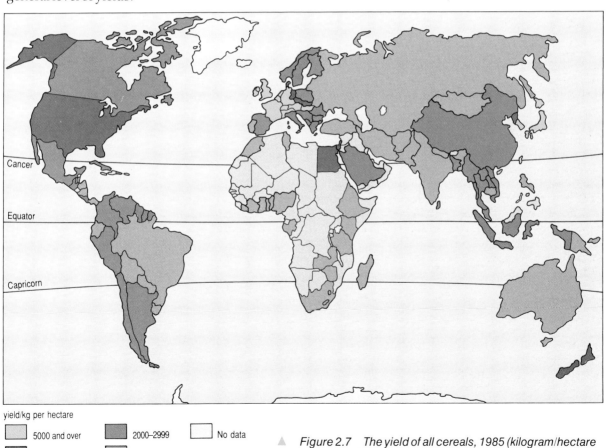

yield/kg per hectare

- 5000 and over
- 4000–4999
- 3000–3999
- 2000–2999
- 1000–1999
- 0–999
- No data

▲   *Figure 2.7   The yield of all cereals, 1985 (kilogram/hectare of arable land). Since figures are by country, output in small areas (such as the Nile Valley) may be generalised to much larger ones (in this case Egypt).*

Q   According to Figure 2.7, where are yields highest and lowest?

A   Cereal yields are highest in north-western Europe, east Asia (Japan and
    South Korea), the United States and Egypt; they are low, not only
    throughout most of the developing world, particularly in Africa, but
    also in several developed regions, such as the Soviet Union and
    Australia.

Q   How would you explain these variations?

A   An explanation of this requires some consideration of the causes of yield
    variations; the major causes are climate, the supply of plant nutrients,
    the crop varieties used and the control of weeds and disease.

Climate

Crop yields are a function of a number of climatic factors, the most important
of which, as has already been seen, are rainfall and temperature. Lack of
moisture gives low cereal yields and much of Canadian and Australian
cereal output is in semi-arid regions as is that of the Soviet Union, Argentina
and the Near East. This limitation can be overcome by irrigation: see Box 2.2.

Box 2.2   Irrigation

Irrigation is a term which covers a wide variety of
practices. In some parts of Asia rivers at high water
are allowed to flood fields, and crops are planted
when the floods recede; in other places, such as
Tamil Nadu or Sri Lanka, each village has a small
reservoir with earth dams, called a 'tank', that stores
monsoon rainfall, to be released in the dry season.
In the south-west of the United States, in Australia and
the oases of the Sahara, water is obtained by pumps
from fossil water stored in the underlying rock. In the
most elaborate irrigation systems, large dams
contain water in reservoirs on the upper parts of
rivers; this is released in periods of low water, and
distributed by canals. Irrigation is not confined to the
traditional arid and semi-arid areas; in modern times
spray systems are used on high-value crops in
eastern England and other parts of western Europe.
    Approximately 15% of the world's arable land is
irrigated. In some regions, irrigation is practised
because without it farming would be quite
impossible, as in the deserts of Egypt and Saudi
Arabia; elsewhere irrigation is used to supplement
rainfall and to overcome the high variability of rainfall
in semi-arid regions, for example, where rainfall is
concentrated into a short period of the year. It is most
common in Asia; yet surprisingly a minority – 36% of
non-Communist Asia – of the continent's rice is not
irrigated although there is a clear connection

between irrigation and rice yields. Because irrigation
provides security against crop failure, it attracts
high-value crops and receives more inputs than dry
land. Thus in the developing countries only 20% of
arable land is irrigated, but receives 60% of the
fertiliser used in these countries and produces 40%
of the value of output.

▲   The modern version of the 'Persian wheel' is a basic
means of lifting irrigation water from wells in the Indus
Plains of Pakistan and north-western India.

There is little that farmers can do about modifying temperatures, although in exceptional cases high-value crops – vegetables, fruit and flowers – are produced in glass-houses. Elsewhere, farmers have to adapt to the prevailing temperature regime.

The supply of plant nutrients

Until the mid nineteenth century, fallowing, manuring and rotation with legumes were the main means of maintaining crop yields. However, with the industrial fixation of nitrogen, with oxygen to produce nitrates, or with hydrogen to produce ammonia, farmers soon turned to commercially produced chemical fertilisers: in 1900, 91% of nitrogen applied to farm crops was organic; by 1913 this was only 40%. Since 1945 their use has boomed: the early 1970s saw the cost of fertilisers fall in real terms and their ease of handling compared with farmyard manure has led to their even greater use. In the 1970s chemical fertilisers provided 75% of the nitrogen, 70% of the potassium and 59% of the phosphorus for plant growth in the UK; the consumption has risen eight-fold between the 1930s and the 1980s.

Equally dramatic rises in the consumption of chemical fertilisers have occurred in nearly all developed countries in the post-war period. Nor has the increase in fertiliser consumption been confined to the developed countries; indeed the rate of increase has been greater in the developing countries, largely because of the very low usage in 1949–51: see Table 2.4.

Table 2.4   Fertiliser usage per hectare of arable, 1949–81 (kg of nutrients/hectare)

	1949–51	1980–1	Increase factor
Latin America	3.1	46	14.8
Far East	1.6	38	23.8
Near East	2.4	34	14.2
Africa	0.4	10	25.0
Asian CPE[1]	–	146	–
Developing	1.4	49	35.0
Developed	22.3	116	5.2
World	12.4	80	6.5

Note: [1]Asian Centrally Planned Economies: China, Kampuchea, Vietnam, Mongolia, North Korea.

Source: FAO (1971) *The State of Food and Agriculture, 1970*, Rome; (1983) *The State of Food and Agriculture, 1982*, Rome.

There are still marked variations in their usage of chemical fertiliser: see Figure 2.8. The highest usage is in western Europe and east Asia, the lowest in Africa, Latin America and south Asia; this reflects the fact that fertilisers are a product of the heavy chemical industry, concentrated in the industrial countries where the real cost of fertiliser is low and, furthermore, agriculture is highly subsidised. The developed countries produce 75% of world fertiliser output, many developing countries relying upon imports from the developed world. But there is not simply a distinction between developed

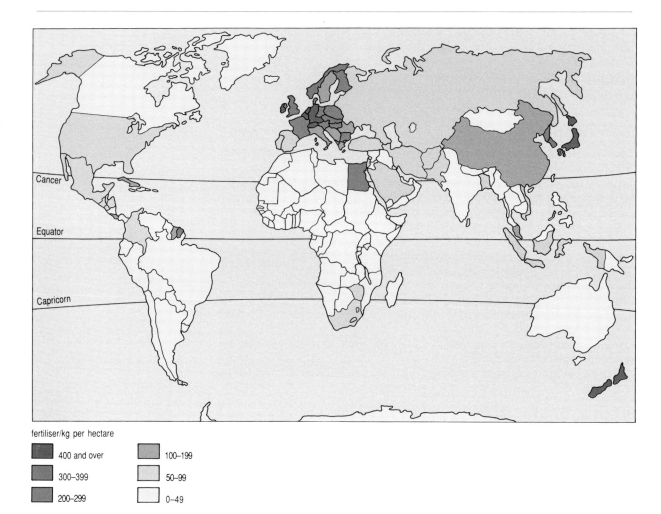

fertiliser/kg per hectare

█ 400 and over   █ 100–199

█ 300–399   ░ 50–99

█ 200–299   ☐ 0–49

▲   *Figure 2.8   Synthetic fertiliser use, 1982 (kilogram/hectare of arable land).*

and developing countries: fertiliser usage per hectare is low in the Soviet Union, North America, Australia and Argentina. Much of the crop acreage in these countries is in semi-arid zones, where the absence of moisture impairs the uptake of fertiliser by plants. Further, much of the farming in these regions is carried out on a large scale, with the aim of maximising output per capita rather than per hectare. Although the use of fertiliser is not the only, indeed not the most important, cause of yield variations, there is a relationship between use per hectare and crop yields: this is shown in Figure 2.9.

New plant varieties

In traditional farming farmers selected their seed for the next crop from their harvest and, until the nineteenth century, one quarter or more of each harvest was retained for this purpose. They were able to select the better seed and slowly improve yield and resistance to disease in this manner. In addition, seed from other regions could be imported. Hence Russian wheats which developed in a short growing season were taken to Canada in the

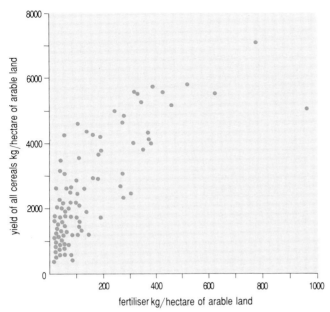

▲   Figure 2.9
*The effect of synthetic fertiliser application (kilogram/hectare of
arable land) on the yield of cereals (kilogram/hectare).*

nineteenth century and made possible the cultivation of the Prairies. But it
was not until the principles of genetics were applied to crop breeding in the
early twentieth century that it was possible to breed varieties with specific
characteristics: tolerance of drought, more rapid maturing, the ability to
absorb fertiliser and immunity to specific disease have all contributed to
higher yields.

The first major impovement came with the breeding of hybrid maize in
the United States in 1922, and by the 1950s it had largely replaced the earlier
varieties. In Europe there were comparable advances, particularly in wheat,
and since 1945 a succession of new varieties have contributed to higher
yields. Indeed approximately half the yield increase in the United States and
western Europe since 1945 is attributed to new crop varieties. Less advance
was made elsewhere except in Japan and its colonies where new rice
varieties were bred and widely adopted in the inter-war period. Advances
made in Mexico and the Philippines in the breeding of semi-dwarf wheat
and rice have led to major changes in the varieties used in Asia. Although
initially only adopted by those with large farms, the new High Yielding
Varieties have spread to small farms, and now substantial proportions of the
farm area are sown with HYV wheat and rice, and hybrid maize (see Table
2.5), particularly in China where the new varieties were locally bred rather
than introduced from Mexico and the Philippines. Africa has least of its area
in the new varieties, partly because rice and wheat are not widely grown.

The substantial increases in yield are only possible, however, under
optimum conditions, and require liberal fertiliser use, irrigation and –
because the new varieties lack the immunity to disease which older varieties
had acquired – the use of pesticides. They thus tie the farmer into new
farming methods which require much greater outlays of capital, not only for
the seed, but for the fertilisers and pesticides which must be used as well in
order to reap the benefit. This favours the large land-owners, or necessitates

Table 2.5   *Percentage of area in wheat and rice sown with*
HYV in 1977, and in hybrid maize, 1983–5

	Wheat	Rice	Maize
Asia	72.4	30.4	6.8
Near East	17.0	3.6	32.0[1]
Africa	22.5	2.7	16.2
China	25.0	80.0	72.0
Latin America	41.0	13.0	50.2

Note: [1] Including North Africa.

Source: D. Dalrymple (1978) *Development and Spread of High*
Yielding Varieties of Wheat and Rice in the Less Developed Nations,
Washington, DC; D. Dalrymple (1988) *Development and Spread of*
Improved Maize Varieties and Hybrids in Developing Countries,
Washington, DC.

high levels of borrowing for the smaller farmer. This is a great problem in
Africa where, although women produce most of the food, they have great
difficulty in being granted loans, because they do not own title to the land;
they are also usually excluded from development programmes and from
membership of co-operatives.

The control of pests and weeds

As we have seen, the conditions that encourage the growth of crop plants
also encourages other plants – weeds – as unwelcome competition for the
supply of nutrients and moisture. The control of weeds has always been a
major aim of farmers and once occupied much of the year. In Europe
ploughing before sowing and ploughing in the fallow year were undertaken,
whilst horse and hand hoeing were practised during growth when crops
such as potatoes, sugar-beet and fodder roots were grown. In most farming
systems the control of weeds was only possible with very large amounts of
hand labour. However, during the late nineteenth century, chemical sprays
that killed weeds – herbicides – were tried in France. But it is only since the
1950s that herbicides have been used in large quantities in North America
and western Europe. Their use has greatly reduced the amount of labour in
crop production. This aspect is not so crucial to third world countries, where
labour costs are low and supply is plentiful.

Traditional farmers had great difficulties controlling crop diseases that
were spread by insects and fungi. Rotations may have reduced the incidence
of plant disease, as did intercropping in the tropics. Early chemical sprays
used inorganic materials to control the diseases of potatoes and the vine in
the 1860s, and the spraying of fruit was common in the 1920s, when aircraft
were first used. But as with herbicides, the rapid growth of usage of
insecticides and fungicides has come only since the 1950s, and is greatest in
North America and Europe, which consume half the world's output. In 1982
there were 4000 registered pesticides in the UK, representing 1000 different
types, and worth nearly £400 million to the chemical industry. Chemical
sprays have had adverse effects on wildlife, and recent work suggests some
foods may contain unhealthy amounts of some pesticides. In the developing
countries their use is largely confined to export crops. The lack of control
over pesticide use and the continued use of chemicals banned in first world
countries give cause for concern over health risks in the third world.

Summary

The differences in yields between different parts of the world – the contrast is largely between Europe, the United States and east Asia and the rest of the world – is thus explained by a variety of factors. The non-tropical location of these regions is one such factor, but more important are the intensity with which inputs are used. In east Asia – China, Korea, Taiwan and Japan – labour is still intensively used in preparing seed beds, weeding and transplanting rice; in Europe, and particularly western Europe, high yields are due more to the use of chemical fertilisers, pesticides and improved crop varieties. In western Europe cereal yields are now over three times those of the 1930s, before the widespread use of chemical treatments or improved varieties. In contrast fertilisers and new varieties are little used in Latin America, Africa and much of Asia.

Yields will be a major contributor to output value, but existing measures of the value of agricultural produce cover a much wider range of produce than just cereals and include livestock as well as crops. The explanation of variations in yields which was given suggests that in many cases a high value of outputs will rely on a high level of purchased inputs. A better measure of the efficiency of farms is therefore value added – the difference between the value of outputs and the value of inputs. Estimates of value added have been published by FAO and the World Bank. These have the disadvantage that data are not available for most socialist countries and that national figures are converted to US dollars using exchange rates which fluctuate. Nevertheless, they do present a striking picture, as shown in Figure 2.10.

Q   What countries stand out as high or low in value added per hectare?

A   Not surprisingly, east Asia and western Europe are high in value added, but are matched by Egypt, Mauritania and Papua New Guinea. Irrigation and plantation crops provide the explanation for the surprises. At the low end of the scale, Ethiopia and Sudan might be expected but Australia, Argentina and North America are all major food exporters. The explanation of their low value added per hectare is partly minimisation of labour costs and partly the low productivity of semi-arid pastoral production, which covers large areas of these countries.

Activity 1

Compare Figures 2.7 and 2.10 and pick out examples of countries performing differently in terms of yield and value added per hectare. Why do the differences occur?

The most dramatic contrasts have already been mentioned: Papua New Guinea and Mauritania are in the lowest cereal yield category but the highest value added per hectare. These are the extremes of a more general phenomenon – the generally better performance of countries near the equator in terms of value added than in terms of cereal yields. This is a reminder of the implicit bias of the cereal yield measure since cereals, with the partial exception of rice, are better suited to the mid latitudes than the tropics and in the case of Africa and Latin America are less preferred than root crops like yams and manioc.

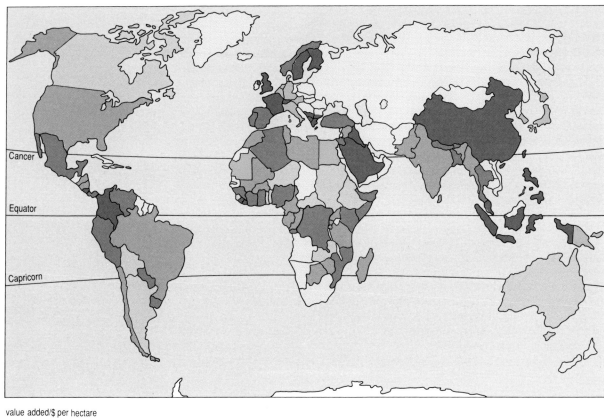

value added/$ per hectare

	2000 and over		250–499
	1000–1999		0–249
	500–999		no data

▲   Figure 2.10
Value added in agriculture, 1982 (per hectare of arable land, in US dollars).

A striking feature of Figure 2.10 is that China is in the same value added per hectare category as the UK and superior to the USA. This certainly departs from most people's images of the productivity of these countries, suggesting that those images are based on a different measure.

3.4   Labour productivity

Although land productivity is an important measure of agricultural productivity, it is not the only one. Indeed labour productivity is more usually used as an index of overall productivity in the developed world. Some indication of international differences can be obtained by dividing the estimated value added in agriculture by the agricultural workforce of each country: this is shown in Figure 2.11. This pattern of productivity is different from that of crop yields and value added per hectare. The highest figures are for Europe, the United States, Canada, Australia and Argentina. Conversely output per head is remarkably low throughout all of Africa and Asia (except Japan); it is slightly higher in Latin America, but still much below Europe

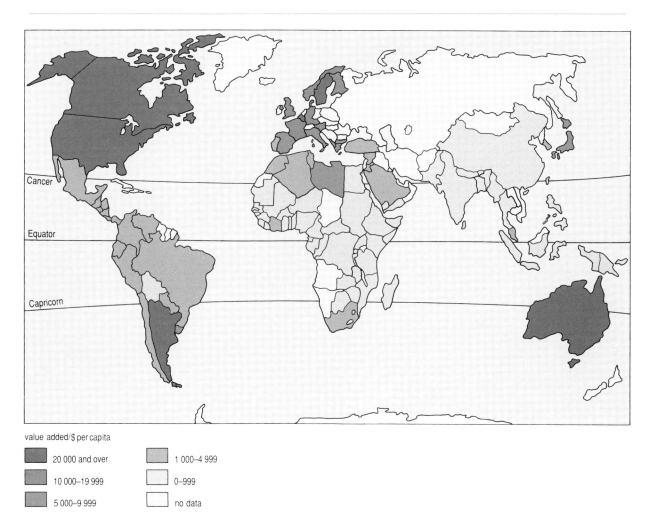

value added/$ per capita

■ 20 000 and over   ▨ 1 000–4 999

▨ 10 000–19 999   ▢ 0–999

▨ 5 000–9 999   ▢ no data

▲   *Figure 2.11*
Value added in agriculture, 1982 (per capita of the population economically active in agriculture, in US dollars).

and the United States. This reflects principally variations in labour per hectare: areas which use a great deal of labour and little machinery have low labour productivities; those with low labour usage and much machinery have high outputs per capita. To understand world differences in labour densities, it is necessary to examine briefly the history of the agricultural population.

Until the eighteenth century the agricultural population made up 75% or more of the population of nearly all countries except Britain and the Netherlands. However, with the spread of industrialisation and the growth in the number of workers in manufacturing, mining and services, the proportion of agricultural workers began to decline, and has declined continuously to the present day. As industrialisation spread from western Europe to other parts of the world so a similar decline occurred there; even in Afro-Asia and Latin America there has been a substantial fall in this proportion since 1950, so that the agricultural workforce exceeded 75% in comparatively few countries in 1985 (see Figure 2.12).

Whilst the decline of the *proportion* of the workforce engaged in agriculture has been universal, changes in the *absolute numbers* engaged in

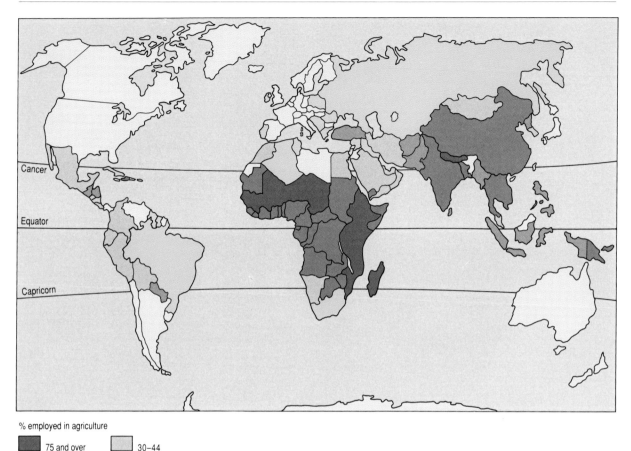

% employed in agriculture

■	75 and over	□ 30–44
■	60–74	□ 15–29
■	45–59	□ 0–14

▲   *Figure 2.12   Percentage of the economically active population engaged in agriculture, 1985.*

agriculture have followed a different course, because industrialisation was accompanied by an increase in population, including the rural population, mainly due to a fall in mortality, but in eighteenth- and nineteenth-century Europe to a rise in fertility as well. As industrialisation got under way in nineteenth-century Europe, the difference between wages in agriculture and in industry attracted people from the farms to the towns, a process that has continued to the present day. But initially the rate of migration out of agriculture was exceeded by the rate of natural increase in the agricultural population, and so employment in farming slowly increased until the late nineteenth century, except in the British Isles where decline began in the 1850s. Elsewhere the decline of the agricultural population began later, either because the onset of industrialisation was later, as in eastern Europe, or because new areas of land were still being colonised, as in Australia, Canada, Argentina and the United States. But by the 1950s the agricultural population of the developed countries was everywhere in decline; between 1970 and 1985 alone it fell by over one-third.

In contrast the agricultural population of most parts of the developing countries has been in continuous increase down to the present; in Latin America, Africa and Asia the cities have attracted many migrants from the

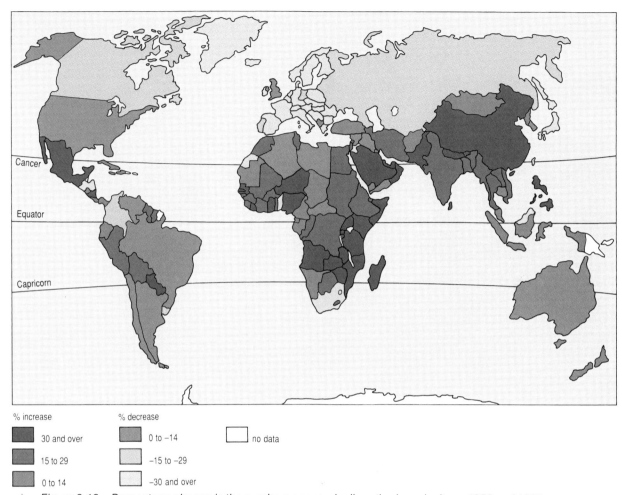

% increase

30 and over

15 to 29

0 to 14

% decrease

0 to -14

-15 to -29

-30 and over

no data

▲   Figure 2.13   Percentage change in the numbers economically active in agriculture, 1970 and 1985.

countryside because of the prospect of better services and higher wages, in spite of the prevalence of urban unemployment. In many parts of Asia rapid rural population growth has led to the subdivision of farms, and this has accelerated out-migration. But the growth of rural populations by natural increase has also been very high, and exceeded the rate of out-migration, so that the agricultural populations have continued to increase in spite of out-migration; indeed the agricultural population of the developing countries as a whole increased by over 25% between 1970 and 1985. Only in a few developing countries has a decline in the agricultural population begun – in parts of Latin America and the Middle East: see Figure 2.13.

In the developed countries agricultural populations have declined because of the opportunities for better incomes in the cities; also because in some cases farmers have replaced labour by machines. The reaper, the threshing machine and other labour-saving implements began to be widely used in North America and Britain in the late nineteenth century; perhaps as important was the tractor, introduced in the early twentieth century, and the combine harvester which was first used in Britain in the 1930s. But it was not until after the Second World War that the tractor finally replaced the horse, and the mechanisation of the United States and western Europe has

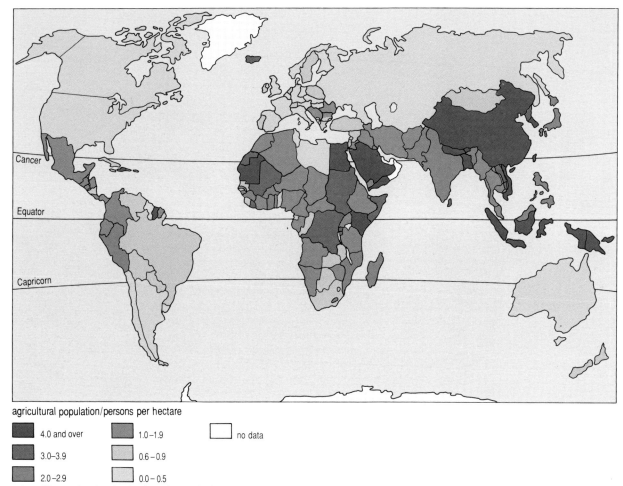

agricultural population/persons per hectare

■ 4.0 and over	■ 1.0–1.9	□ no data
■ 3.0–3.9	□ 0.6 – 0.9	
■ 2.0–2.9	□ 0.0 – 0.5	

▲   *Figure 2.14   Agricultural population, 1982 (per hectare of arable land).*

since proceeded at an unparalleled pace. Mechanisation has proceeded less rapidly in Afro-Asia and Latin America, for there is less incentive when agricultural populations are increasing, and thus wages are low. There are very strking differences in the labour used in agriculture. These are shown in Figure 2.14; agricultural population per hectare is lowest in the developed countries – Europe, the USSR, Australasia, North America and much of Latin America, where mechanisation has made more progress than elsewhere in the developing world. Densities are highest in Africa and Asia but particularly high in east and south-east Asia.

Activity 2

Use the data on productivity to separate countries into four categories:

● high productivity per hectare and per capita
● high per capita, low per hectare
● high per hectare and low per capita
● low per hectare and per capita.

▲   *Campesinos spraying fields near Lima, Peru. Even in less developed countries, large-scale monoculture is well established and requires chemical pest control.*

3.5   Summary

By combining the two measures of productivity – value added per hectare and output per capita – it is possible to recognise several classes of countries. First are those where both labour and land productivity is high. These are in western Europe, with Denmark in the top category for both measures. A second category includes those countries where yields are low, but output per head high – these include Canada, Argentina and Australasia. In these countries agricultural population densities are low, and farming is highly mechanised; but crop yields are relatively low, reflecting the limited use of fertilisers. A third category includes tropical Africa and South Asia, where the productivity of land is moderate to low and labour productivity is very low; although agricultural population densities are high, few modern inputs – fertilisers, new crop varieties or pesticides – are used; nor has mechanisation made much progress. Finally, a small group of countries have comparatively high yields but lower labour productivity. In east Asia and parts of south-east Asia, yields are high because of the intensive use of labour, whilst in the last twenty years an increasing proportion of land is irrigated, fertilisers used and HYV varieties are replacing the traditional rice varieties. These kinds of system, led by Japan, may well be the most relevant to the future need to feed growing numbers of low-income people. (This is discussed further in the next chapter.)

4   Sustainability

4.1   Introduction

The previous section has shown the high levels of productivity which can
be achieved in modern farming systems. Growing populations and rising
living standards constantly demand that agricultural output also increases.
However, concerns have grown about the effects of intensive farming
methods and whether they are sustainable in the long term. The World
Commission on Environment and Development (or Brundtland Report)
(1987) defined sustainable development as '. . . development which meets
the needs of the present without compromising the ability of future
generations to meet their own needs'. This brings into consideration rates of
resource consumption and long-term environmental impacts.

   This section begins by looking at the widespread problems that threaten
the maintenance of ecological balance which is vital to sustaining output.
The dependence of modern agriculture upon large energy inputs will then
be explored. Thirdly, the growing public opposition to chemical farming
methods and their long-term effects on both land and people will be
considered. Lastly, when considering sustainability it is necessary to look at
the interdependence of the global agricultural system and the prospects for
the future.

4.2   Farming and soil

As this chapter has shown so far, farming changes the natural ecology of an
area: it requires the removal of natural vegetation, and the cultivation of a
limited number of crop plants and/or keeping a limited number of animals,
rather than the great variety of species which occur naturally. Land
clearance and crop cultivation remove plant nutrients and, when bare, the
soil is exposed to higher wind speeds, greater temperatures and higher
intensity of rainfall. The overall effect of this can be to substantially alter the
local environment, often in ways detrimental to farming productivity.
Furthermore, many farming techniques, such as irrigation and the use of
chemical fertilisers, have unexpected adverse consequences.

   The term **land degradation** has been used to describe physical and
chemical changes which reduce the long-term productivity of the soil. But
this is difficult to measure; removal of top soil by wind in the American Great
Plains in the 1930s was obvious, as is gullying in parts of Nigeria now, but
slow changes in the chemical composition of soils is less easy to monitor.
However, some ten years ago, the Food and Agriculture Organisation of the
United Nations estimated that one quarter of the world's arable land was
subject to degradation, through salinisation, soil erosion and desertification.
They subsequently raised this estimate to one third.

Acidity, alkalinity and salinity

One of the chemical characteristics of a soil is its acidity or alkalinity. These
are at opposite ends of a continuum which is measured on the pH scale. This
runs from pH 0, which is highly acid, through neutral at pH 7 to pH 14

which is highly alkaline. Soils with a pH rating of 5–7 are suited to the growth of most crops, but outside this range only a few crops thrive and the yields of others is reduced. Ultimately conditions become so extreme that crops will not grow. Although both acid and alkaline soils occur in natural conditions, their pH may be changed by some agricultural practices.

Soil acidity occurs widely in both agricultural and non-agricultural soils and is a particular problem in cool, high rainfall areas. For example, most soils of upland Britain are acid. Soil acidity has several adverse effects. It reduces the capacity of bacteria in the soil to fix nitrogen and it limits the ability of crops to take up plant nutrients from the soil. In Europe it is claimed that deforestation increased soil acidity in the Middle Ages, but soil acidity can be reduced by applying lime, a technique long known to farmers. More recently there has been some concern that acid rain may be affecting crop yields. Industrial smoke emitted over the last two centuries has increased the amount of sulphur dioxide and nitric oxides in the atmosphere; they are converted in the atmosphere into a mixture of sulphuric and nitric acid that returns to Earth in rain. Their effect upon trees has been much discussed, but little is yet known of the effect upon crops. Acid rain may increase soil acidity which slows the growth of most crops, but it also supplies sulphur which promotes growth. Although no generalisations can be made about the net effect, acid rain is thought to have reduced crop yields by 10% in parts of eastern Canada.

Soil alkalinity is encouraged by the build-up of calcium, magnesium, potassium and sodium in the soil. This occurs mainly in arid conditions where there is insufficient leaching to remove these metals in solution. Alkalinity may be worsened by irrigation with water containing dissolved metals, especially if the irrigated land is inadequately drained so that the metals concentrate in the upper layer. The worst cases of alkalinity, with pH as high as 10, are those involving sodium carbonate. No crops will grow under such conditions. In principle, alkalinity can be reduced by flushing with water and/or treatment with gypsum to convert sodium carbonate to sodium sulphate, which is less caustic and more easily leached. Such treatment may often be too expensive to be adopted in practice. However, even if alkaline soils can be reduced to neutrality, they may remain unproductive because of the concentration of salts in the soil water – a condition known as **salinisation**.

Saline soils are a major problem in many parts of the world and occur under three conditions. First, in some semi-arid areas there is saline groundwater which moves to the surface by capillary action, and the salts are deposited by evaporation on the surface as a salt crust. In Australia the removal of deep-rooted forests and their replacement by pasture or crops has led to the salinisation of 5 million hectares, mainly in Western Australia. Second are potential arable soils near coasts in the humid tropics of south and south-east Asia. Some 20 million hectares currently supporting mangrove swamps could be drained to provide excellent cropland if it were not for their high salinity. Third, and more important, is the occurrence of saline soils in irrigated areas. (See Plate 3a.)

In these arid regions water is obtained from rivers or reservoirs and carried to fields by canals; before irrigation the water table – the upper surface of water in the ground – was at a considerable depth, but after several decades of irrigation, water that has leaked from unlined canals and floodwater have led to a slow but continuous rise of the water table. This can be substantial; modern irrigation in the Punjab has lifted the water table 7–9 metres above the level of 1895, and in much of India and Pakistan the water table is now within a few metres of the surface. These underground waters may become increasingly salty with the salts taken down with the water; where the groundwater reaches the root zone, its brackishness will stunt or prohibit crop growth, or even if not salty will kill crops by cutting off the oxygen supply.

The salinisation of irrigated areas is not new; it was widespread in the Tigris and Euphrates valley some 2500 years ago. Nor is it confined to developing countries: 25–35% of the irrigated land in the south-west of the United States is affected by salinisation. But it is in developing countries that these problems are most acute. In the late nineteenth century modern irrigation systems were constructed in many parts of south-west and southern Asia: large concrete dams formed reservoirs from which water was distributed to cropland by canals. These regions are now suffering from a high degree of salinisation and waterlogging. Indeed some authorities believe that half the world's irrigated land is salinised, at best reducing crop yields, at worst causing land abandonment. In India 13 million of the 43 million irrigated hectares are salinised. In Pakistan, with a far greater dependence on irrigation, some 70% of irrigated land is salinised, in Iraq half, in Egypt 30%, in Iran 15%. In Egypt construction of the Aswan Dam has increased the availability of water, allowed more double cropping and reduced the risk of crop failure. But the excessive use of water and the spread of salinisation has in places reduced crop yields by 20%.

In irrigated areas the problems are of excessive water, and the cures are, firstly, more careful management of water, second the lining of canals and, third, the underdrainage of land. All these are expensive, but less expensive than bringing new land into cultivation.

Soil erosion

Soil erosion is regarded as a major threat to land productivity, and there have been many pessimistic statements about its extent and impact upon crop production. But it is difficult to measure and even more diffficult to estimate its effect upon crop yields.

Soil is constantly being eroded by the action of running water and wind. Soil erosion is a natural process, and it only becomes a problem for the farmer when erosion substantially exceeds the formation of new soil. Soil forms in Britain and the United States at about 0.3–1.3 tonnes per hectare per year, or at 0.02 mm–0.1 mm per year.

A net soil loss has a number of adverse consequences. The removal of soil reduces the organic matter, plant nutrients and water retention in the soil and restricts the development of roots. Consequently crop yields may fall unless fertilisers are used. When soil erosion becomes serious, its effects are obvious. Wind erosion removes much of the upper soil, and with water erosion deep gullies appear, which make it physically impossible to work the land. (See Plate 3b.) Although there is historical evidence of soil erosion, it was not until the 1930s that there were efforts to measure soil erosion and to develop soil conservation techniques. The United States Department of Agriculture pioneered research into soil erosion and remains active today. In northern Europe soil erosion has had less apparent effect although it is now accepted that some modern farming techniques are having adverse effects upon the soil.

The United States Department of Agriculture has estimated T-values for the major soil types. A T-value is the level of soil erosion that will permit a high level of crop productivity to be sustained economically and indefinitely. T-values do not exceed 11.2 tonnes per hectare per year on any soil type yet 27% of the cropland in the United States has rates above the T-value, and 10% has rates above 22.4 tonnes per hectare.

The relative importance of the action of wind and running water depends upon local climatic conditions and soil type. In England and Wales *wind erosion* does not occur until wind speeds exceed 9 metres per second. Although such wind speeds occur at least once a year in nearly every part of England and Wales, the south-west and west of the country have the highest frequency of such speeds; but they also have the highest rainfall. As this binds soil particles together, wind erosion is unusual. It is much more common in the eastern lowlands on dry friable soils; peats in the Fens and sands in the Vale of York have most recorded instances of wind erosion, but as yet few farmers see it as a major hazard. It has been estimated that 14% of the arable land of England and Wales is susceptible to wind erosion.

To some extent modern farming practices have increased the risks of wind erosion, notably removal of hedgerows to enlarge fields and thus allow the easier use of machinery. The decline of grassland in the east of England has also increased the risk of both wind and water erosion, for the continuous cover throughout the year protects the land, whilst the practice of bare fallowing increases the risk of wind erosion since bare dry soil is highly susceptible to erosion. This is a particular problem where farming has penetrated into semi-arid areas. It was, of course, in the Great Plains in the 1930s that the most celebrated of all wind erosion events took place and this – the Dust Bowl – persuaded the United States government of the need to finance and promote soil conservation.

In much of the world's arable regions erosion caused by running water is a more serious problem than wind. A number of factors determine the extent of *water erosion*. First is the intensity and duration of rainfall. The size of raindrops and intensity of storms is greater in the tropics than in temperate areas, where rainfall comes mainly as drizzle. There is a marked difference in the erosivity of rainfall between the tropics and temperate regions, and even between northern and Mediterranean France, the former being only 25% of the latter.

◀   Ploughing parallel to the steepest slope on even a very gentle gradient can lead to run-off concentration and initiation of gully erosion.

Second is vegetation: the greater the cover, the less the soil is exposed to the impact of rain or wind. Thus experiments in England have shown that erosion rates are least under woodland, and then increase progressively under grass, cereals, and are highest on bare soils. The latter occur not only on fallow land but in short periods between crops. In England autumn-sown cereals are at risk partly because there is little plant cover in winter but also because this is the period of highest rainfall. Research in the hilly watersheds of the Mississippi, where the natural forest cover had been stripped away, shows the effect of human land uses on erosion rates: from the forested area, only a few hundredths of a ton per hectare per annum was lost; from grassy pasture 4 tons; from areas cultivated for corn an average of 54 tons (ranging from 8 to 106); and on abandoned farmlands where gullies had formed 450 tons were being lost in a year.

A third and very important factor is the angle of slope: the steeper the slope the greater erosive capacity of running water. Not surprisingly some of the more dramatic erosion occurs on steep slopes in uplands where deforestation has taken place. Population pressure has driven farmers to clear forest and plough higher angle slopes in many parts of the world. Serious erosion has been recorded in uplands in Nepal, Bolivia, Kenya, Ethiopia and Central Java. In Colombia slopes of 45° have been cultivated and soil loss has reached 370 tonnes per hectare per year. In Britain the high prices paid to cereal farmers, and the development of tractors that can operate on steep slopes – up to 21° – has led farmers to cultivate grassland on 20° slopes on the South Downs. The effect of slope on soil erosion is well illustrated by an example from Nigeria: when cassava was grown on land with a 1° slope, the rate of soil erosion was 3 tonnes per hectare per year, on 5° slopes 87 tonnes, but on slopes of 15°, 227 tonnes per hectares per year were lost.

Fourth, soil texture plays an important role in determining the rate of soil erosion. Generally the coarser the particles in a soil the more easily

▲   *A highly organised fuel collection service in Niger. The fuel needs of the increasing urban populations in third world countries can lead to large-scale deforestation.*

eroded it will be, and the greater the clay content, the lower the erosion. In England erosion is greatest on sand, moderate on silts and lowest on clays.

Finally, research in both the United States and Britain suggests that some modern farming practices increase the risk of erosion. Before the use of herbicides and pesticides, farmers in Britain and the eastern United States commonly rotated crops and grass and combined crop and livestock production. This increased the amount of organic matter in the soil as well as providing more continuous vegetation cover. There is evidence that organic manures improve soil structure, and so reduce the erodability of soils. Levels of organic matter are reduced under cereal monoculture using artificial fertiliser. The use of heavy machinery compacts soils and reduces infiltration, thus increasing run-off. Continuous crops of cereals leave the land bare for much of the winter, whilst stubble-burning reduces ground cover.

There have been many attempts to persuade farmers to adopt conservation methods. In the United States farmers now practise *contour ploughing* on slopes, ploughing along the slope rather than down it, but in Britain few farmers have adopted this practice, whilst as long as chemical farming is profitable there is unlikely to be a return to rotations or mixed farming. One new technique that does reduce soil erosion is *no-tillage or zero-cultivation*. Instead of ploughing the land and harrowing several times before sowing, farmers only lightly till and drill seed directly into the soil. This is rapidly increasing in the United States, but has made little progress in Britain. Other conservation techniques include planting shelter belts and intercropping, where crops with different growth rates are planted on the same land. These methods are discussed in Chapter 4.

The precise effect of erosion upon the world's arable land is unclear; no one doubts that it is a serious problem, but there are few reliable estimates based on careful research. Some estimates of its extent seem excessive, but a few illustrations will show that there is cause for concern. Thus 61% of India's cultivated area is said to be undergoing some form of degradation including salinisation; 80% of Bolivia's crop and grass area has had a fall in productivity from soil erosion; 80% of Madagascar's crop land is affected by severe erosion; half of Australia's agricultural land is said to be in need of treatment for land degradation.

Traditional farming practices would seem to offer better protection against soil erosion than modern farming methods, but in the United States the cost of accepting conservation methods is extremely high and it has been argued that adoption of the full range of recommended techniques would bankrupt most farmers.

The obverse of the soil erosion problem is that of silt, and this is another problem which besets irrigation schemes. Areas where irrigation systems are vital for agriculture are often those where deforestation has proceeded apace. All the soil from upstream which is eroded by water finds its way into the water courses and is deposited as sediment in the riverbeds and onto the floodplains, bringing renewed fertility but also causing flooding. The silt also finds its way into the canals and other waterworks of the irrigation systems. This necessitates continuing funds and labour for maintenance, and even so drastically shortens the useful life of reservoirs supplying the systems, particularly where the reservoir is small in relation to the flow of the river feeding it. It also reduces the effectiveness for supplying hydroelectric power.

Silt can be seen as the major form of human-caused water pollution in the world and in fact exacts a heavier cost than any other water pollutant, possibly even all others combined.

Agriculture in semi-arid areas periodically affected by drought may have not only the short-term consequence of crop failure but also longer-term effects of land degradation. (Senegal.)

Desertification

In the 1930s a number of writers noted that vegetation in parts of West Africa was deteriorating: poor grass and thorn scrub in the Sahel vegetation zone was in places becoming like desert, whilst some drier savannas – areas of grass and trees – were being encroached upon by the scrub of the Sahel. This was publicised as 'the advance of the Sahara'. In the 1970s famine in the Sahel drew further attention to this problem, and the term **desertification** was coined to describe deterioration of vegetation on the edge of the desert. But the definition was very soon expanded: in 1977 a United Nations report defined desertification as soil stripping, gully erosion, salinisation and alkalisation. Thus desertification would seem to be the end point of land degradation in arid and semi-arid regions.

Initially the expansion of a poor vegetation in the Sahel was attributed solely to climatic change. There is no doubt that there has been a decline in the mean annual rainfall of the Sahel and adjacent savanna areas, and an increase in variability of rainfall, which occurs almost entirely in a short period in the summer. But other factors have contributed. The northern and drier parts of the Sahel zone are occupied by nomadic pastoralists, the south by sedentary farmers. In two decades before 1960 the combination of rising human populations and a run of above average rainfall prompted the expansion of cultivation into parts of the Sahel. This reduced the area available to pastoralists, and their livestock no longer had sufficient land for grazing. Cattle, sheep, goats and camels selectively grazed the more palatable plant species; less palatable species spread, further reducing the capacity of the land to sustain livestock, and sometimes to soil erosion. At the same time the frequency of droughts was increasing after 1960, so compounding the problem.

▲   *Desertification in Burkina Faso, where climatic change has been exacerbated by overgrazing by livestock.*

Overgrazing in arid regions is not confined to the Sahel. It has occurred in Patagonia, where sheep numbers rose rapidly in the late nineteenth and early twentieth centuries; in semi-arid areas of Iran and Syria sheep numbers are estimated to be 3–4 times the carrying capacity of the meagre vegetation. In Africa overgrazing has often been the result of land appropriation, earlier in this century of tribal pastures for European agricultural settlement, notably in Southern Rhodesia (now Zimbabwe) and Kenya, where Masai grazing lands have been reduced by their exclusion from a wildlife park since independence. (See Plate 4.)

Problems of desertification are widespread, and principally result from farmers pushing into lands where rainfall is too low for crop cultivation without irrigation. Environmental refugees, the result of deterioration of agricultural land caused by unsustainable methods, now form the largest class of refugees in the world, estimated at over 10 million.

4.3   Energy and modern agriculture

One of the striking characteristics of modern agriculture is the importance of inputs purchased from the industrial sector. Traditional farmers used seed from their own harvest, fertilisers from animals and power from animal and human muscle – so that, for example, in Sweden in the 1860s, purchased inputs were only 5% of the gross value of agricultural production. In most developed economies now, where farming has been 'industrialised', this proportion is over half, and so farmers are highly dependent upon the price of inputs as well as the price of their products.

Many of these purchased inputs depend upon the use of energy. Obviously tractors and other machines need fuel, electricity is essential for drying grain, heating and ventilating broiler houses and piggeries and powering milking machines. But energy is also needed to produce chemical fertilisers and pesticides. There is thus a great difference in the amount of energy used in modern and traditional farming as can be seen in Table 2.6. Although crop yields in modern agriculture considerably exceed those in traditional farming, the use of commercial energy is far greater: modern production of rice requires 375 times as much commercial energy per hectare as traditional, and uses 80 times as much energy per kilogram of rice produced. These issues of use of energy and relative productivity are considered in more detail in Chapter 3 on the production of wetland rice, and Chapter 4 which looks at temperate agriculture.

Such use of commercial energy is comparatively recent. In the United States the amount of commercial energy needed to produce a given weight of food output rose fivefold between 1900 and 1970. Thus when oil prices rose dramatically in the early 1970s there was concern about the economic viability of modern industrial farming, and there were even suggestions that a return to the use of horses might be necessary. In the event, the real price of energy and fertilisers has since fallen. In the immediate future there seems no likely shortage of fuel, or mineral deposits for fertilisers – natural gas, potassium salts and phosphate rock – for developed countries. However, the economic viability of these types of farming might be in question if the system of protected prices in the EC ended; and if the use of chemical farming spread to the developing countries, prices might rise dramatically. In the longer term, the sustainability of high energy agriculture will depend on achievement of a sustainable energy policy, an issue considered in *Blunden and Reddish* (eds) (1991).

Table 2.6   *Commercial energy used in the production of rice and maize by modern and traditional methods (energy per hectare/10^6 joules)*

	Rice		Maize	
	Modern (US)	Traditional (Philippines)	Modern (US)	Traditional (Mexico)
Machinery	4 200	173	4 200	173
Fuel	8 988	–	8 240	–
Nitrogen fertiliser	10 752	–	10 000	–
Phosphate fertiliser	–	–	586	–
Potassium fertiliser	605	–	605	–
Seed	3 360	–	621	–
Irrigation	27 336	–	351	–
Insecticides	560	–	110	–
Herbicides	560	–	110	–
Drying	4 600	–	1 239	–
Electricity	3 200	–	3 248	–
Transport	724	–	724	–
Total	64 885	173	30 034	173
Yield kg/ha	5 800	1 250	5 083	950
Energy input per kg of output (joules × 10^6/kg)	11.9	0.14	5.91	0.18

Source: FAO (1977) *The State of Food and Agriculture, 1976*, Rome, p. 93.

4.4 Impacts of agriculture, public opinion and subsidy

The profound changes brought about by the industrialisation of agriculture, especially in the USA and Europe, have not only caused soil degradation and dependency on fossil fuels but also had a series of impacts outside agriculture which have in turn opened agriculture to more intense public scrutiny. These impacts stem from the greatly increased use of machinery, chemicals and bought-in animal feed. They range from changes to the rural landscape, through pollution of air and water to public questioning of subsidy regimes and international effects.

The impact on landscape will be explored in more detail in Chapters 4 and 5, but here it is enough to mention drainage of wetlands, ploughing of former pasture as mixed farms are converted to cereal monoculture, removal of small woods and hedgerows to create larger fields in which larger machines can operate and ploughing and reseeding moorland to create more productive pasture. The result is the elimination of wildlife refuges and the creation of visually monotonous landscapes with much reduced amenity value.

Pollution effects are increasingly spreading beyond farms. Concern at the effects of pesticides and herbicides on wild plants and animals was multiplied by Rachel Carson's book *Silent Spring* in 1962 and has continued, although many of the persistent toxic chemicals have been withdrawn from sale in developed countries. However, the increase in scale and intensity of farming has made even beneficial materials like manure into a problem as intensive animal feed-lots produce such large quantities of slurry that they can overwhelm the capacity of even substantial streams to dilute, disperse and decompose. Currently, there is growing concern about nitrates entering streams and underground water supplies in increasing quantities as levels of synthetic nitrates increase and as more animals are intensively reared. Whereas specific pesticides can be replaced by safer alternatives, nitrogen in some form is an indispensable part of intensive crop production, so nitrate pollution raises questions about the balance between intensive production and water purity. At the time of writing the newspapers are carrying reports that the UK Ministry of Agriculture Fisheries and Food will not impose controls on nitrate-liberating activities which are sufficiently tight to bring all UK water supplies below the EC limit for nitrates.

In Europe and North America the 1980s were a time of increasing public and political concern about overproduction of certain agricultural commodities, including dairy produce and cereals. The spectacle of surplus produce being dumped, stored or sold at cut rates to the USSR has caused widespread questioning of the subsidies paid to farmers, a questioning exacerbated by cases where farmers sometimes seemed able to obtain subsidies both for producing more and for producing less of the same product. During this period, many have argued for less intensive forms of agriculture, including organic farming, which would reduce surpluses and harmful impacts on the environment. However, official policy changes, including the EC's scheme for 'set-aside' seem calculated to take some land out of production but to encourage even more intensive use of the remainder.

In recent years the effects of intensive modern agriculture have been queried far beyond the farm gate. The urban population has become increasingly concerned at the effects on food quality. The residues of herbicides, pesticides and antibiotics are traceable right through the human food chain and are compounded by the effects of additives used in storage and food processing. Of course, such residues and additives are subject to government controls, but many members of the public query whether such controls are adequate. In the UK rising rates of salmonella poisoning led to revelations that salmonella was endemic in many large commercial flocks and had for the first time begun to affect eggs. The emergence of a new cattle disease, BSE, was attributed to cattle feed containing the offal of sheep infected with scrapie. Whether these are merely temporary setbacks in the process of intensification or indications of an agricultural system that has become over-industrialised is currently being debated.

Finally, there are those who raise ethical questions about world agriculture, focusing on two sets of issues. First, the ethics of intensive animal-rearing. The morality of veal production and battery chickens has long been disputed, and some animal rights activists have taken direct action. So far, such arguments have not made much headway against the cheapness and convenience of the produce. However, coupled with evidence of infection or of products used to resist infection, this is a balance which could shift in future towards a demand for higher quality.

The second set of ethical objections is at a world scale and may have partly contradictory implications. This is an objection to a world system that overproduces in rich countries and produces chronic malnutrition and

◀   *There are growing ethical objections to intensive animal-rearing*

frequent famines in poor countries. The simplistic suggestion that surpluses should be used to feed the starving still commands widespread support – immediate and practical in the case of appeals for disaster relief for Ethiopia – in spite of expert advice that such aid can harm food producers in recipient areas. More thoughtful critics point to the trade linkages which drive many third world countries to promote crops for export to the first world even while their own populations are malnourished.

Much of the best land which could be used for domestic food production is used instead to grow cash crops for the developed countries of the first world. The five most common are sugar, tobacco, coffee, cocoa and tea. The fluctuations – and often decline – in prices of such commodities make them unreliable bases for national planning and budgeting. Typically, countries are dependent on just one or two crops, which may represent 75% or more of the value of their exports. Further areas brought under cultivation, or intensification of cultivation, may in fact mean a lower return as prices fall. Labourers, working on these estates, are displaced from the land, unable to grow even subsistence crops for their families. The inequalities of land ownership are at their extreme in Latin America, where 80% of the land is owned by 8% of land-owners; smallholders who comprise 66% of all owners have just 4% of the land. However, it is a worldwide problem: 4% of land-owners in the Far East own 31% of agricultural land. Increasingly in Asia, indebtedness of small farmers leads to landlessness.

Prime land in the third world is also used for rearing livestock, chiefly for export. And the levels of livestock production in the developed countries are only achieved through imports from the third world: one-third of the world's grain, two-thirds of oilseeds, half the fishmeal and one-third of milk products are used to feed livestock, the majority of which are consumed by the developed world. This represents a large outflow of protein – in the form of groundnuts from Nigeria, soya beans from Brazil, fishmeal from Peru and so on – from the malnourished countries to feed the well-fed populations of the first world (Harrison, 1987).

Such issues of distribution will have to be addressed, as the current inequitable situation both within and between countries does not provide a good basis for sustainable development. As populations grow and the effective demand for 'westernised' foods – such as wheat in Africa – increases, the need for increased productivity will put further demands on often fragile ecological situations, and may well generate the same kinds of harmful impacts as those which are becoming increasingly obvious in the rich countries of the world.

Activity 3

Monitor the media for discussion and evidence of problems of sustainability of first and third world agriculture. You may well find:

● evidence of the impacts of high industrial inputs on wildlife, soils or water

● policy changes towards set-aside or less intensive use in first world countries

● problems arising from commercialisation in areas of intensive subsistence agriculture

● negative impacts of clearance of tropical forest for agricultural use.

PUNCHLINE
by @CHRISTIAN

FATHER WHY IS IT THAT OUR PEOPLE AREN'T GETTING ENOUGH FOOD TO EAT?

I'M AFRAID THERE'S SOMETHING IN OUR FIELDS TODAY MY SON,...

THAT HAS COMPLETELY WIPED OUT OUR TRADITIONAL HARVEST.

FATHER, WHAT IS IT?! DROUGHT?! LOCUSTS?! RATS?!

CASH CROPS...

5   *Summary and conclusion*

Activity 4

This chapter set out to answer three questions:

- How have agricultural systems adjusted to the variety of ecosystems, soils and climatic zones which exist in different parts of the world?
- Which systems have been and are the most productive?
- What problems have they created?

Spend a few minutes jotting down your own answers to these questions based on your study of this chapter.

Section 2 of the chapter showed that agricultural systems have had to adjust to environmental constraints, notably temperature, available rainfall, slopes and soils, so that only about a tenth of the Earth's land surface is cultivated and a quarter grazed. However, enough has been said about the ten-thousand-year history of agriculture to show that farmers have been extremely active in selecting preferred varieties and modifying ecosystems and water systems to affect what is produced. They have been extremely successful in increasing productivity rates, but in North America and Europe since 1945 there has been a dramatic increase in use of inputs like machinery and chemicals in order to increase outputs; these technologies are increasingly being adopted in less developed countries. The proliferation of non-sustainable practices seems as absurd a direction for policy as some of those which have been applied to encourage and then discourage production in developed countries.

Activity 5

Review Chapter 1, especially reminding yourself of

- the probable growth of world population over the next century
- the location of the regions of fastest and slowest growth

Compare these patterns with the patterns of agricultural productivity and change discussed in this chapter

---

The patterns clearly show a general resemblance, but not a very encouraging one. Broadly, the developed countries have agricultural surpluses and low expected population growth while the least developed countries have food shortages and high expected population growth, with Africa the scene of the highest population growth rates and the worst food shortages. Asia and Latin America have a more mixed picture, some countries having industrialised and/or improved agricultural productivity sufficiently to outrun population growth.

The current growth rates suggest that the future is likely to see a worsening of a trend which is already well established. Overall, the growth in cereal production has progressively outstripped world population growth. In spite of this, in 1990 there were more people in the world who did not get enough to eat than there were in 1980. Estimates put the number whose inadequate diet prevented them from leading productive working lives at in excess of 730 million, or 15% of the total world population. The present problem is that world agriculture produces sufficient food to feed everyone but that the system of distribution does not provide for those most in need. Without major changes in policy, famines and chronic malnourishment will increase.

Given the crucial role of agriculture in feeding the human population, it is vital to promote systems which are sustainable indefinitely. Such systems would have to have fewer harmful impacts on environments than some of those currently in use, though the problem of loss of natural habitats can be avoided only if growth in agricultural productivity can continue to keep pace with population growth in future.

The technology exists and provides the potential to feed a doubled world population, but a dramatic growth in production threatens further environmental damage and provides no guarantee to better distribution.

There have been some important international initiatives which are seeking responses which are efficient, equitable and environment friendly. In 1980 the World Conservation Strategy produced an agenda for sustainable development linking agricultural development with the need to maintain ecological processes: see Box 2.3. The Brundtland Report, *Our Common Future* (1987), called for a series of policy initiatives concerned with 'sustaining and expanding the resource base of the Earth'. In Book Four of this series (*Smith and Warr* (eds), 1991) these initiatives will be analysed in detail in the context of a range of global environmental problems.

Box 2.3   World Conservation Strategy

Living Resource Conservation for Sustainable Development – a Report from the International Union for Conservation of Nature and Natural Resources (IUCN), Gland, Switzerland (1980) – was a diagnostic exercise on a global scale, not constrained by geographical boundaries, on the threat to ecosystems from the processes of agricultural and industrial development, and the basic need to survive.

It proposed *three* principal objectives of resource conservation:

1   The maintenance of ecological processes and life support systems.

2   The preservation of genetic diversity.

3   The sustainable utilisation of species and ecosystems.

Of these objectives, the first is the most critical, the other two being closely linked to it. To achieve stability and sustainability in terms of ecological processes, *three* specific requirements were laid down:

●   the utilisation of good croplands for crops, rather than the raising of cattle;

●   the ecologically sound management of crops;

●   the protection of watershed forests.

A quote from the Strategy underlines the significance of these requirements:

> Only 10% of the world's population live in mountainous areas but another 40% live in the adjacent plains; so the lives and livelihoods of half the world directly depend on the way in which watershed ecosystems are managed.

The Report predicted the irreversible damage of continued deforestation and of the increasing use of fertilisers and pesticides. The Report did not explain how these proposals were to be implemented.

From the global overview of this chapter we shall now take a more detailed look at the basis of productivity and environmental impacts of some of the major agricultural systems. Because rapid population growth makes further growth of output essential, we have chosen to analyse in depth two of the most productive forms of agriculture: the capital-intensive farming typical of the developed countries of temperate zones and the labour-intensive methods of subtropical zones, which reach their peak in the production of wetland rice.

References

HARRISON, P. (1987) *Inside the Third World*, Harmondsworth, Penguin Books.

PIMENTEL, D. and PIMENTEL, M. (1979) *Food, Energy and Society*, London, Edward Arnold.

SILVERTOWN, J. (1990a) 'Inhabitants of the biosphere', Ch. 3 in Silvertown, J. and Sarre, P. (eds).

SILVERTOWN, J. (1990b) 'Earth as an environment for life', Ch. 2 in Silvertown, J. and Sarre, P. (eds).

SILVERTOWN, J. and SARRE, P. (eds) (1990) *Environment and Society*, London, Hodder and Stoughton/The Open University (Book One of this series).

SIMMONS, I. (1990) 'The impact of human societies on their environment', Ch. 5 in Silvertown, J. and Sarre, P. (eds).

WORLD COMMISSION ON ENVIRONMENT AND DEVELOPMENT (1987) *Our Common Future*, Oxford, Oxford University Press.

Further reading

BERNSTEIN, H., CROW, B., MACKINTOSH, M. and MARTIN, C. (eds) (1990) *The Food Question*, London, Earthscan.

GRIGG, D. B. (1974) *The Agricultural Systems of the World: an evolutionary approach*, Cambridge, Cambridge University Press.

1   Introduction

We saw in the last chapter some of the many ways in which people have tried to obtain useful products through varying degrees of 'management' of terrestrial ecosystems. In this chapter we will consider in more detail one of these managed ecosystems: that of wetland or 'paddy' rice cultivation.

This farming system is one of the most important in the history of human settlement, and has assumed a growing importance in global food supply in the second half of the twentieth century. This is because rice constitutes nearly half of the overall cereal output of developing countries, where three-quarters of the world's population live, compared to only 3% of the total cereal output of developed countries. The significance of this in world terms is twofold: firstly, rice is overwhelmingly a crop grown by poor, small-scale farmers; secondly, it is an important food source to many of the world's poorest consumers, who are most vulnerable to food shortages.

By the late 1980s the world average yield of rice per unit of land cultivated was nearly 50% higher than that of wheat. During the three decades from 1957 to 1987 rice output more than doubled, enabling many Asian countries to achieve self-sufficiency in rice in spite of high population growth rates. United Nations statistics show that in 1985 the total cereal output in developing countries overtook that in developed countries for the first time since records were begun, forty years earlier.

This rapid increase in rice production was one of the results of a number of changes in rice cultivation, often known as the 'green revolution'. In this chapter we shall:

● identify the key biological and chemical factors in the ecosystem supporting wetland rice cultivation;

● examine the history of Asian rice cultivation to ask how human efforts to increase production have modified not only the rice ecosystem, but also the form of human society itself;

● analyse the nature of the green revolution in Asian rice cultivation in the twentieth century, and its impacts on environment and on society;

● examine current problems and possibilities for future development of paddy rice cultivation.

2   The ecology of wetland rice

2.1   Wetland rice

Rice cultivation in Asia has a history of at least 7000 years. The major characteristic which distinguishes the historic development of Asian rice production from all other agricultural systems is that the crop was grown principally on flooded or waterlogged land. By contrast, rice cultivation by farmers in Africa and South America was, until the latter half of the twentieth century, principally on 'upland' which was freely drained. (This is not to say that flooded or 'wet' rice cultivation was never practised by farmers elsewhere: systems for growing rice in seasonally flooded valleys were an important part of traditional farming in both West and East Africa. Furthermore, upland rice is important in some parts of Asia.)

Our focus in this chapter will be confined to Asian wetland rice because some 90% of the world's rice is produced in Asia, and 80% of rice production in Asia is associated with the exploitation of soils which have been flooded in a variety of ways: through irrigation, through impounding rainwater, or through the seasonal flooding of rivers. This practice is so different from the use of well-drained soils for all other cereals (and, indeed, the vast majority of other crops) that it is important to understand what advantages there might be in growing rice on flooded soils.

2.2   The wetland ecosystem

We can make a useful start by remembering the two principal processes which define biological activity within an ecosystem. These are firstly the **flow of energy**, or **food chain**, and secondly the **cycle of mineral elements (or nutrients)**. Figures 3.1 and 3.2 depict both these processes in a generalised ecosystem, showing how energy and minerals pass between

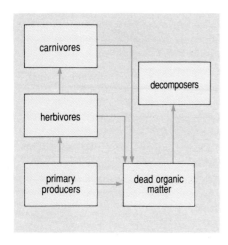

▲   Figure 3.1
Compartments of a 'model' ecosystem, showing the pathways of energy flow.

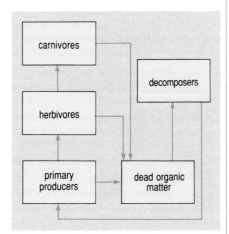

▲   Figure 3.2
The pathway of mineral elements in the model ecosystem.

different types of organisms: from primary producers (plants) to herbivores and then on to carnivores and ultimately on to decomposers. (Readers of Book One in this series (Sarre and Silvertown (eds), 1990) will recognise these diagrams from Chapter 4 of that volume.)

To determine the significance of using wetlands (flooded or waterlogged land) for plant production, we need to concentrate our analysis on the mineral cycle, and in particular on the soil conditions which in all terrestrial ecosystems control the working of the critical link in the cycle where mineral elements are absorbed by the plants.

In order to identify 'wetland' soil conditions, let us consider the ecosystem in which wild rice originated – the swamps of the Himalayan foothills, between north-east India and south-west China.

Q   Using what you already know about the effects of rainfall and temperature on the mineral cycle in other ecosystems, what broad characteristics might be expected in the soils of this tropical swampland?

A   Firstly, tropical soils exposed to high temperatures and rainfall are most typically regarded as having had many of their minerals washed out of them. However, the lower-lying parts of the landscape receive water and minerals washed down from the surrounding hills and they therefore often contain higher concentrations of minerals and, where rain falls only in certain seasons of the year, remain moist for longer than free-draining upland soils. Secondly, unlike waterlogged areas in temperate climates, the high temperatures allow the activity of 'decomposers', the organisms which break down dead organic matter. However, and thirdly, the waterlogging of the soil for long periods means that air is excluded from the soil, which prevents the activity of **aerobic organisms** which need oxygen for respiration. Decomposition must therefore be carried out by **anaerobic organisms** which can live in the absence of oxygen.

For practically all cultivated plants, the lack of oxygen in waterlogged soil prevents respiration in the roots, which are quickly killed as a result. In contrast, the rice plant is able to grow successfully in flooded soil because it has an efficient system of air channels between the root and the shoot. This system (which is four times more efficient than that of barley and ten times more efficient than that of maize, both crops adapted to 'upland' conditions) allows air absorbed from the atmosphere by the shoot to be supplied to the roots growing in oxygen-deficient soil.

These general descriptions of soil in swamps suggest that, to early cultivators with few resources, rice offered the possibility of growing food in a niche in the landscape more fertile than the uplands to which they were restricted by other crop plants. Moreover, in the tropics and subtropics, where the length of the growing season is commonly limited by lack of rainfall during a dry season of several months' duration, the accumulated water in these low-lying areas is often sufficient to significantly prolong the period each year when crops can be grown. A longer growing period could increase the number of crops available for harvest each year.

Research carried out over the past twenty-five years on the chemistry of flooded soils has indicated a number of mineral-cycling characteristics in such soils which make them particularly resilient to continuous intensive crop-growing, and probably more so than many freely drained soils. Because these characteristics have some bearing on the development of rice farming considered in later sections, they will be briefly described.

Minerals and primary production

Before we explore specific characteristics of flooded soils, let us outline some of the general features of the absorption of mineral elements by plants growing in soil. This is fairly straightforward because, although plants differ widely in terms of the *quantities* of minerals that they absorb, all plants seem to need to absorb the same set of minerals, known as *mineral nutrients*. The principal ones are:

- nitrogen
- phosphorus
- sulphur

- potassium
- calcium
- magnesium

In addition very small quantities of the following nutrients must also be absorbed:

- zinc
- copper
- molybdenum
- boron

- manganese
- iron
- chlorine

Q   Where do these mineral nutrients come from?

A   The mineral cycle in Figure 3.2 shows that a part of the mineral nutrients in the soil are derived from the decomposition of organic matter from dead plants, animals and micro-organisms. However, all nutrients except nitrogen are ultimately derived from the rocks from which the soil is formed. These may be rocks underlying the soil, or mineral material such as clay or silt deposited after being transported from elsewhere by wind or water. Nitrogen in the soil is derived not from rock material but from the air, which is 79% nitrogen gas, through the agency of 'nitrogen-fixing' bacteria and algae which can incorporate atmospheric nitrogen into organic material.

The nutrient nitrogen is particularly important in the cultivation of cereal crops, because it is contained in large quantities in the harvested grain. A harvest of 2 tonnes of rice, for example, contains approximately 32 kg of nitrogen, as against only 6 kg of phosphorus and 16 kg of potassium. Because of this heavy demand for nitrogen, the roots of cereals must absorb large quantities of this nutrient from the soil. Moreover, because so much nitrogen is contained in the grain, little is returned to the soil by the decomposition of the dead plant leaves, stalks and roots. Cereal crops therefore move large amounts of nitrogen out of the soil and into other parts of the food chain. In order to maintain this flow, nitrogen must be replaced in the soil, and many systems of cereal farming have evolved to incorporate plants which support nitrogen-fixing bacteria on their roots (legumes) through rotations (for example, in temperate climates clover in pastures one year followed by wheat or barley the next) or through intercropping (that is, growing more than one crop in the same field, such as beans with maize in Latin America). As we shall see, similar techniques involving *Azolla* ferns and blue-green bacteria have been developed for flooded rice fields in Asia.

As Chapter 2 discussed, where farmers sought higher production of grain from the same area of land, they adopted the practice of adding extra nutrients to the soil in the form of organic or mineral fertilisers and, among these, fertilisers containing nitrogen have been the most important. However, when very large amounts of grain are produced repeatedly from the same field, the quantities of many types of nutrients may become insufficient for normal plant growth, so that in addition to the principal nutrients like nitrogen and phosphorus, fertilisers must also contain nutrients such as zinc or copper, which the crop plants require only in minute quantities.

We can see, therefore, that in order to maintain a high flow of energy up the food chain through large harvests from the primary production (crop) part of the ecosystem, farmers have to develop ways of increasing the rate at which mineral nutrients are cycled through the soil.

Q   We have mentioned that mineral nutrients in soil are derived from both organic and inorganic sources, but in what form are they actually *absorbed* by the plant roots?

A   All mineral nutrients are absorbed by plant roots in the form of simple inorganic chemicals which are soluble in water.

The final stage of the decomposition of organic matter in the soil is therefore its **mineralisation** to release mineral nutrients in this simple inorganic form. This is important because the solubility, and hence availability to plants, of these minerals is determined by the acidity and oxygen content of the soil. Flooding changes both of these soil characteristics and so profoundly alters the availability of many of the nutrients needed by plants.

Let us now consider some differences between flooded and freely drained soils.

Some comparisons of flooded and freely drained soils

A first effect of flooding on soil is to change its physical *structure*. The different organic and inorganic components of soil are combined in various physical ways to form *aggregates*: the solid material of the soil. The spaces or *pores* between the aggregates allow the movement of water and air in the soil.

When a soil is flooded, the system of air spaces and pores within it will tend to collapse due to:

• the compression of the air trapped in the pores by the water, leading to small air 'explosions' which break down larger aggregates, or clods, into smaller ones

• the swelling of certain types of minerals, particularly clays

• the dissolution of some of the substances that stick soil aggregates together.

As a result of this collapse of soil pores, water moves through the flooded soil much more slowly: that is, the soil will lose less water through drainage. When the soil surface is covered by water, the oxygen supply in the soil is quickly depleted (in less than a day) in all but a thin layer of up to 1 cm thick, at the soil surface, to which oxygen diffuses from the air through the water. Thus, a flooded soil typically consists of two layers, illustrated in Figure 3.3: a thin upper layer supplied with oxygen, and the underlying bulk of the soil in which oxygen is absent. In this latter layer, the aerobic microbes which function in the presence of oxygen become dormant, or die, and microbial activity is dominated by those anaerobic organisms which do not require oxygen for respiration. Instead of oxygen, these anaerobic organisms transform a wide range of other chemical compounds in the process of respiration, and it is these transformations which very largely account for the differences in chemistry between flooded and freely drained soils.

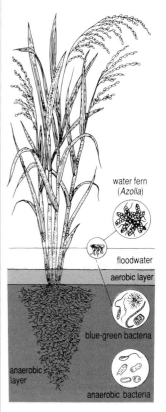

▲   Figure 3.3
Rice plant showing flooded growing conditions and aerobic and anaerobic layers of soil. Nitrogen is fixed by micro-organisms including those shown: blue-green bacteria, free-living or in a symbiotic relation with the water fern Azolla and a variety of other bacteria.

The consequences of these transformations are outlined as follows:

• *Increased nutrient availability for crops*   When a soil is flooded, some important mineral nutrients, such as phosphorus, become more soluble, and hence more available for absorption by plants.

• *Soils become neutral*   In contrast to the situation in cool and cold climates (where waterlogging inhibits decomposition and allows build-up of thick peat layers which acidify the water), in tropical or subtropical areas all soils, whether alkaline or acidic before flooding takes place, become neutral within a month of flooding. While flooded, therefore, soils do not suffer problems of excess acidity or alkalinity which can cause serious reduction in growth of crops growing in freely drained, upland soils.

• *Reduced decomposition of organic matter, but enhanced nitrogen supply*
The decomposition, or mineralisation, of organic matter by anaerobic micro-organisms in flooded soils is slower than that by the aerobic micro-organisms in freely drained soils. Thus, organic matter tends to accumulate more in flooded than in freely drained soils. This might be considered a disadvantage of flooded soils, slowing down the mineral cycle and restricting the movement of minerals into primary (crop) production. However, although *quantitatively* slower, the anaerobic mineralisation has some *qualitative* advantages in relation to the all-important mineralisation of nitrogen, particularly when this nutrient is present in only low concentrations in organic matter.

Q   We have already encountered one example of organic matter with a low
     concentration of nitrogen. What was it?

A   Cereal straw.

In freely drained soils organic matter such as straw, in which the content of nitrogen is lower than about 1.5%, can only be mineralised by aerobic micro-organisms if they scavenge extra nitrogen from elsewhere in the soil, thus mopping up the nitrogen which would otherwise be available for absorption by plant roots. For this reason, addition of large amounts of straw to a field just before a cereal crop is planted may create a temporary 'famine' of nitrogen which will reduce the growth of the crop. In flooded soils, however, the activity of anaerobic organisms is less sensitive to the nitrogen content of the organic matter, so that nutrients contained in material such as straw are more readily available to a crop of rice than, say, a crop of wheat.

• *Advantages of continuously as against intermittently flooded soil*
The collapse of pores and channels in a continuously flooded soil means that less water, and hence nutrients dissolved in the water, will drain through the soil into the groundwater. Flooded conditions effectively conserve water and nutrients in the rooting zone of the crop. By contrast, under conditions of intermittent flooding, large amounts of water will drain through the cracks which open as the soil dries out between periods of flooding. Furthermore, the drying out of the soil allows oxygen into the anaerobic layer, allowing the aerobic decomposition process to begin. An alternation between aerobic and anaerobic conditions in the soil has negative effects on the mineral supply to crops by allowing large amounts of nitrogen in the soil to return to the atmosphere through a process known as **denitrification**. This works in the following way: each time the soil dries out and aerobic micro-organisms can become active, mineral nitrogen will be converted from ammonium compounds to nitrates. Both forms can be absorbed by

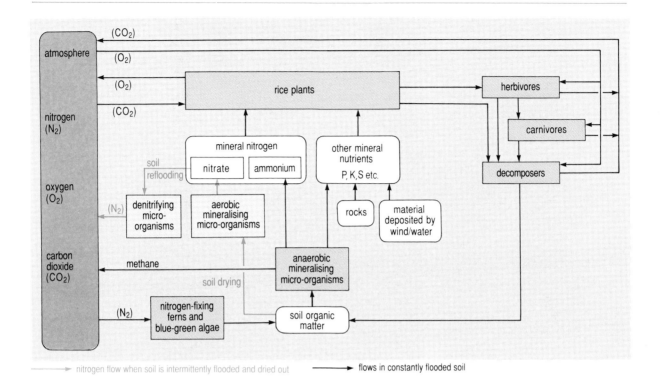

nitrogen flow when soil is intermittently flooded and dried out   flows in constantly flooded soil

plants but the nitrate form has two disadvantages: it is highly mobile, and therefore easily lost in drainage water; also, each time the soil is reflooded the anaerobic organisms convert nitrates to the gases nitrous oxide and nitrogen, which bubble to the surface and are lost to the atmosphere. Inadequate control of water in rice cultivation, leading to intermittent flooding and drying out of the field, results in much lower efficiency in the use of both water and soil nutrients. See Figure 3.4.

Not all aspects of flooded soils are advantageous, however.

• *Disadvantages of continuously flooded soils*   In certain soils with high levels of organic matter and low levels of iron, flooding may cause the formation of hydrogen sulphide gas, which is toxic to rice plants. A major product of the anaerobic decomposition of organic matter in flooded soil is methane (commonly known as 'marsh gas'), which bubbles to the surface and into the atmosphere. Although of no immediate significance to rice farmers, the increasing content of methane in the atmosphere on a global scale has been claimed to be a contributory factor in the increased retention of radiation reflected from the Earth's surface (the so-called *greenhouse effect*). However, the relative contribution of flooded ricefields to increased methane in the atmosphere is as yet unknown. Natural swamps and the digestive system of cattle are other major sources.

▲   *Figure 3.4*
Nutrient flows in a flooded rice field and in a field which is intermittently flooded and dried out.

Summary

From this brief listing of the chemical consequences of flooding soils we can summarise that, compared to freely drained soils, flooded or waterlogged soils in warm climates have a number of mineral-cycling advantages for intensive agricultural production. In particular, they conserve water and nutrients through reduced drainage, conserve organic matter, avoid acidity, and render certain nutrients more available for absorption by the crop. There is therefore an advantage to be gained from extending the principle from naturally occurring swamps to soils which are not flooded in their natural state. Such a strategy is not without risks, however, as when flooding is intermittent rather than continuous, losses of water and of the important nutrient nitrogen will occur. Close control of water is thus intimately linked with the maintenance of fertility of soils in flooded rice cultivation.

Activity 1

Our discussion of the wetland ecosystem in which rice originated has so far concentrated on only two compartments of the system: the decomposers and the primary producers. What type of organisms would you expect to occupy the other compartments (herbivores and carnivores)?

  Sketch out a scheme of the energy flows between the different organisms. Check your answers against the figure given at the end of the chapter.

2.3 Variability, domestication and adaptation of the rice plant

It was stated above that rice is believed to have originated in the foothills of the eastern Himalayas: in north-east India, Indo-China, and south-west China. This geographical origin is suggested by the large concentration of wild rice species in that area. Wild rices include many perennial species, but, in spite of the advantages of permanent flooding for nutrient retention, it was the annual species which were of more interest to human cultivators as they could be more successfully grown in areas which were not flooded for the entire year. The archaeological evidence indicating the earliest date of rice cultivation was found in the Yangzi delta (eastern China), where excavation of a village situated at the edge of a marsh has yielded remains which were carbon-dated to 7000 BP. Other evidence of rice cultivation has been discovered at sites in north-east Thailand which have been similarly dated to 6500 BP.

  Archaeological studies have indicated that the progressive spread of rice cultivation to the rest of southern and eastern Asia took place over a 6000-year period. Thus, the earliest indications of rice cultivation in Vietnam date from 5000 BP, and those in India from 3500 BP. Rice-growing arrived in Japan much later, in about 2400 BP, probably via Korea. In Malaya and Indonesia, rice did not become a major crop until after 1000 BP. See Figure 3.5.

  In many of the areas into which rice cultivation spread, rice increasingly became a staple food, substituting millets and tubers which had previously been the principal food crops. While rice cultivation seems likely to have been originally carried out exclusively in swamps, the spread of the crop to new areas meant that it needed to be adapted to a wide range of environments differing in soil type, temperature, day-length and rainfall. It is clear that farmers were active in this adaptive process, by selecting varieties that were best suited to each local set of conditions. As a result, the range of rice varieties is very broad, varying from those at one extreme

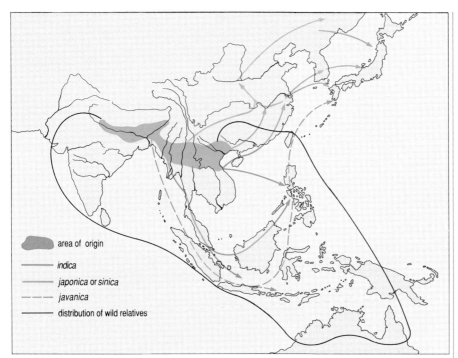

▲   *Figure 3.5   Spread of Asian rice* Oryza sativa *from its area of origin as a wild annual grass: indica, japonica (or sinica) and javanica are the three major geographic races of* Oryza sativa. *The indicas were originally cultivated in the humid parts of the Asian tropics and subtropics; japonicas developed in subtropical temperate regions; javanicas developed in equatorial Indonesia.*

suitable for upload (unflooded) conditions, where they are grown like other cereals, to, at the other extreme, varieties of 'floating' rice which can be grown in water up to 5 m deep.

Not only is the range of rice-growing conditions extremely broad but the discrimination of different characteristics has proved to be very subtle. When the International Rice Research Institute set out in the 1960s to make a collection of the existing rice varieties in the world, it recovered, over a twenty-year period, some 63 000 local varieties of the rice species cultivated in Asia (*Oryza sativa*). This was in addition to over a thousand species of wild rice, and some 2500 cultivated varieties of the African rice species (*Oryza glaberrima*). To give some perspective to this genetic diversity induced by rice farmers, it may be noted that the number of known varieties of wheat (*Triticum aestivum*) is estimated to total only 20 000. The enormous number of local varieties of *Oryza sativa* were practically all developed by Asian farmers before the beginning of the twentieth century. In order to better understand how this came about and the changes which subsequently took place in the twentieth century, we shall briefly consider the mechanics of selecting new varieties of rice.

Selecting new varieties of rice

As was discussed in *Silvertown* (1990, Section 6), in the process of 'domesticating' a wild plant species human cultivators select which seed will form the basis of the next generation of plants on their fields. They may, for example, choose to sow seeds of plants that were taller, or which matured faster, or which had bigger seeds. In so doing they reduce the genetic diversity of the plants on their fields in relation to the diversity of the wild population. This process, carried on over thousands of years by millions of different farmers selecting seed according to different criteria can fairly easily be seen to give rise to many different distinct populations, or varieties, of the same original species.

This selection process was integral to the harvest: the most common method of rice harvesting employed until recently in Asian rice farming was to cut each individual stem just below the grain-bearing head, or 'panicle', with a small knife. This system provided farmers with an opportunity to inspect each panicle separately, and set aside for seed any which were of particular interest. This technique, known by plant breeders as **mass selection**, was by itself sufficient to select and maintain a large number of distinct rice varieties due to the fact that the rice plant is predominantly **self-pollinated**.

Q   What is meant by self-pollination?

A   By self-pollination is meant that flowers of the rice plant are fertilised by their own pollen. That is, grain generally contains genetic material derived only from the plant on which it develops. As a result, a variety of rice resulting from many generations of selection will tend to breed true, and maintain its characteristics from one generation to the next.

However, within this predominant pattern, two factors operate to present some degree of genetic variability in each generation, which allows farmers to select plants which can form the basis of a new variety. Firstly, the genetic material of a population of rice plants will not be completely homogeneous (identical), so that plants will vary in many quantitative ways, such as height, length of growth period before flowering and so on. Secondly, where a number of different rice varieties are grown in the same area, or where wild rice species grow near cultivated rice, a very small amount of **cross-pollination** occurs, and this may also give rise to new types of plant from which farmers are able to select seed to reproduce as a new variety.

Until the mid twentieth century, all domesticated rice varieties in Asia were partitioned between three major subspecies of *Oryza sativa*. The two most important of these were the *indica* subspecies, grown in tropical Asia, and the *japonica* subspecies grown in the cooler and more northern rice-growing areas. A third subspecies, *javanica*, predominated in Indonesia: see Figure 3.5. The principal distinctions between the *indica* and *japonica* rices were:

● grain type: *indica* varieties were long-grain, while *japonica* were short-grain;

● flowering characteristics: *indica* varieties were sensitive to day-length, and so a given variety started flowering only at a particular date, irrespective of when it was planted, while *japonica* varieties are not sensitive to day-length but will tend to flower after a fixed period of growth, which would vary between varieties.

In the twentieth century the process of selecting new varieties of rice was radically changed by the development of new *techniques* and by the adoption of different *criteria* for selection. Simultaneously, the control of the selection process passed from farmers to research scientists.

At the beginning of the twentieth century, Japanese scientists developed a technique of artificially pollinating rice plants of one variety with pollen from another. This enhanced cross-pollination enabled them to

generate a large number of new genetic combinations from which they could
select new varieties, and also gave them the chance of combining the desired
qualities of two or more parent varieties in a single new 'improved' variety.
This work resulted in the production in the 1930s of *japonica* varieties that,
when grown with large quantities of fertiliser, produced yields two to three
times higher than those possible with traditional 'farmers' varieties'.

Cross-pollination between *japonica* and *indica* rices produces very few
fertile plants and was practically unknown before the 1950s. It was at that
time that breeding programmes were set up to promote cross-pollination
between the two subspecies and to closely evaluate plants grown from the
small amounts of fertile seed which such crosses produced. This process of
crossing and selection resulted in the identification by the International Rice
Research Institute (IRRI) of the so-called **high-yielding varieties (HYVs)**
that were the basis of the introduction of the 'green revolution' to tropical
Asia in the 1960s (to be explored in more detail in Section 4).

2.4   Summary

In this section we have explored some of the underlying biological
mechanisms in the Asian rice cultivation system. We have seen that rice
cultivation enabled early cultivators to exploit nutrient-rich swamp soils,
and that agricultural advantages could be gained from reproducing flooded
soil conditions elsewhere. We have also seen that the spread of rice
cultivation depended upon farmers' ability to form new populations, or
varieties, of rice better adapted to new sets of growing conditions.

In Sections 3 and 4 we shall trace the wider socio-economic context of
Asian rice cultivation in two stages: Section 3 deals with the history of
rice-growing in Asia before the twentieth century; Section 4 analyses the
origins and impact of the changes in rice-growing in the twentieth century.

3   Development of rice cultivation up to the twentieth century

In our discussion of the history of rice farming we will identify two basic
trends: the *extension* of cultivated areas, and the *intensification* of production
per unit area of land cultivated.

3.1   Organised farming: the development of water control

We saw earlier how in warm climates a flooded soil environment may
present certain advantages for mineral cycling for primary biomass
production, and that a central feature of wetland rice production systems
was their unique ability to exploit flooded soil environments. Although rice
cultivation appears to have been first carried out in naturally waterlogged
marshy areas, the spread of rice farming required the creation of flooded

fields in areas where they did not occur naturally. The ability to impose these flooded conditions depended upon water control, and the spread and development of rice-growing very largely reflected the development of technologies of water control.

At its simplest, water control involved impounding rainwater on fields by constructing low dykes, or 'bunds', around the field edges. On more sloping land retention of water was achieved by cutting terraces to provide a series of horizontal fields step-like up the slope. The steeper the slope, the smaller the field size necessary to stop water flowing downhill. Some of the earliest terraces believed to be associated with rice cultivation have been found at Gio Linh, in Vietnam, and these are thought to have been constructed in 4000 BP. (See also Plate 5.)

The spread of rice cultivation to areas with lower rainfall required the development of ways to supplement the supply of water to rice fields. Three basic techniques were important in Asian rice-growing. These were:

(a) The construction of *tanks* to store water from diverted streams. This system was important in upper parts of river valleys, and formed the basis for very extensive irrigation systems that supported important medieval states in Sri Lanka, Thailand and Cambodia. The latter was once the Khmer empire, which flourished for over 300 years, and whose irrigated area is thought to have covered some 167 000 ha. The collapse of the empire in the fourteenth century is believed to have been due at least partly to the silting up of the tanks and canal system.

(b) The excavation of *ponds* to collect and store rainwater. The construction of ponds in elevated locations for water storage to irrigate lower-lying fields is believed to date from the first or second centuries in southern and central China, and from the fifth century in Japan. The size of ponds was very variable, some serving a single farm while others might serve an entire village.

(c) Diversion of stream or river water using *contour canals*. In this case a barrier across a stream would partially divert the flow into a canal system whose gradient was designed to distribute the water by gravity to fields at a flow rate slow enough to avoid scouring and erosion of the canal but fast enough to avoid silting up. Systems using these contour canals were developed in medieval times in Indonesia, in the highlands of Laos and Vietnam, and in Japan. In China a very large system of this kind, at Guanxian, irrigating some half a million hectares with water diverted from the Min river, was built as early as 2250 BP.

Although these water control systems varied enormously in accordance with the local characteristics of landscape and social organisation, a number of common features may be identified. We shall note three. In all cases they rely upon *gravity* to distribute water, so that all were constructed in the sloping highland landscapes of upper watersheds, and not in flat river floodplains. A second common characteristic is that all construction was carried out using only *simple manual tools*, but using very *sophisticated design*. This is particularly apparent in contour canal systems, where canal gradients were set with great precision and water was sometimes carried through tunnels or across valleys in aqueducts made of wood or stone. The success of this technology is shown by the fact that in many cases it remains in use to the present day. Thus tank irrigation continues in Sri Lanka; ponds continued to provide as much as 20% of Japan's irrigation until the twentieth century and were subsequently incorporated as part of later irrigation networks; the Guanxian contour canal system remains in use more than 2000 years after its construction, unchanged except that it now irrigates an

▲   *An example of the use of human labour to lift water: an illustration from a medieval Chinese treatise on agriculture showing two different lifting devices – a square-pallet chain pump, and a beam and bucket.*

area double that for which it was originally designed. A third feature of these irrigation systems is that, although they sometimes reached a very large size, the large systems were essentially *multiples of small-scale systems*. That is, the technology employed by an individual farmer or village to build and manage a tank, pond or contour canal was essentially the same as that employed in large systems, which consisted of interlocking networks of these small units.

This characteristic of 'scaling up' irrigation through multiples of small units was reflected in the organisation of irrigation management in two distinct levels: the level of the unit, and the level of the multiple.

At the 'unit' level, the water source (tank, pond or contour canal) was directly run and maintained by those farmers who used it. The farmers' organisations which evolved for this purpose often (and of necessity) achieved a high degree of regulation of water use by individual members, but also constituted an important focus for lobbying on behalf of communities to which they belonged. These village-level irrigation organisations, of which the *subak* system in Bali, Indonesia is one of the best known, still function in many parts of Asia where irrigated rice production has been long established.

The state was responsible for the organisation of water control at the second, 'multiple' level, indeed the management of irrigation was a prime function of the state in medieval Asia. Since rice-growing was the basis of a reliable food supply, and a taxable surplus, the continuation and growth of the power of a state depended on its ability to sustain or extend the control of water for rice. Consequently, state-appointed officials were responsible for resolving conflicts between different communities or groups, for establishing water use regulations, and for the investment of resources in improvement or extension of irrigation.

Q   What do the characteristics of early irrigation systems imply about the characteristics of the states which organised them?

A   The vital need for water, the need for all users to limit water use and to carry out essential maintenance, especially the need for massive expenditure of labour to construct large systems with simple tools, all point towards the need for a state with a high level of authoritarian power. These were often monarchies and the priesthood commonly played a role in legitimising state activities. *Simmons* (1990) also points to the vulnerability of such states to any breakdown in the irrigation system.

Further developments occurred as the need arose to bring under rice cultivation land on which water control required much larger investment than the systems described above. The most important of such investments were needed to establish water control for agriculture on flat river floodplains and deltas, and coastal swamplands. In practice, the increased investment needed in these low-lying areas amounted to greater labour input: to dig drainage ditches in swamps, to build dykes to prevent uncontrolled river flooding and to keep out the sea. Since there was little slope in the landscape, it was much more difficult to use gravity to distribute water, and so energy had to be expended in pumping water. Although medieval states were active in organising rice cultivation in these situations, for example the colonisation of the Yangzi delta through the digging of drainage works in fourteenth-century China, and the flood control measures built in the same period in the Tonkin delta in Vietnam, the emphasis in such projects was on organising conscripted labour. The eighteenth and nineteenth centuries saw a rapid expansion of rice cultivation on river floodplains and deltas in south-east Asia in which capital investment and hired labour played a much more important role.

Q   What do you think were the historical developments that promoted this rapid expansion of rice cultivation in the eighteenth and nineteenth centuries?

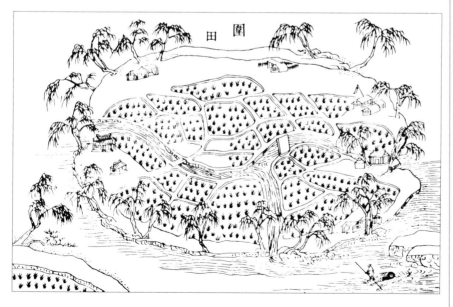

▲   *Water management for controlled flooding of rice fields in lowland areas.*
(Illustrated in the Chinese agricultural treatise Shoushi tongkao *of 1742.)*

A   They were the expansion of European colonialism and international trade. One of the first concerns of European colonists was to expand supplies of commercial products like spices, tea and rubber. This was achieved by establishing plantations managed by Europeans but using local labour. This labour had to be fed, so rice began to be traded over increasing distances and there was a need to expand rice production to produce a greater surplus. The colonial administrations themselves contributed to the increase in rice area by opening up previously sparsely populated deltas like those of the Irrawaddy (Burma), Mekong (Vietnam) and the Chau Phraya (Thailand).

▲   Figure 3.6   Colonial government in rice-growing areas of Asia at the end of the nineteenth century.

▲   A manual method of irrigating the flooded rice fields in Vietnam.

Unlike the highland irrigation systems discussed above, the drainage and
flood-control schemes of the deltas needed expensive capital items such as
sluice gates and pumps. Moreover they needed to be carried out on a large
scale to be effective: they did not consist of multiples of more or less
self-contained small units.

Investment was therefore not only on a larger scale, but could not be
spread as easily over time because the entire scheme had to be completed
before production could be reliably started and return on investment begin.
It is perhaps for these reasons, and also because of the low population
density of the new lands, that investment by wealthy individuals in return
for land ownership rights was a common feature of this type of irrigation.
Although the new 'landlords' subsequently rented out their land to
small-scale farmers, they often remained responsible for ensuring that their
tenants provided the very considerable labour needed to maintain the
irrigation system.

Since the latter half of the nineteenth century, irrigation development
has continued to be largely shaped by state intervention, either through the
consolidation of existing irrigation, as in Japan and China, or by the attempt
to bring new land under irrigation. For much of the first half of the twentieth
century the state in Asia was more often than not that of a European or
Japanese colonial administration and this left its mark on irrigation
development. Thus the irrigation expansion carried out by the Japanese
colonial government in Taiwan and Korea inherited some of the
organisational strengths of irrigation management in Japan, while in
European-ruled colonies emphasis on hydraulic engineering was often at
the expense of organisational coherence.

Summary

In this section we have seen how the spread of rice cultivation was
dependent upon the development of water control techniques to allow
flooded fields to be established in different types of landscape. The control

of water had strong organisational requirements which for thousands of years profoundly shaped the political and organisational character of the Asian rice-growing societies. The expansion of European-dominated international trade resulted in a rapid expansion in rice cultivation in which capital investment played a larger role than before, and this has had an impact on the organisational aspects of water control for rice growing.

3.2   Intensifying production: from medieval China to nineteenth-century Japan

While the development and spread of water control technologies determined the extension of the area under rice cultivation, a number of other farming techniques were developed which allowed a sustained increase in the grain output from each unit of land through an increase in the amount of labour invested in growing the crop. These techniques were developed to greatest effect in China during the later Southern Song, Yuan and Ming dynasties (thirteenth to seventeenth centuries), and in Japan during the Tokugawa period (seventeenth to nineteenth centuries). The principal techniques were:

- the selection of earlier-maturing varieties
- transplanting
- wet-tillage
- the use of organic fertiliser.

The selection of earlier-maturing varieties was important in increasing the number of crops that could be grown on a single piece of land in a year. Where water control is effectively established, the main factor determining the length of the growing period becomes temperature. Rice requires a temperature above 15°C for pollination and grain formation to take place, so that it is more restricted by low winter temperatures than other cereals such as wheat and barley. Thus, in the more northern part of its range – in central China, Korea and Japan – a quick-maturing rice crop may allow another crop to be grown in the same land in the cooler part of the year. In warmer latitudes – for example, in Vietnam and south China – two rice crops could be grown in a year. The search for early-maturing rice varieties has been complicated because earlier maturity has often been associated with lower productivity, so that the development of high-yielding early varieties has had a significant historical impact. One of the earliest such instances was that of the early-maturing 'champa' rices which spread from Vietnam to China during medieval times, passing from farmer to farmer. Just under a thousand years ago the Chinese state actively promoted the use of these varieties to enable the growing of two crops a year in the Yangzi delta, where Chinese farmers were able in the next two hundred years to select higher-yielding strains of these early-maturing rices. The role of the Chinese state in this case is interesting for it may be seen as a forerunner of the role taken by the Japanese state in identifying and disseminating more productive varieties in the nineteenth century.

Transplanting rice means that instead of sowing the seed directly into the field, the rice is grown in a small nursery for between one and two months before the seedlings are planted into the flooded soil of the main field. The advantages of the system are that it uses less seed, that it occupies the main field for less time and hence makes growing two crops a year in the same field easier, and, perhaps most important, it reduces weed growth in

▲   Wet tillage, or puddling, reduces the loss of water from rice fields by greatly reducing the downward drainage of water through the soil. (Yunnan Province, China, 1986.)

the field. Not only does the waterlogged condition of the soil suppress many weeds, but seedlings can be planted in lines, which assists weeding of the growing crop. (See Plate 6.)

Wet-tillage (puddling), that is ploughing the submerged field, was carried out to promote the collapse of soil structure in the flooded field. In its simplest form, puddling was carried out by cultivating the field while wet, before the crop was planted. Cultivation could be done either manually with a hoe, or using draught animals to pull a shallow plough.

Q   Why should this be advantageous?

A   It reduces to a minimum the rate of drainage of water in the field. This not only improves the conservation of water and nutrients, but also lessens the risk of the field drying out. As we saw in Section 2, intermittent waterlogging results in reduced levels of nutrients, particularly nitrogen.

Organic fertiliser use is perhaps one of the most characteristic features of intensive rice-growing in China, where for centuries practically any organic waste has been traded commercially as fertiliser. Associated with the wide range of materials used, which included human and animal manure, food-processing waste (beancurd waste, fishmeal etc.), ashes and crop residues, were composting techniques to render the material suitable for application to fields before planting. A further method of enriching the soil to allow it to sustain continuous crop production is the technique of growing aquatic plants such as blue-green bacteria and the fern-like *Azolla pinnata* in the flooded rice fields. As was noted in Chapter 2, these plants are able to fix nitrogen from the atmosphere, and when they die, after about a month of growth, they provide organic matter from which nitrogen is released in a form which the rice crop may absorb. As we saw in Section 2, shortage of nitrogen in the soil is often the major constraint to grain yield, and this technique, developed particularly in China and Vietnam, is an important way of sustaining soil fertility.

Unlike agricultural development in Europe and America, which pursued the substitution of labour by machinery, many of these technical developments of rice-growing *increased* the amount of labour required to grow the rice crop. Growing rice in nurseries and transplanting the seedlings requires more work (20–30 person-days per hectare) than simply broadcasting, or scattering, the seed onto the soil (1–2 person-days per hectare). The application of organic fertiliser requires work in composting, transporting (several tons per hectare of land) and incorporating the fertiliser into the soil. Furthermore, in order to be effective, all these techniques require a good control of the level of water in the field, and this close control of water is in itself a labour-intensive activity, particularly where manually operated water-pumps are used, as in China and Japan until the early twentieth century.

By the application of large amounts of labour – often of the order of 280 work-days per hectare for a single rice crop – Chinese and Japanese farmers were able to produce between 1.5 and 2.5 tonnes of rice per hectare per season (often two seasons in a year) with considerable reliability at a time when yields from an equivalent area of wheat would have been only 0.5 to 1.0 tonnes. In tropical Asia rice yields were more restricted by lack of irrigation. Less control over water meant that availability of water for the rice crop was erratic, and the effectiveness of labour-intensive fertiliser use and transplanting techniques were diminished.

It is evident that for many of the tasks described above the skill content is high and the resulting productivity made the investment of labour worth while. However, it is perhaps more important that the productivity of rice-growing allowed a *diversification* of farm activities. A well-known system developed in central China involved growing mulberry trees on the dykes round flooded fields to provide food for silkworm culture: the waste from silk production was added to ponds and flooded fields not only to fertilise the rice crop but also to feed fish such as carp and tilapia which provided a valuable source of food and income. Other forms of diversification involved growing a second crop, such as wheat or sugar cane, after draining the rice fields, or growing cash crops, of which cotton and soya bean were the most important, on neighbouring 'upland' fields. This diversified farm output, coupled with primary processing (for instance, silk and cotton), allowed a high year-round absorption of labour in rural areas and a relatively high value of output.

The sensitive management of water and soil required to achieve high output in this type of wet rice cultivation meant that there were few opportunities for economies of scale. Thus, although in both China and Japan ownership of land was highly concentrated in the hands of relatively few landlords, they had little incentive to manage their lands as large-scale production units, and most rice land was divided into small plots which were cultivated by tenants. The relatively high degree of technical management under the control of the tenants placed them in a strong bargaining position in relation to their landlords, and there are indications that over quite long periods of Chinese and Japanese history they were able to improve the proportion of their output which they retained.

However, much depended upon the nature and politics of the state, as the divergent paths of development of China and Japan in the nineteenth century illustrate. As the Chinese economy stagnated in the aftermath of the opium wars, landlords resorted to physical extortion in order to extract rents from increasingly impoverished tenants. By contrast, in Japan the Meiji period which began in the mid nineteenth century saw the state intervene in a number of ways to increase agricultural output as part of its industrialisation drive. In order to sustain both the supply of cheap rice for the growing industrial workforce and a flow of taxation (commonly reckoned to have been about 30%) from agriculture to finance industrial development, the state intervened to limit the level of rents paid by tenants to landlords and pursued a vigorous programme of agricultural research and extension. Although landlords retained a role in some aspects of agriculture, notably that of developing irrigation infrastructure, the state-led research and extension focused inevitably upon those responsible for cultivating the fields, two-thirds of whom were tenants at the turn of the century. To the extent that landlords were not directly involved in cultivating their fields, therefore, they became marginalised in Japanese agriculture and more concerned with industrial investment.

3.3   Summary

In this section we have sketched out some of the major factors shaping Asian rice cultivation over the 6000 years to the end of the nineteenth century. Some of these factors are 'technological':

●   the extension of the wetland conditions suitable for rice through the development of water control techniques

●   the improvement of mineral cycling in rice-fields through the use of composting and manuring

●   the selection of earlier-maturing varieties of rice allowing a larger harvest of primary production through the production of more than one crop in a year

●   the development of fish-farming and silkworm production allowing the 'harvest' to be extended to the herbivores and carnivores of the wetland ecosystem, as well as the primary production.

We saw, however, that these technological developments were driven by socio-economic forces and, in turn, produced socio-economic impact at the level of individual farmers, at the level of communities, and at the level of the state.

Activity 2

Review Section 3 and note down:

(a) different ways in which social and economic developments can be regarded as promoting changes in rice cultivation methods;

(b) ways in which the technology of rice production shaped social and economic relationships.

Then compare your answers with those given at the end of the chapter.

4   The twentieth century: the green revolution in rice production

In this section we trace the transformation in rice cultivation which took place in the twentieth century, from its origins in Japan and China to its wider impact in tropical Asia in the second half of the century. A final subsection analyses the consequences of this transformation in environmental and socio-economic terms.

4.1   Japan and China

Despite an early interest in American and British farm equipment, the Japanese drive to increase rice productivity in the late nineteenth and early twentieth century resulted in little mechanisation. The foreign-made equipment was rejected as being inappropriate for the scale and conditions of wetland rice cultivation, and the only significant mechanisation to take place was the introduction of electric pumps for irrigation, which cut the labour required for irrigation by about two-thirds (from 70 to 22 days per hectare).

With the passing of interest in western farming methods, the major Japanese research effort went into a search for more productive rice varieties, capable of increased yield with large applications of fertiliser; this was becoming possible as cheaper steamship transport opened the way for large-scale importation of fertiliser material, such as soyabean cake from Manchuria. In the nineteenth century the search for more productive varieties had been led by 'veteran farmers' who were responsible for bringing together and testing the large number of rice varieties already developed locally by farmers in different parts of Japan. The role of the state was to provide facilities for these activities and an organisation for distributing seed of the better varieties. By the end of the First World War, however, the pace of improvement in yields was slowing, and the increase in output was falling behind that of consumption. Japanese rice supplies were becoming increasingly dependent upon imports obtained from Japanese-ruled Taiwan and Korea. This dependence provided the impetus for major reorganisation and investment in irrigation by the Japanese administration in those colonies in the inter-war years.

In the late 1920s breeding work was started by the Japanese ministry of agriculture and forestry to develop new rice varieties by artificially cross-pollinating between the existing 'farmers' varieties', and this produced the early-maturing dwarf *Norin* varieties. Because of the short, stiff straw of these varieties, the heavy grain panicles resulting from large applications of fertiliser did not cause them to fall over, or 'lodge', and hence farmers could use greater amounts of fertiliser to increase grain production than with taller, traditional varieties. The *Norin* rice varieties were quickly adopted by farmers – in 1935 they were planted on some 160 000 ha in Japan – and they were subsequently introduced to Taiwan and Korea. However, the impoverishment of agriculture during the Depression, and then disruption during the Second World War meant that the benefits of the new varieties were not fully felt until some twenty years later.

The end of the Second World War saw the elimination of the landlord class as a result of land reforms carried out by United States military administrations in Japan, Taiwan and Korea, and by the communist government in mainland China. In all these countries this produced a rice-farming sector consisting of families farming very small landholdings of less than one hectare. In Japan, Korea and Taiwan this pattern of smallholding remained unchanged, while in China the subsequent thirty years saw a progressive combining of individual farming through mutual aid teams, then agricultural co-operatives, and finally communes.

Despite this difference, the technical development of wet rice production followed much the same pattern in all these countries: improved water control and use of high-yielding dwarf varieties grown with large applications of fertiliser were used to achieve very high land productivity. But in addition, from the 1960s onwards, the development of small motor-driven agricultural machinery – originally manufactured in Japan but later also in Korea and China – allowed a progressive *reduction* in the labour input by mechanising operations of heaviest labour demand, like tillage and transplanting. The labour released by mechanisation was absorbed by the growth of industry, much of which was sited in rural areas for this purpose. In China a significant proportion of the rural labour force (5%, or 17 million people) was also employed full-time on irrigation construction projects undertaken and paid for by the communes. The overall increase in land and labour productivity in Japanese rice-growing may be seen from Table 3.1; some figures for Taiwan are also given for comparative purposes.

Q   According to the figures given in Table 3.1, was the productivity increase in Japanese rice farming between 1900 and 1970 greater with respect to land or to labour?

A   Change in productivity per hectare: 5750 − 2870 = 2880, i.e. an increase of just over 100%.

Change in productivity per day: 39.4 − 10.7 = 28.7, i.e. an increase of nearly 300%.

Table 3.1   Development of land and labour productivity in Japan and Korea in the twentieth century

		Labour input (person-days/ha)		Productivity (kg rice)	
		in rice only	farming total	per ha	per day
Japan	1880	278	353	2360	8.5
Japan	1900	267	397	2870	10.7
Japan	1920	235	384	3940	16.7
Taiwan	1926	96	–	2110	22.0
Japan	1940	206	359	3740	18.1
Japan	1960	214	345	4990	23.3
Japan	1970	146	235	5750	39.4
Taiwan	1972	125	–	5700	45.6

Source: Bray, F. (1986) *The Rice Economies: technology and development in Asian societies*, Oxford, Blackwell.

Q   How has the time spent in rice farming in Japan changed as a percentage
     of total time spent in farming over the same period?

A   In 1900 labour input in rice was:

$$\frac{267}{397} \times 100\% \text{ of the total, or } 67\%.$$

     In 1970 it was:

$$\frac{146}{235} \times 100\%, \text{ i.e. } 62\%.$$

Q   The number of work-days required to cultivate one hectare of rice in
     Japan was lower in 1970 than in 1920, while the reverse seems to have
     been the case in Taiwan. Can you think of reasons for this?

A   Japan was more industrialised at both times, so labour costs would tend
     to be higher and prices of manufactured products lower, both favouring
     mechanisation. In Taiwan irrigation increased from the 1920s onwards,
     allowing greater use of labour-intensive methods in rice-farming.
     Taiwan also experienced rapid population growth after the Communists
     took power on the mainland in 1949 and Nationalists fled to Taiwan.
     This would have increased both demand for rice and the supply of
     labour.

At this point we will compare Asian rice farming with mechanised cereal
farming developed in North America. Comparisons of inputs and outputs of
agricultural systems are complex and, where a diversified farm output is
concerned, a complete picture can scarcely be obtained by considering the
output of only one crop. Thus the data presented in Table 3.2 serve only as a
guide to the different magnitudes of input, output and productivity
measures for different methods of growing cereals. The figures for Japanese
farming are for 1960 and the others have been compiled from various studies
carried out in the 1960s and 1970s; thus these data are not strictly
comparable.
     Table 3.2 sets out the inputs of four different cereal growing systems:
two American and two Asian. For each system a series of productivity
measures (outputs) has been calculated:

●   cereal output per unit (hectare) of land area

●   cereal output per unit (hour) of human labour

●   cereal output per unit of 'commercial energy' (purchased inputs such as
     fertiliser and machinery).

Finally an overall measure of energy efficiency is obtained by converting the
cereal harvest and all the inputs required to produce it to energy-equivalents
(MJ: 1 megajoule = 1 million joules of energy). In this way all the different
inputs may be added together to give a single figure for 'total energy input'.
The energy value of the harvest is divided by this 'total energy input' to
provide a figure for the number of joules of output for each joule of input.
     First we shall compare system 1 (US wheat production) with system 3
(Japanese rice production). Note the dramatic divergence in agricultural
labour use between the United States, where mechanisation reduced labour
use to a mere seven hours for each hectare of wheat, and Japan, where the
same area of rice employed no less than 1729 hours of human labour. As a
result, although the output of rice *per hectare* of land in Japan was more than

double that of wheat in the US, the productivity of agricultural *labour* was
over a hundred times higher in the US.

Q   Which of the two systems used more energy to produce a given weight
    of grain?

A   The amount of energy used to produce grain in the two systems was
    about the same because the Japanese put in about 2½ times as much
    energy to produce 2½ times as much grain per hectare. American
    mechanisation was more than compensated by the much higher energy
    inputs in Japanese wetland rice in the form of labour, fertiliser and
    irrigation.

The figures in Table 3.2 allow us to compare Japanese rice cultivation with
two other systems of rice production: system 2 represents a 'western'
rice-growing system from the southern United States which employs
large-scale land-levelling equipment, combine harvesters, and aircraft to
sow, fertilise and spray the crop; system 4 represents tropical Asian wetland
rice cultivation with a low level of water control and a low level of purchased
inputs. Activity 3 will allow you to make comparisons between these
systems.

Table 3.2   *Comparison of inputs and outputs and their energy equivalents in different cereal growing systems*

System	1 Wheat (USA)		2 Rice (USA)		3 Rice (Japan)		4 Rice (Philippines)	
	quantity per ha	energy MJ/ha	quantity per ha	energy MJ/ha	quantity per ha	energy MJ/ha	quantity per ha	energy MJ/ha
Inputs								
labour	7 hrs	13	17 hrs	33.2	1729 hrs	3387	576 hrs	1271
animal draught							272 hrs	3998
machinery, irrigation (incl. fuel)		5 084		32 145		864.5		174
fertiliser	141 kg	3 578	382 kg	18 178	305 kg	10 303	5.6 kg	357
seed	106 kg	2 938	157 kg	4 787	112 kg	3 415	108 kg	1678
pesticides	0.5 kg	210	13.4 kg	5 503	11 kg	4 397	0.6 kg	183
total energy input		11 823		60 646		30 138		7667
Outputs								
per unit area kg grain/ha	2060	28 552	6160	93 915	4848	73 912	1654	25 217
per unit of labour kg grain/hr	294		362		2.8		2.9	
per unit of commercial energy[1] kg grain/MJ	0.17		0.10		0.18		0.69	
energy efficiency MJ out/MJ in	2.41		1.55		2.45		3.3	

Note:[1] Excluding labour and animal power.
Source: Table compiled from data in Pimentel, D. and Pimentel, M. (1979) *Food, Energy and Society*, London, Edward Arnold.

Activity 3

Use the figures given in Table 3.2 to compare the US (system 2), Japanese (system 3) and Philippine (system 4) rice cultivation systems. Rank the three systems (from highest to lowest) in terms of:

- labour input
- total energy input
- land productivity
- labour productivity
- overall energy efficiency.

Which system do you consider to be the most efficient? Compare your answers with those given at the end of the chapter.

Let us now make two observations on these comparisons. Firstly, we can see that, with the technologies developed in twentieth-century agriculture, increased output of grain from a given area of land required an increase in *energy* use. The sustainability of such systems depended, therefore, upon the cost and continuing availability of energy for this input. Secondly, in rice-growing areas of Asia, human labour was for centuries the form of energy with which increased output from a fixed amount of land was achieved. In the twentieth century, other forms of energy have increasingly supplemented, and then displaced, human labour.

In the brief account of Chinese and Japanese rice farming given in earlier sections we saw that the technological changes which accompanied the increased investment of human labour allowed an increase not only in the amount of grain produced by a single crop but also in the number of crops the land could produce in a year. However, in spite of the fact that labour productivity in rice may have increased fivefold since the late nineteenth century (see Table 3.1), our comparisons with labour productivity in US agriculture highlight the fact that rice-growing by such labour-intensive methods is a relatively poor source of *income*. The importance of wetland rice cultivation in China and Japan was that it provided a secure supply of surplus food that enabled farmers to develop other income sources from livestock, cash crops and rural industry. This was of primary importance not only for farmers' incomes, but also for the Japanese economy: from the 1870s to the 1920s the share of silk production in the value of agricultural output rose from 5 to 15%, and in the 1920s silk exports accounted for 30% of Japan's foreign exchange earnings. The industrial development of Japan in the twentieth century was accompanied by an increasing location of industry in the countryside and a move towards part-time farming. Thus, by the 1980s, the number and size of farms had changed little from the time of the post-war land reforms, but over 70% of farmers earned more from non-agricultural activities than they did from farming.

Summary

This section has described how Asian industrialisation, principally in Japan, both increased the need to produce more from a fixed land area, and enabled this to be achieved through the use of large applications of cheap fertiliser. Since heavy fertiliser doses caused traditional rice varieties to grow tall and collapse, Japanese researchers produced shorter, stiff-strawed varieties

capable of converting increased fertiliser into increased grain yields. This
'biological–chemical' technology of breeding crops to grow with very high
levels of mineral nutrients and well-controlled irrigation later became
known as 'green revolution' technology when used to increase cereal yields
(wheat and rice) in tropical Asia.

4.2   The green revolution in tropical Asia

Our account of the development of wetland rice farming in the twentieth
century has so far centred upon the development in Japan of the 'biological–
chemical' technology of rice varieties bred to take advantage of large
applications of fertiliser. The new varieties were of the *japonica* subspecies
(see Section 2.3), and similar varieties were swiftly bred and adopted in
other areas growing rice of the *japonica* type: China, Taiwan and Korea. The
subsequent success of the new varieties in increasing rice production in
these countries prompted moves to seek varieties of the *indica* subspecies
that could serve the same purpose in tropical Asia.

Since the characteristics required in the new varieties (short straw, early
maturity, flowering insensitive to day-length) were in many respects the
opposite of those found in the best *indica* varieties (tall and leafy, flowering
and maturity dependent upon day-length), the search for new varieties
concentrated on efforts to obtain fertile hybrids between *japonica* and *indica*
varieties. The establishment in 1960 of the International Rice Research
Institute (IRRI) in the Philippines with funding from the Ford and
Rockefeller Foundations provided a focus for these efforts, and in 1962 the
Institute produced a short-strawed variety, IR8, with grain type intermediate
between *indica* and *japonica*, from a cross between the varieties 'peta' from
Indonesia and 'dee-geo-woo-gen' from Taiwan. In the following two
decades many such high-yielding varieties (HYVs) were produced at the
IRRI and by national research organisations, and were introduced
throughout the rice-growing areas of the Indian sub-continent, Indo-China,
Malaysia, Indonesia and the Philippines. As a result, and despite
consumers' dislike of the culinary properties of the new rice varieties, rice
production in these areas increased by 60% and countries which
traditionally imported rice, such as the Philippines, Malaysia, India and
Indonesia, were able to achieve a large measure of self-sufficiency, or even
become exporters of rice. It was this transformation which became known as
the **'green revolution'**.

For a number of reasons, however, the effect of the green revolution
upon rice-growers' living standards in these countries was more equivocal
and has been the subject of much criticism. In particular, in contrast to the
radical land reforms implemented in Japan, China and Korea, the European
and American administrations which resumed control of their tropical Asian
colonies after the end of the Second World War left the influence of rural
landlords undiminished. Thus, at the time that the higher-yielding varieties
were introduced into south and south-east Asia in the 1960s and 1970s, not
only was tenancy a predominant condition for rice farmers, but also the
terms of tenancy often placed the landlord in a strong position to gain from
increased productivity, because the rent was a proportion of the crop rather
than a fixed value. While the details of tenancy arrangements varied greatly
between and within countries, the prevalence of share rents has been
documented by studies such as that carried out by the United Nations
Research Institute for Social Development (UNRISD) (see, for example,
Pearse (1980)). These indicate that landlords had the right to as much as

50% of the crop where the tenant paid for inputs such as seed and fertiliser, but that the landlord's share might rise to as much as 75% if he provided inputs.

Against this unpromising background for tenant farmers to increase their income through higher productivity, the early promotion of new rice varieties in the form of a technological 'package' created further difficulties. The 'package' approach meant that farmers were encouraged to use the new varieties only if they also applied the recommended rates of fertiliser and insecticide, for without this agrochemical input the new varieties were unlikely to outyield traditional *indica* varieties. The package at once diminished cultivators' influence over technical decisions in rice-growing. But, more importantly, the need to purchase inputs increased the working capital necessary to grow rice, and so moved control sharply in the landlords' favour because of their greater access to capital, from either their own resources or from institutional (bank) credit secured against their land. Not only were landlords in a position to lend money to tenants for input purchase – debts on which interest could be claimed – but, because the inputs came from outside the rural areas, landlords were also well placed to act as intermediaries in the input distribution chain. Although these mechanisms did not always operate in every situation, all can be found in the UNRISD case studies.

Share tenancy did not persist uniformly in tropical Asia. Land reform implemented in the Philippines in the 1970s converted share tenancies to fixed-rent tenancies with an option to purchase the land over a 15-year period. However, tenant farmers' scope for an improved livelihood continued, even in the 1980s, to be constrained by the scarcity of alternative sources of income, by comparison with small-scale farmers in Japan, Taiwan or Korea in the 1950s. Among the reasons for this were the legacy of rice monoculture inherited in some cases from the expansion of irrigated rice-growing during the colonial era (see Section 3.1), and the relatively greater penetration of industrial manufactures into rural areas in competition with local 'artisanal' manufacture. The lack of high-value agricultural or rural industrial production left the growing rural population the alternatives of migration to the cities in search of work, staying in their villages to engage in unremunerative household-based trading and food-processing activities, or further intensifying their output from rice farming.

On land where irrigation permitted year-round crop production (about 30% of the rice-growing area of tropical Asia in the 1980s), the introduction of the early-maturing HYVs made possible the growing of two crops in one year in tropical Asian countries like the Philippines where it had been impossible with the traditional *indica* rice varieties. Indeed, with irrigation it now became feasible to grow two crops of rice and a third, different, crop (mung bean was a common choice) in the same field in a single year. However, such cropping schemes introduced extreme peaks of labour demand in order to harvest one crop in time to plant another and the 1980s witnessed the rapid adoption of labour-saving technology. In some cases technological change was remarkably simple: the substitution of the sickle for the *ani-ani* harvesting knife in Indonesia reduced the labour required for harvesting. But of no less importance were the use of:

- machinery such as small-scale motorised tractors and portable mechanical threshers originally manufactured for rice-growing in Japan and Korea, and increasingly built in less industrialised countries like the Philippines

- herbicides developed for mechanised rice-growing in the United States.

▲   *Small tractors, developed during the 1950s and 1960s in Japan, and now manufactured in many parts of Asia, allow mechanised tillage in rice fields. (Sichuan Province, China.)*

The second of these was particularly attractive because it not only reduced greatly the work of weeding the crop but also allowed the labour-intensive work of transplanting rice seedlings to the field from a nursery to be abandoned in favour of broadcasting (scattering) seed directly onto the field. Without herbicide, the practice of broadcasting HYV seed produced weed growth of practically unmanageable proportions because the soil could not be kept covered with water while the rice seed germinated, and during this germination period weeds would also germinate. Under these circumstances the large fertiliser applications would feed rampant weed growth, rather than the crop.

It is important to note that whereas the introduction of labour-saving technology into rice-growing in Japan, Taiwan and Korea allowed farming families to take up more productive off-farm employment, in much of tropical Asia labour saving technology in rice-growing is a means of cutting costs in what may often be the most remunerative form of employment available to farmers. Unless some form of shared ownership of machinery is undertaken, ownership of even small power-tillers will inevitably be concentrated among wealthier farmers, who will be able to hire their equipment to poorer neighbours. The use of herbicide, on the other hand, is more accessible to farmers with little capital because it is more divisible – it need only be purchased in the quantity needed for immediate use. Furthermore the expiry of patents on many commonly used herbicides has resulted in a decline in their cost relative to manual weeding.

The labour so displaced from rice farming in tropical Asia is principally hired labour, those who have little or no access to land, and who, in the absence of alternative remunerative employment, must suffer a decline in living standards.

4.3   Food production, rural development and the environment

In 1987 rice production accounted for 55% of all cereal supplies for the 3 billion people in Asia. Overall, rice output in Asia increased steadily by between 1.5 and 2% each year from the late 1950s onwards. In tropical Asian countries like the Philippines, Indonesia, Thailand and Malaysia the annual rate of increase during the 1960s and 1970s was much higher, at between 3 and 5%. In earlier sections we have seen how this increase has resulted from technological change in rice farming. At the centre of these changes is the improvement of water control which allows more than one crop per year, and the selection of early-maturing rice varieties that can make use of high fertiliser rates to produce more grain. As we have seen, when this new technology was first introduced, it tended to increase the amount of labour needed to grow rice. By the late 1970s, however, the availability of mechanical and herbicide technology for small-scale rice farming resulted in their use as a substitute for agricultural labour. In this section we will consider how these changes have affected the impact of wet rice cultivation upon the physical environment. The section will end with a consideration of the future development of agricultural systems based on rice-growing.

Wetland hazards

In the intensive rice-growing systems developed in China and Japan up until the twentieth century, the emphasis on maintaining flooded soil conditions meant that 'leakage' of water and plant nutrients was low. The absence of soil channels impeded water drainage from the field soil into groundwater and, although several tons of organic fertiliser was commonly applied to each hectare of rice, losses to the groundwater could similarly be avoided as long as the fertiliser was incorporated within the oxygen-free anaerobic layer of the flooded soil. Under these circumstances the only movement of material out of the soil, except that into the crop, was the production of gases, particularly methane, which bubbled to the surface and into the atmosphere. Once the soil was drained, however, and oxygen allowed to enter below the top centimetre of the soil depth, the chemical transformation of some nutrients, of which nitrogen was the most important, would result in significant losses when the soil was next flooded (as we saw in Section 2). A further hazard of intermittent flooding should be noted. Water consumption for a rice crop grown under intermittent flooding may be as much as three times that required with continuous flooding, and most of this extra water constitutes drainage into the groundwater. As a result, the level of the water table may rise, and in dry climates with high evaporation rates the minerals dissolved in the groundwater will accumulate as salt at the soil surface. As outlined in Chapter 2, this process of **salinisation** will, within a few years, make it impossible for the soil to support the growth of any crop. Salinisation is an important environmental hazard where rice is grown under irrigation in arid climates – in Pakistan, some parts of India and in many parts of Africa.

More generally, perhaps the greatest environmental hazards in this system of rice cultivation were the increased exposure of farmers to diseases associated with standing water. The most important of these are malaria and schistosomiasis, or Bilharzia. Malaria affects some 200 million people worldwide and is carried by mosquitoes which need stagnant water in

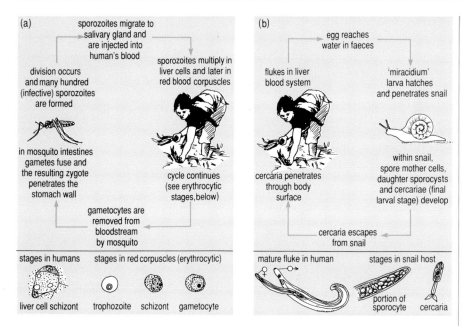

▲   Figure 3.7   (a) The life-cycle of Plasmodium vivax (causing benign tertian malaria). (b) The life-cycle of Schistosoma mansoni (causing bilharzia).

which to develop their larval stage: see Figure 3.7(a). Schistosomiasis is caused by a range of parasitic worms which live alternately in the human bloodstream or intestines and in aquatic snails: see Figure 3.7(b). It affects 500 million people and is frequently associated with the development of irrigation, but it appears to be less widespread in Asia than in Africa or Latin America.

Further disease risks stemmed from the use of animal and human excrement as fertiliser in wet rice fields. The risk of transmission of pathogens and parasites was eliminated to some extent, however, when effective composting was carried out before application to the fields. The addition of animal manure directly to ponds to encourage the growth of fish for human consumption was potentially more problematic, although the very few studies carried out to assess this risk of pathogen and parasite transmission from animal manure to humans via fish have indicated that the risk may be low.

Fertiliser hazards

The introduction of HYV was coupled first and foremost with the use of heavier applications of nutrients to the soil, and in order to achieve this recourse was made increasingly to industrially manufactured 'chemical', or inorganic, fertilisers.

Q   Why was this?

A   The main reason was that the concentration of plant nutrients in organic fertilisers is relatively low. The content of important plant nutrients like nitrogen are usually in the range 1–5% in animal manures, and in the range 7–15% in fishmeal. By contrast, nutrient contents of inorganic fertilisers like superphosphate and urea are over 40%. Thus the effort required to transport and apply high doses of nutrients is considerably reduced by the application of inorganic fertilisers.

A further, though somewhat double-edged, advantage of inorganic fertilisers is that all the nutrient content is in soluble form. The advantage of this is that nutrients can be rapidly absorbed by the growing crop and the effect on the crop can be immediate. A disadvantage is that if the crop is unable to absorb all of the nutrients supplied by fertilisers shortly after their addition to the soil, which is frequently the case when the crop plants are small, then nutrients may be wasted through drainage, absorption by weeds or micro-organisms, or transformation into a chemical form which cannot be absorbed by the crop. This disadvantage is particularly important in the case of nitrogen fertilisers, and in order to avoid losses of nutrients the total amount of fertiliser applied to the crop is usually divided into a number of doses applied at different stages of the crop's growth.

In wetland rice farming this presents a problem, because in order to be absorbed by the rice roots the fertiliser nitrogen must be introduced into the subsurface soil layers and – unlike applications of fertiliser to the soil surface in upland crops on freely drained land – the percolation of rainwater through the soil pores cannot do the job. In fact, most recommendations of fertiliser use in flooded rice advise incorporating the first dose into the soil before planting and then lowering the water level in the field at each subsequent dose to allow the fertiliser to come into contact with the soil. In practice, farmers keen to save labour are more inclined simply to scatter fertiliser into the flooded field. In the case of urea, the most commonly used nitrogen fertiliser, this practice results in the formation of ammonia in the surface water, which is then lost to the atmosphere as ammonia gas. Research has indicated that over half the nitrogen nutrient contained in the fertiliser can be wasted in this way. This is significant, for each kilogram of nitrogen represents 2 kg of fossil fuel expended in its manufacture and transport.

Q   With normal nitrogen application rates in the region of 50 kg per hectare of rice field, what is the wastage of fossil fuel per hectare?

A   Of 50 kg of nitrogen up to 25 kg may be lost, and every kilo of nitrogen represents 2 kg of fossil fuel, so that total losses may be equivalent to 50 kg of fossil fuel per hectare.

Pesticide hazards

Although twentieth-century rice growing can be wasteful of high-energy fertiliser inputs, it is the use of pesticides which has caused more immediate concern for environmental consequences. Insecticides were used fairly widely in rice farming in the 1950s and early 1960s, even before the introduction of the high-yielding varieties. In the Philippines 60% of rice was reportedly being sprayed as early as 1965. However, the first HYV introduced into tropical Asia – IR8 – was very susceptible to damage by insect pests such as stem borers (*Chilo suppressalis*). Consequently the use of insecticide was considered a necessary component of the technological 'package' recommended to farmers starting to grow the new variety. Insecticide use was in some cases subsidised by governments anxious to increase rice output. In the Philippines it was effectively supplied free through spraying carried out by the government's Bureau of Plant Industry,

using pesticides provided as part of bilateral aid programmes. In Indonesia, the 1967–70 BIMAS programme to introduce a high-yielding rice 'package' to farmers was contracted out to, among others, the Swiss-based agrochemical manufacturer CIBA. By the late 1960s it was common for insecticide to be routinely applied to every rice crop.

Since many of the insecticides used, such as dieldrin, DDT and endosulfan, are toxic to fish, an immediate consequence of this policy was a drastic reduction in the fish in flooded rice fields. In parts of Malaysia the decline in fish harvests has been estimated at 50–60% (Tait and Napompeth, 1987). Not only does this remove a significant, and in some cases major, source of dietary protein for rice farmers, it also blocks off a potential route to diversification of farmers' sources of income. In addition to the damage to fish production, pesticide use in Asian rice farming posed a direct threat to human health, through the absence of adequate protective clothing for those preparing and applying the chemicals, and the ease with which contaminated water from sprayed rice-fields could drain into watercourses used for livestock and domestic purposes. This danger became even greater as farmers substituted chemicals such as DDT, considered dangerous because of their residual and cumulative effect, by products such as carbufuran, which could kill insects within the plant but which were more immediately toxic to humans. Although many cases of acute pesticide poisoning have been documented among Asian rice farmers, the effects of chronic exposure to lower levels of pesticide over a long period of time are still practically unknown. Risks to farmers and the environment are compounded by the fact that pesticides are often used in the third world long after they have been banned in first world countries because of proven harmful effects.

The final irony of insecticide use on rice was that it was fairly unsuccessful in protecting the crop. Reports from both the Philippines and Malaysia indicate that insecticide spraying in the 1970s to control one pest, the stem borer, was commonly followed by resurgence of another pest, the brown plant-hopper (*Nilaparvata lugens*), necessitating further spraying, and so on, leading to a 'chemical treadmill'. The development of a new variety of rice, IR36, resistant to the two known strains or 'biotypes' of plant-hopper, appeared to provide the answer in the early 1980s, and in 1983 this variety was being grown on about 10 million hectares. By the mid 1980s, however, a third biotype of the plant-hopper, hitherto unknown and against which IR36 had no resistance, was causing considerable damage, despite the repeated spraying of rice fields. Although IRRI's plant breeders quickly released a new variety, IR56, reputed to be resistant to the third plant-hopper biotype, the United Nations Food and Agriculture Organisation (FAO) was experimenting, with some success, with an alternative approach known as **integrated pest management (IPM)** in Indonesia. This strategy concentrated on promoting control of the pest by natural predators such as spiders, and therefore eliminated the use of some 57 insecticides used in the past which were toxic to these predators. Insecticides that have little effect on the predator species are still permitted where plant-hopper damage threatens, but the Indonesian experiment showed that a reduction of insecticide use of about 80% was possible while at the same time increasing yields. As the FAO experiment was extended in 1988 to other countries in tropical Asia, and to China, it raised the prospect of a radical reduction in insecticide use in Asian rice farming by the end of the twentieth century.

Reduction in herbicide use, however, was less likely. As we have seen in the previous section, herbicides are an important means by which farmers can reduce hired labour required for transplanting and weeding, and so increase their income. The long-term consequences of herbicide use in rice farming have yet to be studied and documented. It is certainly known that some herbicides are toxic to both humans and fish, so that the hazards described above for insecticide use will certainly apply to herbicide use. In addition many herbicides will have negative effects on the blue-green bacteria and *Azolla* plants which are widely planted (or 'inoculated') in rice fields in order to provide a source of nitrogen for the rice crop. FAO estimates that about 1.3 million hectares of rice are cultivated with *Azolla* in China alone. Many herbicides attack only specific plants and it is quite possible that herbicides will be identified which are compatible with both fish and *Azolla*. Until that has been achieved, however, farmers using herbicides on rice risk losing options for agricultural diversification in the pursuit of short-term gains in income from rice.

4.4   *Future prospects for Asian rice cultivation*

The green revolution in Asian rice farming has exposed sharply both the strengths and weaknesses of twentieth-century science as an instrument for improving livelihoods in poorer, agriculturally based societies. It has demonstrated a capacity to produce enough food for a population believed to have grown perilously beyond the 'carrying capacity' of the fixed amount of land available. It has simultaneously demonstrated that this, though necessary, is not by itself sufficient to improve rural food security or living standards. We have seen that social and institutional factors play an important part in determining the benefits of improved agricultural productivity. Certainly, the conditions under which people have (or do not have) access to land is one of those factors, but this operates in a wider context of the alternatives which exist for people to earn a living.

We may take, as an extreme example, the case of Indonesia, where, with some 58% of its population nominally engaged in farming in 1983, rice production was sufficient to cover the food requirements of its people. However, on the densely populated island of Java, rice farmers with land of their own produce as little as 1 kg of rice for each hour of their labour. This is about a quarter of the labour productivity in rice production in Japan and Taiwan (as shown in Table 3.1). But in rural Java, rice growing is one of the most remunerative forms of work available. For the 50% of households who have no land other than that on which their house stands, the productivity of their labour is even lower (White, 1982).

In such situations it is easy to perceive the economic pressures which encourage poor people to have large families. The low productivity of their labour allows parents little opportunity to accumulate savings during their working lives. Large numbers of children – who work rather than go to school – are a means whereby parents try to increase family income and provide security in their old age. (You may wish to refer back to the discussion of economic development and demographic transition in Chapter 1, and in particular to Caldwell's theory of fertility change and inter-generational wealth flows in Section 4.2.)

In considering the future development of Asian rice growing it is necessary to separate the need for rice production from the need for improved livelihoods. As we have seen, many rice-producing countries in Asia have achieved self-sufficiency or are net exporters of rice. By the late 1980s governments in Japan and Taiwan were confronting problems of overproduction of rice, similar to those of overproduction of food in the European Community. As in Europe, political pressure from farmers had resulted in the use of wealth generated by highly productive industry to pay higher prices to rice producers, who in turn used higher levels of inputs to increase rice output further, leading to surpluses of rice too expensive to sell on the world market.

If such conditions apply in richer, industrialised economies, what are the prospects of improved livelihoods for peasant rice-producers in the non-industrialised economies? As in Japan, a half century earlier, the question of *diversification* of rural employment, into industry or high-value agricultural production, is central to improved living standards in Asian rice-growing areas. Some observers have commented that in the case of Japan, Taiwan and Korea, industrialisation was made possible by earlier development of high labour productivity in agriculture founded upon a closely managed and highly developed water control infrastructure. They point to the relatively small proportion (20–30%) of cropland which is irrigated in tropical Asia as an obstacle to agricultural diversification. This in turn has been attributed to 'social barriers to efficient resource allocation to land infrastructure' (Hayami and Ruttan, 1985) which means that the relationship between rich and poor effectively prevents local collaboration to develop and manage irrigation and other works such as soil conservation, which have a public rather than strictly private utility. According to this analysis, the barriers to improving the productivity of agricultural labour in tropical Asia are therefore political rather than physical.

We shall conclude this chapter by briefly considering the fate of one attempt to overcome such barriers: the formation of the communes in China in the late 1950s (see Box 3.1).

The low efficiency of many of the small-scale rural industries established by the communes made them viable only while all alternative supplies for urban large-scale industries were excluded from the rural areas. This was, in fact, the policy carried out by the central state authorities, which prompted one writer to observe 'small and beautiful, if it is not to be wiped out by competition, presupposes the big and bureaucratic' (Kitching, 1989). While future attempts to diversify the income opportunities of rice producers by developing rural industry may be expected to avoid some of the errors of the Chinese communes, in the era of the global market the capacity for any small-scale rural industry to withstand international competition must be open to question.

The Chinese experience in the latter part of the twentieth century emphasises how closely the continued high productivity of land and labour in rice production systems depends on large-scale environmental management. The decline in the maintenance of irrigation infrastructure which has accompanied the break-up of the communes comes at a time when concern is mounting about a more general failure of environmental management in China. Unregulated deforestation of the upper watersheds of the Yangzi and Yellow rivers has caused a marked increase in the siltation rates of these rivers in recent years. Reduced and erratic river flows pose a direct threat to Chinese irrigation, and suggest that in the twenty-first century rice production will require stronger and more wide-ranging social and institutional collaboration than ever before.

Activity 4

Based on what you have read in this chapter, write down ways that the future options of small-scale rice farmers in Asia differ from, or are similar to, those of farmers in other parts of the world.

Box 3.1   The communes in China

As originally conceived by Mao Zedong, the communes were part of a three-tier structure of rural self-management: the communes were subdivided into brigades, which were further divided into work teams. In principle, election of officials at each of the three levels of organisation ensured that the communes represented the interests of their peasant members and acted to defend those interests against coercion by the centralised state bureaucracy.

In Mao's conception, the economic role of the communes was to pursue diversification through rural industrialisation and to increase agricultural productivity through the construction of infrastructure such as irrigation and hydro-elecric power. The emphasis was to be on local self-sufficiency, and particularly the generation of local savings for local investment.

In practice, the economic role of the communes was severely undermined by the failure of their political function: the authoritarian state and party structure effectively pre-empted local democracy, with the result that commune officials were party nominees and state employees. The development of rural industry, particularly during the 'Great Leap Forward' (1958–1960), was, as a consequence, heavily influenced by the industrialisation policy of the centralised state. This resulted in inefficient and wasteful small-scale heavy industry (epitomised by 'the backyard blast-furnace').

Agricultural diversification was severely constrained by centrally defined priorities emphasising grain self-sufficiency, which translated into pressure for grain monoculture.

The Great Leap was a failure, with widespread famine occurring in the early 1960s, and the role of the commune in economic management was subsequently reduced, with the planning role being taken over by the centralised state and the farm management being carried out at brigade and subsequently work team level. In the 1980s collective farm management was made responsible for agricultural output through a contract system.

Despite the evident failure of the communes to develop high-productivity rural industry, they achieved a very significant investment of human labour in the creation of irrigation and other infrastructure with long-term benefits to the productivity of both land and labour in farming. The magnitude of this achievement is indicated by the fact that 97.3 million new workers were absorbed by the agricultural sector from 1957 to 1975.

The pattern of events which followed the final dissolution of the communes in the 1980s is instructive. In the first five years in which agricultural production was carried out by households on an individual basis, grain output rose, reaching an all-time record level (407 million tons) in 1984. However, in subsequent years grain shortages became common. Two reasons have been given for this decline. Firstly, farmers diversified into higher-value farm products, particularly meat, whose production consumed part of their grain output. Secondly, the dismantling of the communes eliminated the local authority with responsibility for organising the collective effort to maintain the irrigation works, and some deterioration occurred.

 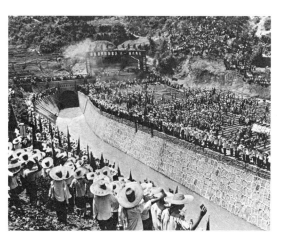

▲   Effective water management requires investment in infrastructure: in China, such investment was achieved in the 1960s and '70s by employing 5% of the rural labour force (17 million people) on irrigation construction projects. Left, digging an irrigation canal near Zibo in Shandong Province, China; and, right, the opening ceremony in 1970 of the Ouyanghai Irrigation Project which brought more than 23 000 hectares of farmland in southern Hunan Province under irrigation.

References

HAYAMI, Y. and RUTTAN, V. (1985) *Agricultural Development* (rev. edn) Baltimore, Johns Hopkins University Press.

KITCHING, G. (1989) *Development and Underdevelopment in Historical Perspective*, London, Routledge and Kegan Paul.

PEARSE, A. (1980) *Seeds of Plenty, Seeds of Want*, London, Oxford University Press.

SILVERTOWN, J. (1990) 'Ecosystems and populations', Ch. 4 in Silvertown, J. and Sarre, P. (eds).

SILVERTOWN, J. and SARRE, P. (eds) (1990) *Environment and Society*, London, Hodder and Stoughton/The Open University (Book One of this series).

SIMMONS, J. (1990) 'The impact of human societies on their environments', Ch. 5 in Silvertown, J. and Sarre, P. (eds).

TAIT, J. and NAPOMPETH, B. (1987) *Management of Pest and Pesticides: farmers' perceptions and practices*, Boulder, Col., Westview Press.

WHITE, D. (1982) 'Population, involution and employment in rural Java', in Harriss, J. (ed.) *Rural Development*, London, Hutchinson.

Further reading

BARKER, R., HERDT, R. and ROSE, B. (1985) *The Rice Economy of Asia: resources for the future*, Washington, DC.

BRAY, F. (1986) *The Rice Economies: technology and development in Asian societies*, Oxford, Blackwell.

BULL, D. (1982) *A Growing Problem: pesticides and the third world poor*, Oxford, Oxfam.

PEARSE, A. (1980) *Seeds of Plenty, Seeds of Want*, London, Oxford University Press.

SANCHEZ, P. (1976) *Properties and Management of Soils in the Tropics*, New York, John Wiley.

Answers to Activities

Activity 1

Herbivores:

- insects (leaf-eating, sap-sucking)
- fish
- birds (such as ducks and grain-eating species such as *Quelea quelea*)
- small mammals (such as rodents).

Carnivores:

- insects (such as mosquitoes)
- fish
- amphibians (frogs etc.)
- reptiles
- birds (feeding on insects, frogs and fish).

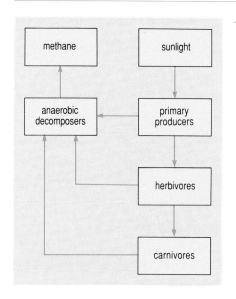

◀   *Diagram of energy flows.*

Activity 2

(a) Examples of social and economic developments that promoted changes in rice cultivation methods:

●   prior to the expansion of European influence in the eighteenth and nineteenth centuries, the growth of population and extension of state power in Asia was the main force behind the extension of irrigation to new areas and the search for technologies allowing higher land productivity (for example, double cropping, and the use of fertiliser);

●   the relative shortage of capital in this period of Asian history meant that irrigation and rice-farming technology were relatively labour-intensive;

●   the absence of large-scale manufacturing presented rice-growers with many opportunities to diversify their economic activity through high(er)-income, household-scale processing (such as silk);

●   the growth of European-owned plantation production was responsible for more capital-intensive expansion of irrigation oriented principally towards rice monoculture;

●   the industrialisation of Japan led to increased pressure for higher yields of rice and made available larger supplies of fertiliser; subsequently, industrialisation led to pressure for mechanisation of rice production.

(b)   Some aspects of rice production techniques which shaped socio-economic relationships are:

●   the need for close control of water promoted the development of farmers' water management organisations. The need for overall co-ordination of water use promoted the development of authoritarian, centralised states;

●   the labour-intensive production methods for rice promoted high densities of population settlement;

●   the intensive management of the rice fields required to manage the water and to carry out operations such as transplanting and manuring at the right time, placed much of the control of the production process in the power of the cultivators and hence increased their bargaining power in relation to land-owners and the state.

Activity 3

Comparisons of rice-growing systems, ranking from highest to lowest:

Labour input	Japan	1729 hr/ha
	Philippines	576
	USA	7
Total energy input	USA	60 646 MJ/ha
	Japan	30 138
	Philippines	7 667
Land productivity	USA	6160 kg/ha
	Japan	4848
	Philippines	1654
Labour productivity	USA	362 kg/hr
	Philippines	2.9
	Japan	2.8
Overall energy efficiency	Philippines	3.3 MJ out/MJ in
	Japan	2.45
	USA	1.55

These comparisons indicate that from the standpoint of total energy efficiency the low-input Philippine system is more efficient than the other two high-input systems. However, from the point of view of land and labour productivity, the US system is most efficient. This is particularly the case for *labour* productivity. It is clear that the assessments of efficiency will depend on which of the factors (land, labour or energy) we consider the most important. It should be noted that the figures for this exercise relate to studies in the 1960s and '70s, and that input and output levels are likely to have changed considerably in the 1980s in both the Philippines, as the result of the green revolution, and in Japan, as a result of fast economic growth.

Activity 4

Future options for small-scale rice farmers in Asia may be considered to be similar to those of farmers in other parts of the world in that rice is now in surplus supply in many Asian countries and, as in North America and Europe, farmers can expect the prices of agricultural goods to decline relative to the prices of manufactured goods. This long-term trend will produce a tendency for agricultural incomes to decline relative to urban incomes, and a pressure to diversify rural incomes from food production.

The situation for Asian rice farmers is different from that of their American and European counterparts in that their existing incomes are lower (due to smaller farms and less mechanisation), they have less access to industrial jobs and, unlike Europe and North America, governments in the less wealthy economies of Asia are unable politically or economically to finance higher incomes for farmers by making urban food consumers pay higher prices for food.

▲ Plate 1
Ethiopia

▲ Plate 2 A poster in China exhorting the population to keep to the 'one couple, one child' policy. Although this campaign met with great difficulties, during the 1970s China's birth rate was halved.

▲ Plate 3a
An irrigated beet field in Colorado in the United States blanketed with salt, a result of poor drainage.

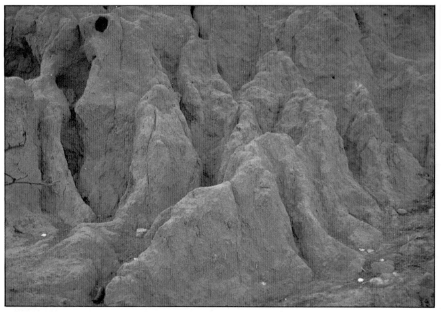

▲ Plate 3b An example of severe soil erosion in the Gambia. Following loss of protective vegetation cover, water erosion has created deep gullies, making the land useless for productive purposes.

◀ *Plate 4*
Masai with flocks of sheep and goats near Lake Natron in Kenya. In some areas desertification is the end-result of overgrazing through the keeping of larger flocks than the area can support.

▲ *Plate 5   Terraces in the Philippines: water management for making flooded rice fields in upland landscapes.*

▲ *Plate 6   Transplanting rice seedlings into flooded fields in Yunnan Province, China. Note the earthen 'bunds' or dykes which ensure that water is adequately distributed in different parts of the field.*

◄ *Plate 7*
Oger village in the
Champagne region of
France, showing the
prairie-like landscape
created by EC policies
in the cereal-producing
lowlands.

▲ *Plate 8*
Extensive cattle ranching in North America.

▲ Plate 9
Exmoor, looking south-
west from Deddy Combe.
Coastal heather and gorse
is in the foreground, with
heather moorland protected
by its status as Common
Land in the background.
In the middle on the right
can be seen the 'traditional'
in-bye of small fields
enclosed by hedgebanks,
while larger-scale, post-war
moorland reclamation is
shown on the left.

◀ Plate 10
Wear and tear along the
Pennine Way. Some of the
popular parts of this track
have become so badly
affected by over-use that
the surface has had to be
artificially covered.

◄ *Plate 11*
The major limestone quarry at Tunstead can dominate visitors' experience of the Peak National Park, even though it is sited just outside the park boundary.

▲ *Plate 12   The redevelopment of Canary Wharf on the Isle of Dogs in London's Docklands.*

▲ *Plate 13   A view of Rocinha, the largest favela in Rio de Janeiro, Brazil, where 200 000 people live.*

▲   Plate 14   A construction site in Bangalore, India, with twenty-five workers
passing cement up to the fifth floor of the building. The rapid increase in the
population of third world cities creates problems of job supply.

Plate 15   An aerial view of Mexico City, showing the very extensive built-up area and the flat terrain of this former lake-bed.

◄   *Plate 16*
Air pollution over Mexico City, taken from the Latin American Tower looking east towards Netza, the largest barrio of Mexico City, which itself has a population greater than that of most other Mexican cities.

1   Introduction

Temperate agriculture probably exemplifies, as well as any other human activity, the conflict between maintaining economic well-being on the one hand and the quality of the natural environment on the other. Some of the most technologically advanced farming practices are being applied in temperate agriculture; through food trade and aid, the food surpluses generated play a crucial role in sustaining the populations of developed and developing countries alike. But the same farming practices are producing damaging environmental impacts, the scale of which has been appreciated only within the last decade.

This chapter aims to analyse the changes that have occurred in temperate agriculture in recent years. No part of agriculture has remained untouched, from the inputs purchased for farming, such as fertilisers, machinery and seeds, through the mix of activities and methods of production on each farm, to the ways in which farm produce is processed and distributed between the farmgate and the consumer. We will find that each agricultural change has had its particular environmental impact.

The argument progresses in four stages, each taking us into a more detailed examination of the relationship between agriculture and the environment. Section 2 assembles some of the concepts and empirical evidence from Chapter 2 on farming systems and their locations, to give an overview of temperate agriculture. In particular it develops a conceptualisation of farming as a modified agroecosystem whereby understanding the changing inputs to and outputs from each farming system can help us to understand both the nature of agricultural changes and their environmental impacts.

Section 3 is a detailed examination of recent trends in temperate agriculture, with evidence from the European Community. Temperate farming around the world displays many similar features, often summarised in the term 'the industrialisation of agriculture', involving change in inputs, production trends and marketing of crops and livestock.

The next stage in the argument, in Section 4, is an examination of a number of temperate farming systems to establish the variety of relationships that exist between agriculture and the environment. Limitations of space dictate that just five systems can be selected here for detailed consideration. They are a range of intensive and extensive farming systems, with crop as well as livestock products: extensive arable, intensive arable, extensive grassland (livestock), intensive grassland (livestock) and intensive (non-grassland) livestock. This mixture of 'intensity' with 'land use' forms a common approach in many classifications of farming systems.

Section 5 focuses in detail on two farming systems in the United Kingdom: hill sheep-farming and intensive cereal-farming. They lie at either end of the environmental impact continuum and illustrate the nature and scale of temperate agriculture's environmental impacts.

2   *Defining and locating temperate farming systems*

In Chapter 2 you met some ecological concepts underlying the development
of farming. In this chapter this idea of agricultural systems depending on
and modifying ecosystems is formalised into the concept of an
agroecosystem.

As you saw in the last chapter in the case of wetland rice, an ecosystem
(environmental unit) can be viewed as an integrated network of energy and
mineral flows in which the major functional components are populations of
plants, animals and micro-organisms. Each system is regulated and
stabilised by the cycling of mineral nutrients for re-use and powered by
energy from the sun. Although a given ecosystem comprises several
thousand species of plants, animals and micro-organisms, each is
continuous to some degree with adjacent systems. (A forest ecosystem, for
example, can merge with an adjacent grassland ecosystem.)

Q   Can you apply the concept of an ecosystem to an agricultural context
and suggest what might be meant by an **agroecosystem**?

A   An agroecosystem can be defined as an orderly set of interdependent
and interacting components, or elements, within a defined farming area
(nation, region, sub-region or farm), none of which can be modified
without causing a related change elsewhere in the system. Five major
aspects of any farming system can be identified: its goals (objectives),
boundaries, activities (components) and their internal relations,
external relations and the relationship between the internal and external
relations.

One of the principal differences between natural and managed ecosystems
lies in the simplification of the latter to a relatively few species of crops and
animals. In broad terms, the greater the simplification of the agroecosystem,
the greater the quantity of energy that must be introduced into it, not least to
control pests and diseases, and the greater its potential instability. The
concept of agroecosystems can offer an interdisciplinary approach to
understanding the relationships between agriculture and the environment.
It enables a holistic description of the relationships to be established by
incorporating the socio-economic, political, environmental and
technological elements of each farming system. Equally, the approach
enables the interrelationships between small subsets of components in a
farming system to be isolated for detailed examination.

The practical difficulties of analysing a farming system, especially
measuring the material and energy flows, usually result in farming systems
being defined loosely and used mainly as conceptual devices. Nevertheless,
by focusing on the components of a farming system, and the structure of
flows within it, changes to the farming system can be identified and their
impact on the interacting components evaluated. The impact of changes in
the human subsystem, especially farm inputs, upon the environmental
subsystem is the central concern of this chapter.

Central to a discussion of this subject is the concept of **type of farming**.
Duckham and Masefield's (1971) typology shown in Table 4.1 is very useful
in this respect.

Table 4.1   A typology of farming systems

	Tree crops		Tillage with or without livestock		Alternating tillage with grass, bush or forest		Grassland or grazing of land consistently in 'indigenous' or 'improved' pasture	
	Temperate	Tropical	Temperate	Tropical	Temperate	Tropical	Temperate	Tropical
Very Extensive	Cork collection from Maquis in southern France	Collection from wild trees, e.g. shea butter	—	—	Shifting cultivation in Negev Desert, Israel	Shifting cultivation in Zambia	Reindeer herding in Lapland. Nomadic pastoralism in Afghanistan	Camel-herding in Arabia and Somalia
Extensive	Self-sown or planted blueberries in the north-east of the USA	Self-sown oil palms in West Africa	Cereal growing in Interior Plains of North America, pampas of South America, in unirrigated areas, e.g. Syria	Unirrigated cereals in central Sudan	—	Shifting cultivation in the more arid parts of Africa	Wool-growing in Australia. **Hill sheep in the UK** (Sheep in Iceland.) Cattle ranching in the USA.	Nomadic cattle-herding in east and west Africa. Llamas in South America
Semi-Intensive	Cider apple orchards in the UK. Some vineyards in France	Cocoa in West Africa. Coffee in Brazil	Dry cereal farming in Israel or Texas, USA	Continuous cropping in congested areas of Africa. **Rice in south-east Asia**	Cotton or tobacco with livestock in the south-east of the USA. Wheat with leys and sheep in Australia	Shifting cultivation in much of tropical Africa	Upland sheep country in North Island, New Zealand	Cattle and buffaloes in mixed farming in India and Africa
Intensive	Citrus in California or Israel	Rubber in south-east Asia. Tea in India and Sri Lanka	Corn Belt of the USA. **Continuous cereal growing in the UK**	Rice and vegetable growing in south China. Sugar-cane plantations throughout tropics	Irrigated rice and grass beef farms in Australia. Much of the east and south of the UK, the Netherlands, northern France, Denmark, southern Sweden	Experimental stations and scattered settlement schemes	Parts of the Netherlands. New Zealand and England	Dairying in Kenya and Zimbabwe highlands

Note: Bold type indicates case studies in Chapters 3 and 4.

Source: Duckham, A. N. and Masefield, G. B. (1971) *Farming Systems of the World*, London, Chatto and Windus, p. 16.

Activity 1

Use Duckham and Masefield's typology in Table 4.1 to answer the
following questions.

Q   What are the three attributes used to construct the typology?

A   • The input intensity of the system
    • the dominant land use of the system
    • the climatic regime within which the system operates.

(Make a note of the farming types that occur under temperate climatic
regimes.)

Q   What are some of the limitations of the typology for temperate
    agriculture?

A   The typology omits intensive livestock (pigs and poultry), even though
    they form an important part of agriculture in many temperate farming
    systems; it incorporates no direct measure of the level of technology
    being applied in a farming system; and it contains no indication of the
    type of social organisation being practised. (By this we mean the mode
    of production, especially the distinction between capitalist and socialist
    (communist) forms of social organisation, including the different
    economic principles by which farming is organised – (modified) market
    versus central planning.)

The third concept we need to employ is that of the **agricultural region**:
that is, the dominant presence of a farming system over an area of space.
Figure 2.6 in Chapter 2 shows the set of regions at the world scale proposed
by Derwent Whittlesey in 1936 which have withstood the test of time.

Activity 2

Examine Figure 2.6 and revise Chapter 2 to answer the following
questions.

Q   What five attributes are used in the typology?

A   (a) The crop and livestock association (e.g. grain and/or dairy);
    (b) the methods used to grow crops and produce livestock (e.g.
    herding or plantations);
    (c) the intensity of application to the land of labour, capital and
    organisation, and the outputof product which results;
    (d) the disposal of the products for consumption (used for subsistence
    on the farm, or sold for cash or other goods – commercial);
    (e) the ensemble of structures used to house and facilitate farming
    operations (explicit in small farms and plantations; implicit in, for
    example, commercial grain or dairy).

Q   Which criteria are found both in Table 4.1 and Figure 2.6?

A   Type of land use, degree of farming intensity and climatic regime.

Q   Which types of agricultural region are not found under the temperate
     climatic regimes?

A   Types 3 (primitive subsistence), 4 (intensive subsistence) and 5
     (plantations).

These classifications imply – and the concept of an agroecosystem explicitly
states – that farming systems integrate a variety of social, technical and
environmental factors. These can be seen as a hierarchy of constraints. At a
general level, features such as soils, climates and topography define the
ecologically feasible farming systems at any location, from which the farmer
can make a choice.

   At a second level, human or infrastructure factors are influential, such
as farm size, available capital, population density, distance from market,
market prices and state intervention in agriculture. Together these features
define the *economically feasible* enterprises at any location from which a
farmer can make a choice. Such a choice includes artificially extending the
range of ecologically possible farming systems by manipulating the
agroecosystem; this can be achieved through such practices as irrigation,
housing for livestock and glasshouse cultivation.

   A third level of constraint is provided by *operational considerations* in
farming: for example, steep slopes or small units might constrain the size of
machines to be used, seasonality of rainfall might require particular
conservation practices or the best seed varieties may be unavailable in a
particular area.

   A final constraint on the farming system is provided by the *personal
behaviour* and *preferences* of individual farmers, for example in relation to
features such as profit maximisation versus conservation, the level of
information on farming methods or commitment to a particular breed of
livestock.

   This hierarchy of constraints can explain the choice of farming systems
at most locations. As we will see later in this chapter, when profit-
maximising behaviour in a farming system is pursued to its logical
conclusion, and when governments intervene in agriculture to stimulate
production, the consequences for the environment can be damaging, often
in unpredictable ways.

3   The dynamics of temperate agriculture

3.1   Introduction

Before turning to a selection of case studies, we need to gain a more detailed
understanding of the general changes that have been taking place within
most temperate farming systems. It is the impact of these changes on the
rural environment that so concerns society at the present time. To focus the
discussion, attention is restricted to capitalist farming systems thereby
excluding temperate agriculture in socialist eastern Europe, the Soviet

Union and China. However, many of the changes observable in capitalist agriculture are also present in centrally planned farming systems. To assist in organising the material, we will first consider the inputs to temperate agriculture, then the production process on farms, and finally the marketing of crops and livestock through the food chain to the consumer. Illustrative data are provided on temperate agriculture within the European Community (EC), noting that the EC has grown from six to twelve countries during the period considered.

3.2   Inputs to temperate farming systems

Conventionally, inputs to agriculture, or **factors of production**, are classified under the main headings: land, labour and capital. The term 'land' is used to denote the sum of the components of the natural environment (climate, soil and topography) and is often used in the context of the quality of the physical resources available to farming. Most countries, for example, employ land capability maps on which land is classified into grades according to the physical limitations imposed on agriculture. In the United Kingdom, for instance, only 1.8% of agricultural land falls into the Grade I (best) category, with 33.7% in Grade V (poorest). The quality of farmland can be modified only with the expenditure of capital and energy on items such as organic (animal and green manures) and inorganic (chemical) fertilisers, drainage and irrigation. The quantity of farmland is another input for farming systems. In most countries farmland has been a declining input as land has been transferred to alternative uses such as forestry, urban development and roads, and water catchment. But, at the same time, new farmland is being created by draining wetlands, ploughing moorlands and felling woodland. Each of these strategies impinges on natural ecosystems and the total farmland input is in a constant state of flux. In the EC, for instance, there has been a net loss of farmland in the order of 0.3% per annum for the last decade, although this proportion would have been higher but for the considerable areas of semi-natural habitats that have been 'improved' for agriculture to offset the losses for urban and industrial development.

The term 'labour' includes the managers, owners and tenants of farmland, together with their families, hired workers and those who supply services on contract for drainage, ploughing, harvesting and crop-spraying operations. Like the farmland base, labour has formed a declining input into temperate agriculture for many decades. The EC, for example, experienced a 37% reduction of the agricultural workforce between 1960 and 1970, a 29% reduction from 1970 to 1980, and a further 16% fall between 1980 and 1986. This left just 7.2 million people employed in agriculture in the ten countries which then made up the Community, compared with 19 million in 1960. We need to be cautious in accepting these figures at face value; there are real problems in determining who is employed in agriculture, not least because the labour input can be casual, seasonal, spare-time, part-time or full-time in nature. Indeed the proportion of farm-owners with more than one occupation is increasing in most temperate farming systems: in the EC, 30% of farmers also have gainful occupations outside agriculture.

Considerable variation exists in the rate of change amongst the different categories of agricultural labour. For example, until recently the number of full-time, hired farm-workers was falling at a faster rate than the number of owners and tenants of farms. At present hired workers are in the minority and most farms no longer employ full-time workers. Within the 'hired'

category, though, full-time workers have been in more rapid decline than
seasonal, casual and part-time workers, especially women.

The trends in land and labour are closely related to the third category of
input – capital. Capital is now by far the most significant factor of production
since it can substitute for both land and labour. On land, capital can be used
to 'purchase' additional hectares through inputs of animal feed. In the
context of the EC, for example, in 1987 5.7 million tons of cereals were
imported to manufacture animal feed; this is equivalent to more than a
million hectares of farmland, assuming an average European cereals yield of
5 tons per hectare. In addition 21.8 million tons of cereal substitutes, such as
manioc, and 29.5 million tons of protein-rich products, such as soya cake,
were imported for animal feed. The productivity of the land resource can be
also raised by the application of capital to other inputs such as chemical
fertilisers, genetic materials in the form of improved seed varieties and
livestock breeds, and agrochemicals such as pesticides, herbicides and
fungicides. The volume of all of these inputs has been rising in temperate
agriculture for several decades. In the case of fertilisers, for example, both
the total volume and the average rate of application per hectare of
agricultural land have increased, albeit at different rates between farming
systems, and show no signs of being reduced (Table 4.2). As we will see in

Table 4.2   Total consumption of inorganic fertilisers[1] in selected countries,
1956–1985 (000 tonnes; kg/ha in brackets)

Year	West Germany	France	Netherlands	United Kingdom
1956	2114 (148)	1924 (56)	468 (201)	– (–)
1965	2897 (209)	3123 (93)	566 (250)	1555 (79)
1975	3300 (251)	4850 (152)	638 (306)	1800 (95)
1985	3185 (265)	5694 (181)	701 (346)	2524 (135)

Note: [1]Nitrogen, phosphate and potash.

Source: Author's calculations from agricultural statistics (Eurostat 1960, 1970, 1988: Brussels).

◀   Agricultural workers
in East Anglia. Although
the number of full-time
farm workers has declined
dramatically, casual, often
female, labour is still used
on a seasonal basis.

more detail later, excessive applications of fertilisers can have damaging consequences for groundwater supplies as well as surface water in streams, rivers and lakes. In the case of agrochemicals, increasing concern is being expressed about their impact on food health (Figure 4.1).

Activity 3

You can monitor the national and local press to build up your own file of cases where attention is drawn to the impact on food health of the use of agrochemicals in agriculture. You should divide the material between criticisms and defence of the use of agrochemicals.
    Read the extracts in Figure 4.1 and then answer the following questions.

Q What national government departments and agencies in the United States and the United Kingdom are mentioned as having a role to play in the control of agrochemicals?

A United States: Environmental Protection Agency.
     United Kingdom: Ministry of Agriculture Fisheries and Food (MAFF); MAFF Advisory Committee on Pesticides; River Authorities; Department of the Environment.

Q Which environmental organisations and pressure groups are mentioned as having drawn attention to the dangers of using agrochemicals?

A Natural Resources Defence Council; Friends of the Earth; World Health Organisation; Parents for Safe Food.

Turning now to substitutes for the labour input, capital can be used to purchase a wide range of farm plant and machinery, as well as petroleum for the motive power. From a position only fifty years ago when farming operations employed mainly labour and horsepower, today almost all are mechanised to some extent; no temperate farming system has been exempt from the trend. Modern machinery can plant and harvest most crops, automatically deliver feed and water to livestock, and wash, grade and process farm produce. But the mechanisation of agriculture has led to its own environmental impacts. For example, the use of heavy machinery for successive farming operations, such as ploughing, seeding, fertilising and harvesting, has caused soil compaction in some regions; in addition, mechanised trimming has had a damaging impact on trees and shrubs in hedgerows.

    When the capital needed to purchase increasingly expensive farmland is added to the costs of fertilisers, machinery and agrochemicals, it is understandable why temperate agriculture can be described as 'capital-intensive'. Figure 4.2 shows the full range of inputs for EC farming systems in 1987, with data for the United Kingdom included for comparison. Animal feed is by far the most important purchased input (41% of the total by value), followed by fertilisers (12%) and farm machinery (12%). By comparison, fossil fuel (petroleum – 10%) and agrochemicals (5.3%) are not major inputs by value for the farming systems of the Community, although when converted into energy equivalents (see Section 4.3 below), high inputs per hectare and per labour unit are revealed (Simmons, 1989, pp. 239–55). All

Crop spray link to cancer

James Erlichman, Consumer Affairs Correspondent

MAKERS of fungicides linked with cancer have drastically reduced their use in the United States, but have not ordered cuts in Britain.

US farmers have been told by Rohm & Haas and three other manufacturers to stop spraying the fungicides on most of their crops. The blacklist, issued last month, covers 70 out of 83 previously permitted crops including apples, beans, cabbage, cherries, lettuces, melons, oats and strawberries.

The fungicides have been widely used in Britain for nearly 40 years on a similar range of crops but no instruc-tions to curb their use have been issued either by the manufacturers or by the Ministry of Agriculture.

Rohm & Haas spokesman, Mr George Bochanski, defended the company's failure to alert British farmers: "We continue to believe that these products are safe and it is not our job to pre-empt the regulatory bodies in the UK."

The company says that residues found in British foods are low enough to meet any restrictions imposed by the US agency.

The Ministry of Agriculture said yesterday that it knew of the US crop withdrawals. Its Advisory Committee on Pesticides is reviewing new data in "the area of consumer risk".

The voluntary cuts in the US follow threats by the Environmental Protection Agency to ban or severely restrict the use of mancozeb, maneb and zineb, fungicides in the ethylene bis-dithiocarbamate (EBDC) family.

The US agency believes that continued use of the EBDCs may cause at least 125,000 additional cancer cases among the population of 250 million. Children are believed to be most at risk because of their high fruit consumption, low weight, and the length of time they have to develop cancer.

Scientists are most concerned about ETU, a breakdown chemical found in the fungicides which causes cancer in animals and accumulates most in heat treated foods like tomato paste, ketchup, and apple juice.

Forty-year fertiliser legacy comes home to roost

Nitrates

EXCESSIVE amounts of nitrate, a mineral form of the nitrogen naturally present in soil, are toxic, according to the World Health Organisation, whose guideline is 100 milligrams a litre.

Nitrate is converted in the body to nitrite which combines with haemoglobin in the blood to reduce the uptake of oxygen, putting young babies at potential risk of blue baby syndrome. Cases are rare in Britain and water authorities with high nitrate levels have provided bottled water for babies.

Studies in other countries suggest babies could suffer oxygen deficiency without showing symptoms from concentrations around the EEC limit. Friends of the Earth says this should be urgently investigated.

Nitrite is also converted into substances which cause cancers in laboratory animals but there is no clear link with gastric cancer in humans.

Throughout much of east and central England, 40 years of increasingly intensive farming has sent a steady trickle of nitrates down into underground water sources which provide 30-40 per cent of local needs.

When the drinking water directive came into force in 1985, around 50 supplies contained more than the permissible maximum concentration of 50 milligrams a litre. The Government freed suppliers from the obligation to observe these limits on the grounds that there was no health danger with a concentration below 100 mg/l.

A complaint by Friends of the Earth to the Common Market Brussels Commission brought a threat of legal action and last year, the Government withdrew these waivers, or derogations. It was also forced by the EEC to alter the method of testing compliance with the law from an average level over three months to a single result.

As a result the number of people receiving supplies over the limit rose from a million to 4 million overnight.

The authorities mainly involved, Severn Trent, and Anglian, are working to meet the limit by closing contaminated sources and blending water.

They have sent their clean-up programmes to the Department of the Environment which will soon announce its strategy for complying with the EEC directive.

Cleaning up supplies may take several years. The main problem, however, is to halt the rise of nitrate levels underground, and in rivers where concentrations are expected to start reaching the limits over the next 10 years.

The Water Bill will allow water authorities and the National Rivers Authority to limit or forbid the use of nitrogenous fertilisers in protection zones around boreholes. Compensation for farmers has been agreed in principle.

Apple spray sales halted

ALAR, the apple spray linked to cancer, was withdrawn from sale for food use by its maker, Uniroyal, yesterday after disclosure of more tumours in animal tests.

The Ministry of Agriculture, which had repeatedly said the spray was safe, will now have to revoke the product's licence, most likely tomorrow when the Advisory Committee on Pesticides meets.

Mr Walter Waldrup, at the US Environmental Protection Agency, said yesterday that lung tumours were found in a "low dose" study of mice which was received from Uniroyal at the beginning of October. Liver tumours were found in rats.

Mr Malcolm Tyrell, Uniroyal's European sales manager, said the company could no longer offer "a totally clear data package" and had formally asked the US authorities to revoke Alar's licence.

Concern about Alar and its use in Britain was first disclosed by the Guardian last May following a report from the Natural Resources Defence Council, a US environmental group. It predicted that 5,500 American children would eventually develop cancer directly from Alar-sprayed apples.

Pressure from the NRDC prompted the US Environmental Protection Agency to demand new laboratory studies from Uniroyal. These tests showed "an inescapable and direct correlation" between the use of Alar and "development of life-threatening tumours". The US authorities then instigated a ban on Alar from next year.

But the Ministry of Agriculture, after reviewing the same studies, gave Alar the all clear and refused to halt sales. In June, Uniroyal withdrew Alar from the US market but refused demands from Parents for Safe Food, the pressure group formed by the actress, Ms Pamela Stephenson, to withdraw it in Britain.

Figures compiled in 1983 suggested that about 100 million apples, or about 7 per cent of the British crop, were sprayed with Alar.

▲ Figure 4.1 The impact of agrochemicals on food health and water quality.

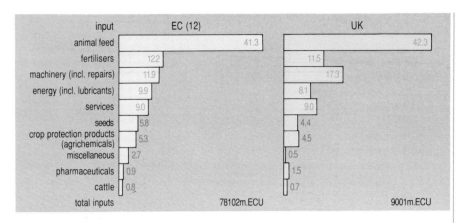

input	EC (12)	UK
animal feed	41.3	42.3
fertilisers	12.2	11.5
machinery (incl. repairs)	11.9	17.3
energy (incl. lubricants)	9.9	8.1
services	9.0	9.0
seeds	5.8	4.4
crop protection products (agrichemicals)	5.3	4.5
miscellaneous	2.7	0.5
pharmaceuticals	0.9	1.5
cattle	0.8	0.7
total inputs	78102m.ECU	9001m.ECU

▲   *Figure 4.2   Inputs to UK and European Community farming systems, 1987
(percentage of total inputs).*

these inputs have their origins outside agriculture in the industrial sector of
the economy: as labour has been displaced from farming, so it has been
gained by those industries supplying the inputs. At the same time farming
systems have become interrelated by creating inputs for each other, such as
animal feed for livestock for fattening, and they in turn have become part of
the larger industrial economic system. The most significant feature for the
environment, however, is the increasing volume of purchased inputs into
temperate agriculture and the energy flows that they represent.

3.3   *Production trends in temperate agriculture*

The upward trend in purchased inputs, both per hectare and per person,
employed in agriculture, has produced an increased level of intensification
in most farming systems. The degree of **intensification** still varies from
system to system, being most developed in pig, poultry and horticultural
production, and least in grassland systems of beef and sheep farming,
especially in uplands and mountains. There is a direct relationship between
inputs and outputs per hectare from farmland; consequently the
productivity (yield per hectare) of most temperate farming systems also
shows an upward trend. This can be measured in terms of the per hectare
yield of a crop, the density of livestock per hectare, or the annual output of
meat or livestock product (eggs, milk) per animal. Again using data for the
EC, the upward trend in the intensification of agriculture can be
demonstrated through crop yields. There is naturally some variation in crop
yields from year to year, but Figure 4.3 illustrates an overall trend of a
general rise in the yield of most crops: low for oats, rye and barley, quite
large for wheat and maize and very large for soya beans. Taken together
with changes in the allocation of land between different crops and livestock,
increased yields have raised farm production to the greatest extent for fats
and oils, wheat and poultrymeat, although decreases in production have
been recorded by a few products, especially potatoes, fresh fruit and
vegetables: see Table 4.3.

   Not surprisingly, many of these production trends have had an adverse
impact on the environment. Looking just at one example, in the
Netherlands the number of pigs and dairy cows have increased to such an

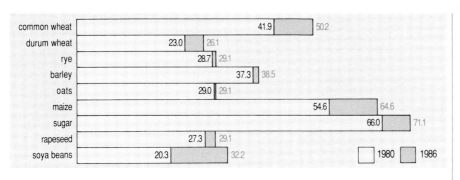

◀   Figure 4.3
Yields of selected crops in the European Community (12), 1980–1986 (100 kilogram/hectare).

Table 4.3   The changing volume of agricultural production in the European Community (9) (1987–88 as % 1971–72)

Large increases		Small increases		Decreases	
Vegetable fats and oils	192	Sugar (beet)	124	Vegetables	92
Wheat (soft and hard)	158	Wine	122	Fresh fruit	85
Poultrymeat	152	Barley	119	Potatoes	76
Beef and veal	142	Eggs	106		
Sheepmeat	139	Milk (raw)	104		
Maize grain	135				
Pigmeat	134				

Source: Author's calculations from agricultural statistics (*Eurostat* 1976, 1988: Brussels).

◀   *Incorporation of organic material from animal slurry or, as here, human sewage helps to maintain soil structure.*

extent that in some regions disposing of their urine and dung now poses a major environmental hazard. The quantity of manure is so great that the soil and field plants cannot absorb all the available nutrients; rainfall washes the nutrients from the manure when it is spread on the fields, resulting in accumulations in soil and water bodies. Some nutrients may be toxic in high concentration in drinking-water, all tend to promote algal growth and hence reduce oxygen in water, sometimes killing fish and plants. These problems have resulted in controls being placed on the quantity, frequency and timing of manure spreading in affected regions of the Netherlands.

While the output of temperate agriculture has been increasing, the domestic demand for food has been rising at a slower rate. This reflects the low level of population growth in most developed countries, and also the tendency to spend a lower proportion of income on food as incomes rise. The outcome for temperate agriculture has been a rising level of surplus production as reflected in the level of self-sufficiency in food production. Table 4.4 demonstrates the problem for the EC, with overproduction for the domestic market evident in all products, but especially whole milk powder and butter, sugar and cereals. In a free market, equilibrium would be restored through depressed product prices, but this has not occurred in temperate agriculture for two reasons. First, individual farmers are locked into a technological 'treadmill'. That is, as new output-increasing technology is developed, innovative farmers adopt that technology to reduce their unit costs of production. For a time they gain an economic advantage over non-adopting farmers. But gradually other farmers are forced into adopting the same technology so as to remain competitive and in business. Eventually output is increased for all those farmers who have not become marginalised and a further round of adopting new technology ensues. Farmers wishing to remain in business have little option but to remain on this technological treadmill.

Second, most states have intervened in agriculture to maintain the prices of farm produce which otherwise would be driven downwards in an oversupplied market. (This intervention takes place for a variety of reasons which will be outlined in Chapter 5.) A wide range of support measures has been introduced into temperate agriculture from import levies, guaranteed prices and support buying by intervention agencies, through direct income supplements and headage subsidies on cattle and sheep, to financial subsidies on the purchase of fertilisers, farm buildings and machinery. Only recently have some governments and the EC turned to supporting 'environmentally sensitive' farming practices. Rather, by subsidising production, governments in all developed countries have effectively encouraged and supported the increased intensification of agriculture with damaging environmental consequences.

Table 4.4   Self-sufficiency in the European Community, 1975–1985 (% total supply)

Product	1975 (EC = 9)	1980 (EC = 10)	1985 (EC = 12)
Wheat (soft and hard)	100	123	126
Barley	103	112	124
Potatoes	98	100	102
Sugar	105	135	129
Wine	98	104	105
Milk:			
whole milk powder	–	378	334
skimmed milk powder	171	128	118
Cheese	104	106	107
Butter	97	119	133
Eggs	100	102	102
Beef	101	103	108
Pigmeat	99	102	102
Poultrymeat	101	110	107

Source: Commission of the European Community, *The Agricultural Situation in the Community*, 1978 and 1988 Reports, Brussels.

Activity 4

Environmentally Sensitive Areas (ESA) in Britain attempt to relieve the pressures on agriculture for further intensification and specialisation.

Read the extracts from the Countryside Commission's publications in Figure 4.4 and answer the following questions.

Q   How many ESAs had been designated in the UK by December 1987 and where were they located?

New ESA options

Cereal farmers in East Anglia and the South Downs are being encouraged to convert arable land back to heathland or grassland, in the new Environmentally Sensitive Area (ESA) schemes announced by the Ministry of Agriculture at the end of November.

Annual payments from £100 in Breckland to £200 in the Suffolk River Valleys are being offered for every hectare of cereal land which reverts.

Breckland farmers also have the option of payments of £300 per hectare to leave six-metre strips of uncropped land at the edge of arable fields, to allow natural regeneration and encourage wildlife. Another option, in return for £100 per hectare, is to limit spraying at the cropped edges of arable fields, creating 'conservation headlands' – an initiative particularly welcomed by the Game Conservancy.

Altogether there are six additions and two extensions to the ESA list in England and Wales. To the six designated in December 1986, are added Breckland, North Peak, Suffolk River Valleys, Test Valley, Shropshire Borders and the Lleyn Peninsula. Extensions have been made to the South Downs and Cambrian Mountains ESAs.

The North Peak scheme is the first to encourage heather moorland conservation. Payments of £10 to £20 per hectare are available to sheep farmers carrying out appropriate moorland management in this area. The higher rate of grant requires the regeneration of at least one hectare of moorland per year.

There are now 1,290 square miles covered by ESA schemes in England, and 560 square miles in Wales.

In addition, Scotland now has five ESAs – Breadalbane, Loch Lomond, the Machair of the Uists and Benbecula, Whitlaw/Eildon and Stewartry – covering 865 square miles. Northern Ireland has two: Mourne and Slieve Croob and the Glens of Antrim, 185 square miles in total.

A promising start

The Government is to designate six areas of England and Wales as the country's first environmentally sensitive areas (ESAs). It has accepted in full the Commission's proposed boundaries for the Broads, Pennine Dales, Somerset Levels and West Penwith, plus the eastern end of the South Downs and northern and southern sections of the Cambrian Mountains.

The Ministry of Agriculture says it hopes that schemes for incentive payments to farmers will be set up early next year, once the formal designation order has received parliamentary approval. Meanwhile the management prescriptions for each area and the levels of payment to be offered are still under discussion between ministry officials and farmers' representatives.

Welcoming the Government's move to protect these landscapes threatened by agricultural change, Sir Derek Barber, Chairman of the Commission, said that the chosen areas would provide good experience for the future development of ESAs. He hoped farmers would take up the payments offered in return for joining the management schemes.

"I suspect that the chances of further areas being designated may well depend on the success of these six in attracting farmers' support," he added.

In April, the Commission submitted to ministers a list of 14 'priority' areas which it felt met the criteria for ESA designation, together with management prescriptions and suggestions for the levels of payment appropriate to each. Other areas on that list were Anglesey, Breckland, Clun, the Lleyn Peninsula, North Peak, Radnor, Suffolk River Valleys and the Test Valley in Hampshire.

▲   *Figure 4.4   Environmentally Sensitive Areas in the United Kingdom.*

A   19. (12 in England and Wales, 5 in Scotland and 2 in Northern Ireland.)
They are widely distributed to cover a range of farming systems and
landscape types of special merit. (See Figure 5.6 for a map locating the
ESAs.)

Q   What protective measures for the environment are offered within the
boundaries of the ESAs?

A   Payments to subsidise approved (traditional) farming practices;
management schemes under which farmers agree to abide by approved
farming practices; conversion payments for placing arable land into
grassland or heathland; conservation headland payments.

At the same time as increasing their inputs to agriculture, farmers have
gained economic benefits from simplifying their production systems. The
term **specialisation** can be applied to the process whereby farmers focus
their resources of land, labour and capital on an increasingly narrow range
of crops and livestock. Usually the least profitable enterprises are discarded
to enable economies of scale to be achieved in producing the remaining
products, for example, just cereals with oilseeds or beef with sheep. It is
increasingly common for only one product to be the outcome of a farming
system, for instance pigs, poultry or milk. Of course, new strains of crops
and livestock are always being introduced and these diffuse as an
innovation through a farming system. The spread of oilseed rape and maize
through the United Kingdom in the 1970s and 1980s are two well-known
examples. Also, the economic fortunes of different products change,
through alterations in either domestic demand, supply conditions in the
international market, or government policies. In these cases the enterprise
balance in a farming system, for example between beef and sheep, can be
altered. These processes, therefore, introduce elements of diversification
into temperate farming systems that otherwise show increasing
specialisation. The trend towards diversification is gathering pace in the late
1980s as governments try to scale down the very high costs of supporting the
food surpluses from existing farming systems. In the EC, for example,
farmers are now being offered financial incentives ('set-aside') to place land
into alternative uses including woodlands, fallow, crops and livestock not in
surplus and long-term conservation reserves. (Chapter 5 discusses these
developments.)

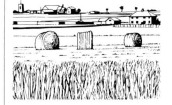

   An indication of the level of specialisation in agriculture within the EC
can be obtained through the proportion of national agricultural production
accounted for by individual farm products: this is illustrated in Figure 4.5.
In the Netherlands, for example, a high level of specialisation is evident in
milk, pigmeat and vegetables: together these products account for over half
of national farm output by value. In the United Kingdom, 35% of national
farm output comes from milk and beef/veal; lower levels of specialisation
exist in other countries. In Greece, a more recent member of the EC, only one
category – fresh vegetables – exceeds 10% of the output from a relatively
diversified agricultural sector.

   As has been noted in Chapters 2 and 3, the trend towards increased
specialisation reduces the stability of agroecosystems. For example, the
genetic variety within each crop and livestock type has been reduced,
thereby limiting the capacity of farming systems to withstand changes in
climate (weather) or attack from pests and diseases. The specialised systems
require increased quantities of pesticides and fungicides, with increased
danger of pollution by residues.

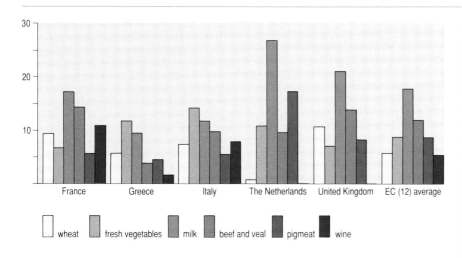

◀   *Figure 4.5*
*Agricultural production
in selected countries and
products, 1987
(% total value of production).*

Government subsidy of farm prices has not prevented their real value from being eroded through time by price inflation. Indeed governments have allowed this erosion to accelerate in the 1980s as a way of reducing the real cost of supporting farm prices. Input costs, on the other hand, have continued to increase, in some cases in real terms and in others at the rate of inflation. Consequently, farmers have been caught in a 'price–cost squeeze' and some have been forced out of farming by bankruptcy. Indeed given the number of family farms, the massive reduction of the labour input could not have been achieved without this process. Under capitalism, small farms are those most likely to be bankrupted, with their land purchased by the remaining, larger farm businesses. The costs of the latter are thereby spread over more units of production, while individual farm families are able to accumulate wealth. Through time, therefore, land becomes owned by fewer, larger farm businesses, a process described generally as **concentration** in agriculture. In some farming systems polarity is evident in the farm-size structure: small numbers of large farms control most of the land resource, while a large number of small farm units occupy the remaining farmland. This degree of concentration is present in the farm-size structure of some regions in the United States, for example California, and in western Europe, for instance the Highlands of Scotland, southern Italy and southern Spain. Elsewhere, however, more medium-sized farms have been maintained despite the inceasing dominance of large farms in the control of the land resource. One consequence for the environment of this process of concentration lies in the environmental attitudes of those who occupy the larger farming units. It has been found that occupiers of large farms have less sympathetic attitudes towards the environment and the need for active measures on conservation than small farmers.

An increasing concentration is evident in the structure of farm production as well as land occupancy. As farms grow larger and more specialised, so the proportion of output controlled by a few farms increases. We can measure this degree of concentration by the proportion of production controlled by the largest producers. Concentration is greatest for farming systems concerned with intensive livestock (pigs and poultry), and least for extensive farmland with beef, cattle and sheep. In the case of pig production in the EC, for example, the largest 5% of herds controls 63% of all animals. For beef production, the largest 20% of herds contains 61% of all cattle, while in dairying a similar percentage of herds accounts for 50% of milk cows.

When large groupings of farms are considered, we find variations between farming systems and agricultural regions in the rates of intensification, specialisation and concentration (Bowler, 1981). One outcome has been the increased regional specialisation of farming through which differences between agricultural systems and regions have become drawn more rather than less sharply. Also, the processes described in this discussion have introduced methods of production into farming that are increasingly industrial in character. These parallels include the purchase of inputs from outside the farming system, specialisation in the labour and production function, mechanised methods of farming and, as we will now see, the onward transfer of farm produce for specialised processing and packaging. Not surprisingly the term **industrialised farming** is now widely applied to temperate agriculture, although it is a term more appropriate to intensive (pigs, poultry, dairy, cereals, horticulture) rather than extensive farming systems.

3.4   *Marketing the outputs of temperate agriculture*

It is no longer useful to think of agricultural systems as ending at the farm gate. The farm, as a production unit, is now part of a much broader economic system, sometimes referred to as the **food chain**, which includes the processing and distribution of food as well as the manufacture of purchased inputs. Only a small proportion of farm production now reaches the consumer without some form of value-added processing, even if this takes the form only of washing, grading and packing the produce. Moreover, the marketing channels whereby food reaches the consumer have become increasingly complex. In temperate agriculture, a significant proportion of farm produce passes initially through either state-financed intervention boards or producer-controlled marketing boards, both of which act to keep prices artificially high. The Intervention Board for Agricultural Produce, for example, acts in the United Kingdom as the agent of the EC: the Board purchases, stores and subsequently markets surplus farm products, often at considerable cost to taxpayers in the Community. The normal channels of food distribution from the farm, however, are shown in Figure 4.6.

Activity 5

Examine the information on the UK food chain in Figure 4.6 and answer the following questions.

Q   What proportion of the value of food (domestically produced and imported) passes through the food manufacturing sector?

A   54.5% ([£3 100m + £2 900m ÷ £5 700m + £5 300] × 100): this demonstrates the key role played by the manufacturing sector in the food chain.

Q   After food manufacturing ([£6 000m ÷ £12 000m] × 100 = 50%), which sector in the food chain adds the greatest proportional value to its inputs?

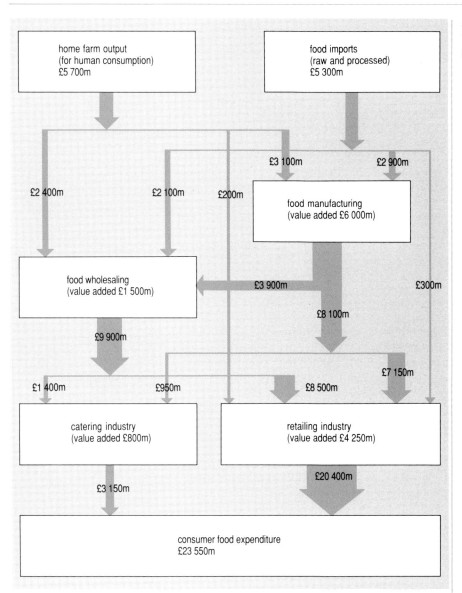

◀ *Figure 4.6*
The UK food chain
(1979 prices).

A   The catering industry (25%); food wholesaling is 15%, and the retailing
industry is 21%. The catering industry (restaurant, hotel and
institutional trade) serves a fast-growing sector of consumer food
expenditure.

Usually food-processing firms, amongst which there is considerable
concentration in most countries, hold back from direct ownership of farms,
but assure their supplies by placing forward contracts with individual
farmers. For example, within France nearly 50% of poultrymeat and 93% of
vegetables are marketed under contract and figures for the Netherlands are
90% for each of these products. Forward contracts allow the processor to
control the price, quantity and quality of produce delivered from the farm.
This degree of control can be so rigid that the farmer becomes little more
than a 'landed labourer': the farmer supplies farmland and labour, while

capital, materials, farming operations and marketing are controlled by the processor. In these circumstances, the environmental impact of agriculture is determined not so much by the farmer as by decisions taken by the managers of food-processing industries.

Contract farming has been an important catalyst in the development of co-operative marketing groups in some farming systems. By grouping together to offer a product of assured uniform quality and quantity, producers are sometimes able to negotiate more favourable prices with processors. This form of marketing varies in importance between farming systems and countries, for it is culturally as well as economically defined. Pig, vegetable and dairy producers in Denmark, pig producers in France and vegetable producers in the Netherlands, for example, have been particularly amenable to marketing their products co-operatively. Much greater resistance to this form of co-operative behaviour is evident in countries such as Italy and the United Kingdom.

The retailing sector, with its large multiple retailers, is increasingly able to determine the price, quantity and quality of food purchased from the manufacturing and wholesaling sectors or directly from larger farms. The catering industry, especially restaurant and fast-food chains, is also increasing its sales and becoming a significant element in how food reaches the consumer. With all of these developments, the price of food is determined more by the value added beyond the farm gate than on the farm itself (look again at Figure 4.6). This observation has a broader implication. If we become concerned with the efficiency with which temperate farming systems use resources such as energy, then that use needs to be placed within the context of the energy consumed by the whole food chain, including packaging, transportation and distribution. Pimentel and Pimentel (1979), for example, show that only 45% of the energy needed to produce a loaf of bread is consumed on the farm; the figure for a can of sweet corn is 15%. On the other hand, for products where there is little processing, most energy is consumed in farm production – 98% in the case of beef. Concern with the energy-intensive nature of temperate agriculture needs to be extended beyond the farm down the whole food chain.

3.5   *Summary*

Temperate agriculture is characterised as being energy and capital intensive, with decreasing inputs of land and labour. Individual farming systems show evidence of increasing intensification, specialisation and concentration, although these trends vary within agriculture. Nevertheless, one common outcome of the industrialisation of agriculture is the merging of farming systems with larger industrial systems as regards both purchased inputs and the processing of food outputs. In this way energy and nutrients enter temperate farming systems from the industrial sector, while losses occur when produce (crops, livestock and livestock products) leaves the farm gate to pass down the food chain to the consumer.

Within the food chain, decisions reached on the marketing of food in the retail and manufacturing sectors are passed back to individual farms: these decisions influence the volume, variety and methods of food production in temperate agriculture, with direct consequences for the environment. Not all of these impacts need be negative. In the late 1980s, for example, consumers have expressed a demand for 'organically produced' food, that is food produced without the use of chemical fertilisers, agrochemicals such as pesticides and added hormones in livestock. Large multiple retailers, realising the market potential of this demand, are beginning to place contracts for 'organic' farm produce and thereby stimulate a more environmentally sensitive form of agriculture. Nevertheless, the environmentally damaging consequences of modern temperate agriculture tend to predominate and the next section looks at a number of temperate farming systems to examine these impacts in more detail.

Activity 6

One way of focusing your attention onto the environmental impacts of temperate agriculture is to speculate on the form that an 'environmentally friendly' farming system would take. List the features you would favour in such a system:

- What would be the pattern of inputs?
- What farming practices would be included/excluded?
- What energy flows would take place within your model farming system?
- What outputs would be produced?
- What would be the environmental impacts of your system?

4   Case studies of temperate farming systems

4.1   Introduction

The previous section looked at some of the general trends to be found in temperate agriculture and began the task of identifying their associated environmental impacts. However, Section 2 drew our attention to the wide variety of farming systems within temperate agriculture and it would be surprising if evironmental impacts, as well as their severity, were similar in all the systems. In this section, therefore, we examine five temperate farming systems in greater detail: firstly, to expose the varying agriculture–environment relationships to be found in each system; secondly, to estimate the relative seriousness of the impacts; and, thirdly, to begin an assessment of the need for remedial action. The five case studies are: extensive arable farming; intensive arable farming; extensive grassland farming; intensive grassland farming; and intensive livestock farming. These farming systems range over a variety of crop and livestock types, include both intensive and extensive farming practices, and cover different types of physical environment. Attention is focused on the degree of ecosystem manipulation that each represents.

4.2   Extensive arable farming systems

Extensive arable (crop) farming takes place mainly at the *extensive margins of cultivation*, where commercial crops are at their ecological limits because of deficiencies in rainfall or temperature (and therefore growing season) or both factors acting together. Historically the agroecosystem had been simplified to continuous cereal cultivation, mainly wheat, punctuated by fallows of between one and three years' duration depending on soil moisture conditions. But in recent decades rotational cropping has been introduced, including grain, sorghum and grass leys for beef cattle and sheep. Despite the adoption of high-yielding crop varieties and the periodic application of chemical fertilisers, outputs per hectare remain characteristically low and variable, whereas farming operations are highly mechanised so as to produce high crop yields per worker. In order to maintain the economic viability of farm businesses, farm sizes must be relatively large with production costs per hectare kept to a minimum. One farm practice in North America, for example, is to rely on peripatetic contractors to harvest the cereal crop, rather than having to employ farm labour all year and own the harvesting equipment. The following are examples of large-scale, specialised grain-farming regions: the spring wheat region of the Dakotas and eastern Montana, together with the adjacent part of the Canadian prairies; the winter wheat belt of Kansas, Colorado and Oklahoma; the Palouse country in Washington; the Cordoba–Santa Fé–Bahia Blanca region of Argentina; the spring wheat region of western Siberia; and the South-Australia–Victoria–Queensland wheat belt of Australia (type 7 on Figure 2.6).

With their location at the semi-arid margins of cultivation, extensive arable farming systems are very vulnerable to climatic and economic fluctuations. Taking the Great Plains of the United States as an example, 'boom' periods of cereal farming can be identified in the initial period of permanent settlement following the 1862 Homestead Act, the first two decades of the twentieth century, the years immediately following the Second World War and, more briefly, the late 1960s. Conversely, 'bust' periods have been experienced in the 1890s, 1930s, 1950s and 1980s. However, it is not easy to distinguish between the effects of climatic and economic fluctuations on some of these cyclical movements. The run of dry years which produced the infamous Dust Bowl and land abandonment of the 1930s, for instance, coincided with a downturn in the world economy leading to the Great Depression. Similarly, the 1940s witnessed a coincidence between relatively high rainfall years and an increasing demand for wheat in war-torn Europe. On the other hand, the economically depressed conditions of the 1980s can only be accounted for by a change in government policy towards agriculture: price supports for cereals were severely and sharply reduced, leading to a downturn in the incomes of extensive grain producers. Table 4.5 gives data for a county in Colorado on the Great Plains which show the continuing decline in the number of farms as well as the rural population, but fluctuations in the number of hired workers, reflecting the contemporary state of 'boom or bust' in the cereal economy.

Specialised, large-scale grain production has tended to replace natural grasslands formed under semi-arid continental climates. Farmers have sought to cope with this marginal agricultural environment by manipulating the agroecosystem using a variety of dry-farming techniques:

- clean tillage where stubble is ploughed in during the autumn using a mouldboard plough

- conventional tillage where stubble is surface disc ploughed in the autumn or spring

- conservation tillage where stubble is undercut in the spring to remain on the surface as a mulch

- minimum tillage, as above but with less ploughing of mulch and weeds
- chemical tillage, again as for conservation tillage but with weeds controlled by herbicides.

In each case the objective is the exercise of farm-level control over the **soil moisture budget** by a number of methods: reducing weed growth to a minimum between harvest and planting; keeping wheat stubble upright for as long as possible in order to increase snow accumulation and reduce wind velocities; preserving a straw mulch until planting time to reduce wind impact, evaporation and run-off; maintaining a rough field surface with large clods of earth during fallow and after planting so as to reduce wind velocities and trap snowfall; and returning plant residues to the soil so as to maintain the nutrient cycle (Figure 4.7).

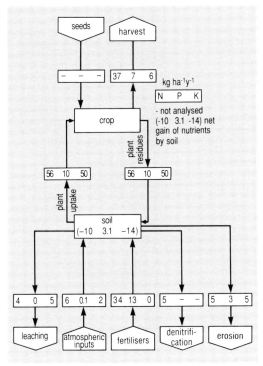

◀ *Figure 4.7*
The nutrient cycle of a wheat farm in central Kansas, USA.

Source: Briggs, D. J. and Courtney, F. M. (1985) *Agriculture and the Environment: the physical geography of temperate agricultural systems*, London, Longman Group.

Table 4.5   Socio-economic indicators in Sedgwick County, Colorado, 1910–82

Year	Total population	Hired labour	Number of farms	Average farm size (ha)
1910	3061	—	448	144
1920	4207	399	487	195
1930	5580	—	560	222
1940	5294	213	505	232
1950	5095	145	474	268
1960	4242	279[1]	376[1]	335[1]
1970	3405	571[2]	327[2]	428[2]
1980	3266	390[3]	253[3]	520[3]

Notes: [1]1959; [2]1969; [3]1982.

Source: Spath, H. J. (1987) in Turner, B. L. and Brush, S. B. (eds) *Comparative Farming Systems*, New York, Guildford Press, p. 319.

When farmers make inappropriate modifications to the agroecosystem in these semi-arid environments, the consequences can be disastrous. For example, clean and conventional tillage, which leaves no protective stubble on the field surface after harvest, proved catastrophic for parts of the Great Plains during the sequence of dry years in the 1930s. Although this farming practice has nearly been eliminated, wind erosion of the soil remains a significant problem in particularly dry years, for example 1975: see Table 4.6.

Activity 7

Examine Tables 4.6 and 4.7, then answer the following questions.

Q   What features of chemical tillage recommend the farming practice to profit-maximising farmers? (Table 4.7.)

A   Farmers are able to trade off reduced machine operations (discing, ploughing, weeding), with lower energy inputs, against higher inputs of chemicals. The loss of soil moisture is reduced (fallow efficiency rises), cereal yields are raised and the ratio between total energy outputs and inputs increases. You should note that while the dependence of dry-farming on purchased energy inputs is reduced, chemical tillage suppresses both weeds and other flora and fauna.

Q   Are there any underlying trends in the three different wind-erosion conditions in Colorado between 1969 and 1983? (Look at Table 4.6.)

A   Despite the well-known problem of wind erosion, the area suffering cropland damage appears to be increasing in Colorado; the area of crops destroyed shows little long-term reduction, although the area under emergency tillage is falling.

▲   *Extensive arable farming: combine harvesters in Czechoslovakia.*

▲   *The morning after a windstorm in the Texas Panhandle, one of the United States' most productive cotton-growing regions. During a critical time between harvest and regrowth while the soil was bare, the wind lifted the silt and left the sand.*

Table 4.6   Wind erosion in Colorado, 1969–83 (ha)

Year	Cropland damage	Crops destroyed	Emergency tillage[1]
1969	10 988	56 356	29 525
1972	29 525	20 011	68 396
1975	261 737	388 189	535 681
1978	168 083	76 184	50 791
1981	925 830	19 213	35 843
1983	147 187	31 003	14 345

Note: [1]By producing large soil clods, deep tillage can serve as emergency tillage for wind erosion control.
Source: Spath, H. J. (1987) in Turner, B. L. and Brush, S. B. (eds) *Comparative Farming Systems*, New York, Guildford Press, p. 320.

Table 4.7   Tillage systems and their agro-ecological features (north-east Colorado)

Tillage system	Number of mechanical operations[1]	Fallow efficiency (%)	Yield (kg/ha)	Energy output/input ratio
Clean tillage	5–8	20–24	1680–2352	5–15
Conventional tillage	4–6	24–27	2016–2688	10–15
Conservation tillage	4–5	30–33	2352–2688	15–20
Minimum tillage	2–4	30–40	2688–3360	20–30
Chemical tillage	1–3	33–45	3024–3696	20–35

Note: [1]Ploughing, harrowing, discing, spraying, weeding, sowing, harvesting.

Source: Spath, H. J. (1987) in Turner, B. L. and Brush, S. B. (eds) *Comparative Farming Systems*, New York, Guildford Press, p. 330.

4.3   Intensive arable farming systems

Intensive arable farming is characterised by crop rotations and high inputs producing high yields per hectare. The crops found in these farming systems include cereals (wheat, barley, oats, maize), oilseeds (sunflower, soya bean, colza), roots (sugar beet, turnips) and vegetables (cabbage, carrots, potatoes and so on). Whereas extensive arable farming systems aim to regulate the soil moisture budget, intensive systems are designed primarily to manipulate the nutrient cycle. Intensive arable systems employ high throughputs of nutrients but relatively simple and minor internal circulations.

Each annual crop cycle terminates with the removal of nutrients in the harvested crop for commercial sale, the removals being replenished by organic or purchased chemical fertilisers. In this sense the farming system acts as a converter of mainly chemical inputs (nitrogen, potassium and phosphorus) into useful food products. Figures 4.8(a) and (b) show the nutrient cycle for an intensive arable farm in the Netherlands growing potatoes, wheat and sugar beet in rotation. Under the rotation, each crop makes slightly different demands on the soil in terms of nutrients; in addition the farmer can exercise greater control over pests and diseases while enjoying the economic benefits of spreading risk over several crops. Figures 4.8(a) and (b) can be compared to gain an appreciation of the importance of fertiliser inputs as well as the management of crop residues. While the latter return important soil nutrients to the system, especially nitrogen and potassium, unless carefully managed, crop residues can also harbour pests and diseases for subsequent crops, together with any toxicity remaining after the spraying of agrochemicals. Figures 4.7 and 4.8 also permit a comparison of the nutrient cycle under extensive and intensive arable systems: it shows the relatively high level of fertiliser applications needed to maintain intensive systems, together with the high losses of nutrients from leaching, denitrification and harvesting. As we will find when examining intensive cereal farming in the United Kingdom, the high losses of nutrients through leaching pose a major environmental hazard both for supplies of drinking water and for wetland and river habitats.

Like extensive agriculture, intensive arable farming is found throughout the world. When intensive crops (often under irrigation) are combined with tree fruits (olives and citrus) and rain-fed wheat, a characteristic Mediterranean agricultural system can be recognised (type 6 in Figure 2.6). When crops are combined with livestock in rotation, the term 'mixed farming' is commonly employed (type 8 in Figure 2.6): it is a particular form of agriculture in both eastern and western Europe, eastern North America and parts of other regions of European settlement in the Argentine pampas, south-east Australia, South Africa and New Zealand. Even so, large areas largely devoid of livestock can be found within these regions, for example in the intensive cereal-growing areas of eastern England and north-central France.

Dorel (1987) offers us a detailed view of one such intensive cereal-growing area on the chalky plains of Champagne, located to the east of the Paris basin. From being one of the poorer agricultural regions of France, with small farms and much land in either forest or fallow, the region has been transformed since the Second World War. Forests were cleared and land drained; farms were amalgamated to create large businesses, and intensive cereal production (wheat) set within a crop rotation of wheat/barley/sugar beet/wheat/peas/wheat was rapidly developed. The transformation was so rapid – only twenty years – that Dorel remarks on 'the

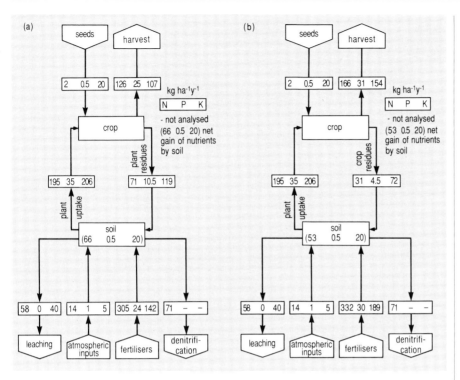

◀   Figure 4.8
*The nutrient cycle of an
intensive arable farm with
potatoes-wheat-sugar beet
rotation on clay soil in the
Netherlands.*
*(a) Crop residues retained
on the land.*
*(b) Crop residues removed
from the land.*

Source: Briggs, D. J. and
Courtney, F. M. (1985)
*Agriculture and the
Environment: the physical
geography of temperate
agricultural systems*,
London, Longman Group.

uniform, regional farm patterns reminiscent of the Great Plains of the
United States – the general flatness, the small number of trees, the large
cultivated fields, the scattered homesteads'. The principal causes of this
transformation, through the intensive applications of fertilisers,
agrochemicals and mechanisation, have been identified already: they were
the financial incentives offered by the price support system of the Common
Agricultural Policy and the penetration of agriculture by agri-inputs and
food-processing firms. The outcome, however, has been a transformed
landscape: enlarged fields to accommodate the powerful tractors and
combine harvesters of modern cereal farming; hedgerows and woodland
swept away, together with their habitats for flora and fauna; modernised
farm buildings on those holdings still in production, with decaying or
converted buildings on those farmsteads no longer actively engaged in
agriculture. (See Plate 8.)

The energy-intensive nature of modernised arable farming is caused by
successive management operations which include seedbed preparation,
sowing, fertiliser application, pesticide spraying, harvesting and residue
disposal. Each operation requires the expenditure of energy through the use
of machinery and other materials produced off the farm. In the 1970s,
concern over the apparent 'energy dependency' of modern farming systems
spawned a wide range of studies, each attempting to measure the elusive
concept of 'energy efficiency'. Our discussion at the beginning of this
chapter provides a background to this analysis. Figure 4.9, using data for
1971–72, shows the principles involved in calculating an energy ratio for an
individual (arable) farm. Clearly the calculated energy ratio between
outputs and inputs of 2:1 means little on its own; the figure only gains value
when set alongside similar calculations for other farming systems.
However, researchers in this area are unable to agree on the details of the
computations: they differ on the range of inputs to be included, their

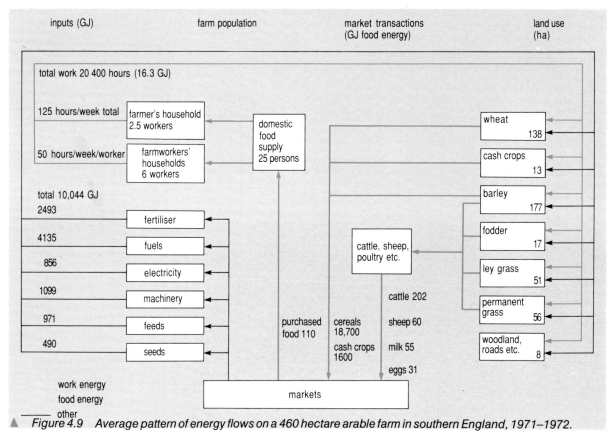

| inputs (GJ) | farm population | market transactions (GJ food energy) | land use (ha) |

total work 20 400 hours (16.3 GJ)

125 hours/week total — farmer's household 2.5 workers

domestic food supply 25 persons

wheat 138

50 hours/week/worker — farmworkers' households 6 workers

cash crops 13

total 10,044 GJ

barley 177

2493 — fertiliser

fodder 17

4135 — fuels

cattle, sheep, poultry etc.

856 — electricity

ley grass 51

1099 — machinery

cattle 202

permanent grass 56

971 — feeds

purchased food 110 — cereals 18,700 — sheep 60

490 — seeds

cash crops 1600 — milk 55

woodland, roads etc. 8

eggs 31

work energy
food energy
———— other

markets

▲ Figure 4.9   Average pattern of energy flows on a 460 hectare arable farm in southern England, 1971–1972.

$$\text{Energy ratio} = \frac{\text{Crops sold} + \text{animal products sold}}{\text{Work input} + \text{total subsidies}} = \frac{20\,300 + 348}{16.3 + 10\,044}\,GJ\ = 2.1$$

imputed energy costs and the crop and animal yields to be assumed. Varying assumptions are also employed on the labour input to different farming operations: Spath (1987, p. 342), for example, excludes harvesting, drying and transportation operations from the energy budget since the energy inputs occur after the production process in the field is complete. Other researchers, however, include these inputs, arguing that the totality of the production process should be examined. There is also some dispute over which index of energy use should be employed: Bayliss-Smith (1982), for example, offers a choice between energy productivity, surplus energy income and energy yield, in addition to the energy ratio itself.

Pimentel and Pimentel (1979) provide us with the most comprehensive review of energy budgeting. Their calculations produce comparable statistics for crops and livestock farming systems in the United States. The budgets divide fossil energy inputs by protein outputs: this equation demonstrates the greater energy efficiency of crop as compared with livestock farming, and extensive as compared with intensive crop or livestock systems. What this calculation shows is that for each unit of protein of output obtained, the fossil fuel input required is much smaller for vegetable crops than for livestock crops (only rice is an exception to this) and that extensive farming systems for producing beef, eggs and lamb are very considerably more efficient than intensive systems: see Table 4.8.

Table 4.8   Energy ratio for crop and livestock products in the United States (fossil
energy input/protein output)

Crops		Livestock	
Soya beans	2.06	Beef (rangeland)	10.1
Oats	2.70	Eggs	13.1
Wheat	3.44	Lamb (rangeland)	16.2
Brussels sprouts	3.51	Broilers	22.1
Maize	3.63	Pork	35.4
Potatoes	4.25	Milk	35.9
Rice	10.01	Beef (feed-lot)	77.7

Source: Adapted from Pimentel, D. and Pimentel, M. (1979) *Food, Energy and Society*, London,
Edward Arnold, pp. 56–9.

◀   *A cereal field showing
the monoculture of modern
industrialised agriculture.*

◀   *Crop spraying is
favoured in intensive
arable farming to
achieve high yields.*

Even so, most temperate farming methods are inefficient in the conversion of energy in the sense that only a small proportion of total energy inputs is ultimately consumed as food. But energy accounting is simply a tool for describing a farming system. It does not prescribe a healthy diet, nor quantify animal welfare, amenity or landscape aesthetics, nor value the amount of food capable of being produced by intensive farming methods. In most parts of the world, the main concern with farming systems is their ability to generate profits and/or deliver food to a population rather than their energy efficiencies.

4.4   *Extensive grassland farming systems*

Extensive grassland farming systems (ranching) tend to occupy locations beyond the margins of cultivation in either excessively arid, cold or mountainous environments. Large farm units predominate to exploit previously natural, but now modified, grasslands (rangelands) using low input-output farming methods for the production of beef cattle or sheep. The major ranching areas lie on the prairie rangeland of western United States, the llanos of Venezuela, the sertão of Brazil, the pampa of Uruguay, the chaco of Patagonia, the karoo of South Africa, the arid interior of Australia and part of South Island, New Zealand (type 2 in Figure 2.6). (See Plate 7.)

Ranching emerged as a major agricultural system only in the second half of the nineteenth century, the main factor being the growth in demand for beef and wool in the urbanised areas of North America and western Europe. Consequently, the initial marketing infrastructure of these farming systems tended to be export-oriented, with transport networks and meat-processing plants focused on ports so as to serve distant markets. In recent decades other farming systems have been able to produce beef, wool and sheepmeat at competitive prices; consequently, ranching has had to adopt the same process of intensification as found in other farming systems in order to survive. In this way the rangeland and environment have come under increasing pressure from extensive grassland farming.

The central feature of rangeland management is the livestock-carrying capacity of the native grasses, herbaceous plants and shrubs. In the sense that the very act of grazing transforms herbage composition, little 'natural' grassland remains. For example, in Australia the widespread adoption of sheep-grazing led to the removal of kangaroo grass, a predominantly summer-growing species, and its replacement by essentially winter-growing species such as *Danthonia* and *Stipa*. Nevertheless, a distinction can be drawn between those pastures that receive little management and those that are subject to improvement through rotational grazing, reseeding, controlled burning and fertilising. Improving the grassland by these methods fundamentally changes its character and composition, but allows higher densities to be achieved. Grassland improvement has been introduced along the more humid margins of rangeland areas, including the cultivation of some fodder crops. Such developments have moved the farming system towards a mixed agricultural economy but led to a continuing reduction in the extent of semi-natural grassland. Even on the 'unmanaged' pastures, the pressure to increase farm output has tended to lead to higher stocking densities, overgrazing and soil erosion by both wind and water. Excessive grazing depletes the vegetational cover, reduces the reincorporation of organic matter into the soil, compacts the soil and initiates soil displacement on sloping areas. Indeed the first signs of

overgrazing can be seen in the down-slope movement of soil caused by
'trampling displacement'. The terraced livestock paths leave the topsoil
vulnerable to rill and gulley erosion.

Figure 4.10 shows the structure of a grassland system of farming. It
highlights the interrelationships between soil, grassland and livestock. In
ranching, grazing is the chief manipulation of the environment. The stock
are replenished by breeding and only a regulated number of animals leave
the system each year. Adjusting the number of cattle or sheep to rangeland
conditions on an annual or even monthly basis is central to good
management practice. In the highly variable semi-arid environments of
extensive grassland farming, a balance has to be struck between the forage
consumption rate of different types or ages of stock, grass yield (biomass),
the species composition of different rangeland areas, and the need to leave
approximately half of total forage growth for the pasture to recover for the
following year.

Similar considerations apply to extensive grazing systems in upland and
mountain areas located within otherwise intensive farming regions. Cattle
and sheep farming on the moorlands of the Scottish Highlands and the
Cambrian Mountains of Wales, as well as the alpine meadows of western
Europe, are cases in point. Nevertheless, from the perspective of the llanos
or the sertão, with carrying capacities in the range of 2–6 hectares per sheep,
hill sheep farming in these areas appears to be a relatively intensive farming
system at 0.8–4 hectares per sheep. A more detailed consideration of upland
and hill sheep farming in the United Kingdom is provided in Section 5.2

Judged in relation to extensive and intensive arable-farming systems,
significant environmental damage from extensive grassland farming
appears to be relatively limited and localised. This observation suggests the
existence of a continuum of environmental impacts: from farming systems
with relatively low to those with high and damaging consequences for the

Source: Briggs, D. J. and
Courtney, F. M. (1985)
*Agriculture and the
Environment: the physical
geography of temperate
agricultural systems*,
London, Longman Group.

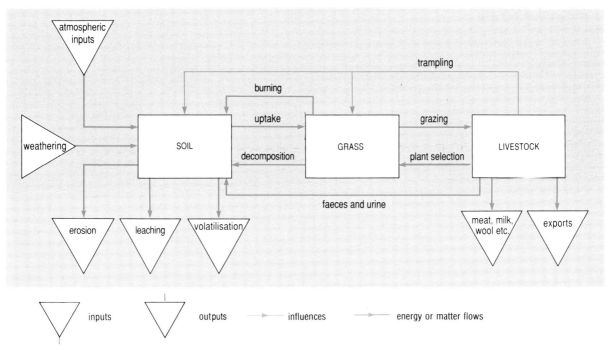

Figure 4.10   *An extensive grassland farming system.*

environment. With their localised occurrences of over-grazing, soil trampling and induced soil erosion, the extensive grazing of cattle and sheep can be placed towards the low-impact end of the continuum. But an alternative view can be taken on some grazing systems. For example, throughout the Mediterranean basin over-grazing by goats is widely viewed as a major contributor to the serious problem of soil erosion, especially along watersheds. In the western USA poisonous burroweed has become common and many woody species have invaded the grassland, for example mesquite, sagebrush and juniper. In Tasmania the overgrazing of pasture has encouraged the spread of unpalatable tussock grass and thorn bush.

4.5   *Intensive grassland farming systems*

Intensive grassland farming systems produce meat (veal, beef, lamb and mutton) as well as livestock products such as milk, hides and wool. Both cattle and sheep graze artificially grown pasture of three main types: permanent pasture, rotation pasture (leys) and temporary pasture. In general, rotation and temporary pastures contain more nutritious grasses – ryegrass, timothy and clover – with higher yields of forage. Turning to Figure 4.11, intensive grassland farming regulates the components of soil, grassland and livestock to a greater extent than under ranching. With rotation and temporary pasture, for example, the sward is periodically ploughed and reseeded, while nitrogenous fertilisers are applied to promote leaf growth. With so much nitrogen removed by harvest and grazing, as well as that lost in drainage waters, replenishment is needed to maintain biomass yield. Nevertheless, as with fertilisers used in arable systems, careful management is needed to reach the optimum rate of application per hectare. If the forage is too nitrogen-rich, for example, cattle can be in danger of nitrate poisoning.

Rotation pasture is usually renewed in a five- to ten-year cycle, whereas temporary grass, being part of an arable rotation, usually has a life of only one or two years' duration before being ploughed in. In both cases, grass-seed mixture is selected so as to produce a high forage yield throughout the year. Permanent pasture, in contrast, is ploughed only infrequently and is refreshed by surface treatment of lime, nitrogenous fertiliser and grass-seed. There is a long-standing debate in agriculture over the relative merits of temporary as compared with permanent grass; if managed well, however, there is little to choose between the two, and both can achieve stocking rates of between 3 and 4 cattle per hectare.

Intensive grassland farming is found mainly in association with areas of European settlement in western Europe, North America, North Island, New Zealand and parts of coastal south Australia. Farm size tends to be small but, as with ranching, the success of the intensive system depends on the quality of management supplied by the individual farmer. Three particular management practices should be noted. First, grass is conserved either as hay or silage to feed livestock during the winter months when the growth of the pasture ceases. Removing grass from the field in this way involves major losses of nutrients. Consequently, and secondly, the growth of the pasture is promoted using fertilisers. Thirdly, the grazing of the pasture is controlled using a variety of techniques. Under a *'free range'* system, for example, livestock are allowed to graze at will over the whole area of available grassland. Under *set stocking*, however, the stock are rotated from field to field on a daily or weekly basis so as to exploit the full potential of the available fodder. *Paddock grazing* is an elaboration of this technique: fields

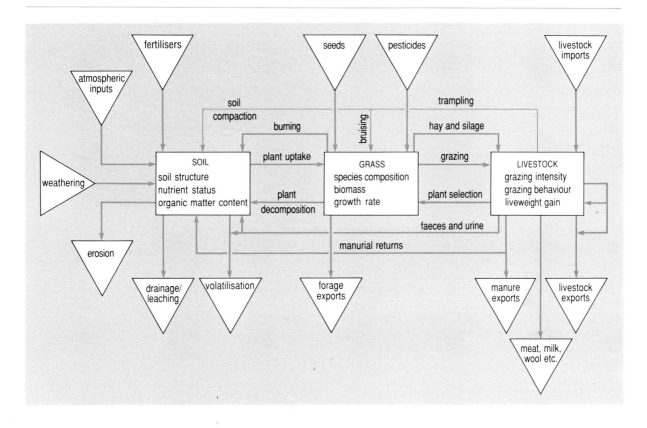

are subdivided into small, fenced areas (paddocks) and the stock are grazed intensively on each in turn. *Strip grazing* introduces a yet more intensive practice: an electric fence is moved daily or hourly in stages across the pasture; at each stage livestock have access to only a narrow strip of grass which is grazed to the full. Finally, under *zero-grazing* the grass is cut daily and taken from the field to the stock which are housed in stalls or open yards. This system minimises the waste of forage involved in trampling and fouling under field-grazing methods, while the stock expend little energy in obtaining their food. On the other hand, the nutrient losses are significant and there is no recycling of nutrients through animal faeces. Indeed, the problem of disposing of the slurry effluent created by cattle kept at high densities has been mentioned already, while accidental leakages and spillage from storage areas (tanks or lagoons) can have a devastating effect on the ecology of local streams and rivers. Indeed so toxic is the effluent that in many countries – including the UK – farmers can be fined for leakages into water courses, especially where public water supplies are involved. In Denmark new environmental laws have been applied to the storage and application of manure and slurry so as to control the pollution of groundwater. Farms with more than twenty animals have to be able to store a minimum of six months' production of slurry and manure; strict construction standards have been applied to slurry pits and lagoons; animal housing must be placed at certain distances away from domestic water supplies; and restrictions have been placed on the use of nitrogen on pastures.

The manipulation of the agroecosystem is most developed in dairy farming (type 9 in Figure 2.6) with high levels of stock density, capital and labour inputs achieving high milk yields per hectare and per cow. Livestock

▲ *Figure 4.11*
An intensive grassland farming system.

Source: Briggs, D. J. and Courtney, F. M. (1985) *Agriculture and the Environment: the physical geography of temperate agricultural systems*, London, Longman Group.

▲   The containment and disposal of slurry is an enormous problem: 2.7 million
dairy cows produce 41 million tonnes per annum. (Above) a slurry store in a
sleeper-walled compound; (below) good practice in solid and liquid slurry stores:
surface rainwater on the muck soon drains out when it stops raining.

diversity is minimised: Holstein and Friesian dairy breeds are dominant,
with some regional specialisation in breeds such as Normandy, Guernsey
and Ayrshire. Successively lower intensities of inputs and outputs are found
in cattle and sheep production but, with the increasing economic pressure
on agriculture, even these systems are beginning to adopt more intensive
methods of management. In sheep farming, for example, winter housing
has been introduced, together with supplementary feeding of concentrates
during the winter and spring months, especially around lambing time.
     A wide variety of farming practices can be found within these broad
features. Dairy farmers in North Island, New Zealand, for example, benefit
from the growth of grass all year; there is no need for energy-intensive grass

▲ *A modern milking parlour*

conservation or winter housing for the stock. In beef and sheep production, some farms breed, rear and fatten stock, for example in the Welsh borderland of the United Kingdom, whereas only one or two of the three stages of livestock production are practised elsewhere. To give one example: the permanent pastures of south-east Leicestershire have been used traditionally to fatten, but not breed or rear, beef cattle and sheep.

To some degree, all intensive grassland systems are supported by state farm policies. The farming system employs a relatively large number of farmers and hired workers, but its products tend to be in over-supply on domestic and world markets. So as to yield a socially acceptable farm income, most states offer price supports and market intervention for products such as milk, beef and sheepmeat. The milk quota scheme operated under the Common Agricultural Policy of the European Community is a recent but typical example of such state intervention.

4.6   *Intensive livestock farming systems*

Intensive livestock farming is among the most regulated of the agroecosystems, and comparable with intensive horticultural production under glass. The system has been applied to a number of livestock products including stall-fed veal, feed-lot beef and zero-grazed dairy cows. However, the term 'intensive livestock' is most commonly applied to the production of pigs and poultry.

There are a number of distinctive features in the farming system. Firstly, the stock are housed in buildings with closely regulated temperature and lighting conditions. Poultry and pigs are kept at high densities in cages and pens respectively, with feeding, watering, egg collection and slurry removal carried out by mechanical means. Economies of scale are obtained through the large number of stock handled by each production unit, and not surprisingly the system is widely described as 'factory farming'. These

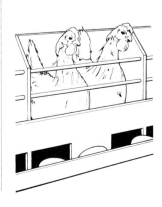

▲ *Intensive livestock rearing, in this case for veal. High inputs of energy are needed to maintain a controlled environment, but a high value output is produced.*

farming practices have attracted increasing criticism from the aspect of animal welfare, while the food health standards of beef and poultry products have also been questioned.

Secondly, intensive livestock farming is primarily a method of converting cereals into a food product such as bacon, pork, eggs and poultrymeat. The feed conversion efficiency of the livestock determines the profitability of the enterprise. In a sense, therefore, land is incidental as cereals are usually purchased as the output of another farming system. Since a significant proportion of the cereal inputs come from third world countries, the 'land' supporting intensive livestock farming is international in its distribution.

Thirdly, rather than having a large number of independent family-owned farms, intensive livestock farming is concentrated into a small number of very large agribusinesses in which vertical integration is commonplace, with feed mills, egg hatcheries, production units and processing plants all placed under one ownership.

Fourthly, compared with other systems, intensive livestock farming is characterised by the absence of state regulation. Of course, there are exceptions to this generalisation. The increasing incidence of salmonella has led to the compulsory testing of poultry in this country. In Canada the poultry sector functions under supply management (i.e. production quotas), but across the international border, in the United States, the market is not regulated. As a result, the family structure of poultry production has been retained in Canada, whereas agribusinesses are dominant in the United States.

As with intensive grassland farming systems, the main environmental problem associated with intensive livestock systems is the disposal of animal effluents. When intensive farming units are dispersed amongst other farming systems, the effluents (slurry and manure) can provide useful sources of nitrogen, phosphorus and potassium when spread on neighbouring farmland. But when large numbers of such units are

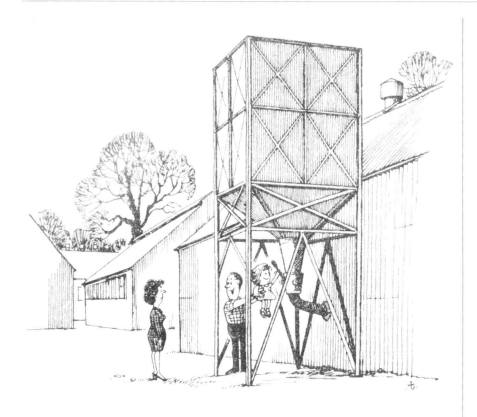

'She loves feeding the animals'

concentrated in a relatively small area, for example, in northern parts of
Brittany (France), the Po Valley (Italy) and East and West Flanders,
including the Kempen area (Belgium), disposal of the effluent creates
environmental hazards in terms of ground and surface water pollution and
soil toxicity.

4.7 Summary

This chapter has discussed only a few of the very many farming systems
found in temperate agriculture. Nevertheless, the case studies reveal
differences in the internal structure of the systems and the varying extent to
which the agroecosystem is manipulated. This understanding should now
lead us to approach generalisation about temperate agriculture with some
caution, although the farming systems tend to have one feature in common:
a dependency on energy inputs purchased off the farm. Nevertheless, the
farming systems vary in the efficiency with which that energy is converted
into useful food products, intensive livestock farming being relatively
inefficient in this respect. The discussion has also identified some of the
environmental effects of the different farming systems, together with the
need to place each system along a continuum of low–high impacts. The next
section takes an even more detailed view of these agriculture–environment
relationships by focusing on just two types of agriculture in the United
Kingdom: hill sheep and cereal farming.

5   The environmental impact of temperate agriculture

5.1   Introduction

Concern over the damaging environmental consequences of modernised –
some would say industrialised – agricultural systems was first expressed in
the United States as part of the evolving environmental movement. Rachel
Carson's *Silent Spring* (1963) was amongst the first popular expressions of
anxiety over the damaging impact of pesticide residues on the ecosystem, an
anxiety that later spread to fertilisers, farm effluent, soil erosion and the loss
of habitats. Transferred to a British context, official concern was expressed
as early as 1970 about the impact of modern farming on soil structure, and
later on the wider environment, while the environmental debate was given a
higher profile in agricultural circles following Marion Shoard's book, *Theft of
the Countryside* (1980), and debate on the 1981 Wildlife and Countryside Act.
Today 'agriculture and the environment' is high on the political agenda in
most countries. Indeed a considerable literature has been developed around
the topic which we can deal with here in only a partial way. Rather than
attempt a summary, attention is focused on two farming systems in the
United Kingdom that lie at each end of the environmental impact
continuum. Hill sheep farming has been selected to represent a relatively
'low impact' system, while intensive cereal growing acts as an example of
'high impact' farming.

5.2   Hill sheep farming in the United Kingdom

With upland areas accounting for approximately 40% of Britain (7.7 million
hectares), the land resource occupied by hill farming has considerable
ecological significance. In particular, the moors and heaths of the uplands
act as a refuge for many threatened species of flora and fauna, including
several rare species such as the red kite. Three main environmental impacts
can be identified: moorland reclamation, grassland species composition and
bracken incursion. In the wider perspective it can be argued that none of
these impacts is particularly severe; nevertheless, all three have the effect of
reducing both the diversity of natural and semi-natural habitats and the
visual amenity (landscape value) of hill and mountain areas.

   Moorlands and heathlands in Scotland, Wales, the Pennines, North
York Moors, Dartmoor and Exmoor were largely created by woodland
clearance. Contemporary improvement, commonly known as *moorland
reclamation*, therefore, continues a historic trend by bringing such land into
cultivation. In some cases the pre-existing vegetation (for example *Calluna*,
Vaccinium and *Pteridium* species) can be cleared by light surface cultivation,
burning or spraying with herbicides; the soil can then be prepared by
applying lime and chemical fertilisers, followed by the sowing of preferred
grass species such as ryegrass, meadow grass and clover. Where soil
conditions are very wet, however, deep ploughing and drainage may be
necessary before surface cultivation can commence. Quite marked
reductions in the area of moors and heaths have been recorded in the 1950s

and 1960s in regions with hill sheep farming. On Exmoor, for example, over 4000 ha of moorland (17% of the total area) were reclaimed between 1947 and 1979, while similar figures have been recorded for the North York Moors between 1950 and 1963 and the Brecon Beacons from 1948 to 1975. Most reclamation and enclosure occurs on the fringes of the open moors and heaths, and considerable areas are secondary reclamations of land that fell out of cultivation in the early part of this century, especially during the 1930s. Much upland remains under threat from any further intensification of hill farming.

The motives for land reclamation are relatively straightforward. As hill sheep farms have come under economic pressure, so their owners have attempted to raise farm output by increasing the number of hill ewes and cattle. Reclaiming hill pastures raises the carrying capacity of a farm and enables more stock to be fed. But the high capital costs of moorland reclamation, when faced by the relatively low prices of lambs and cattle for fattening, render the practice economically marginal. Consequently, successive governments in the United Kingdom have provided both grant aid to farmers per hectare of reclaimed land, and support for their incomes by headage payments on cattle and sheep. Although the grant aid has now been discontinued, the headage payments remain as Hill Land Compensatory Allowances (HLCA) under the Common Agricultural Policy. By 1986 these had increased in value up to £62.48 per hill cow and £7.33 per hill ewe. All the hill and upland areas of the United Kingdom are now eligible for these direct income supplements under the European Community's Less Favoured Areas Directive (see Figure 5.1).

The ecological effects of reclamation are disputed. On the one hand, reclamation clearly changes the character and composition of upland vegetation from heather and coarse-grass species – cotton grass, bent-grass, purple moor-grass – to agricultural grasses. In addition the diversity of habitats is reduced, while the buffer zone between intensive agriculture and open moorland is removed. Such changes impinge on the animal species which are dependent on the moorland habitat for food, cover and nesting ground. But other research has shown that drainage, fertilisers and fencing can increase rather than decrease populations of insects, wood mice, pygmy shrew and field voles, as well as their predators – foxes and owls. Consequently the ploughing and fencing of open moorland continues to be a contentious issue, with Exmoor providing a particular cause célèbre. A long-running battle has been fought between conservation and farming interests, with origins that can be traced back to the 1960s. A formal enquiry was held in the early 1970s, under Lord Porchester, to investigate the problems surrounding moorland reclamation; it resulted in financial compensation for some of the land-owners who gave up their plans to plough the moorland in exchange for management agreements. These financially expensive arrangements were later formalised under the 1981 Wildlife and Countryside Act and have served to preserve limited areas of moorland with high ecological and amenity value. Nevertheless, the remaining area of moorland is now fragmented and vulnerable to further piecemeal reclamation on a farm-by-farm basis, especially in the dark areas shown in Figure 4.12. (See Plate 9.)

Turning now to the second major environmental impact, *species composition*, the activities of burning and grazing have considerable impacts on the species found in upland pastures. Heather burning is carried out mainly in the interest of grouse for gameshooting as discussed by *Silvertown* (1990, Section 4.2). Figure 4.13 summarises the successional transitions that occur in moorland habitats under different burning and grazing regimes.

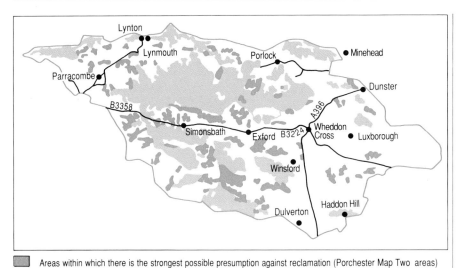

◁ *Figure 4.12*
Exmoor moorland, 1980.

Areas within which there is the strongest possible presumption against reclamation (Porchester Map Two areas)

Other areas of moor and heath (Porchester Map One areas not included in Map Two)

Non-moorland areas

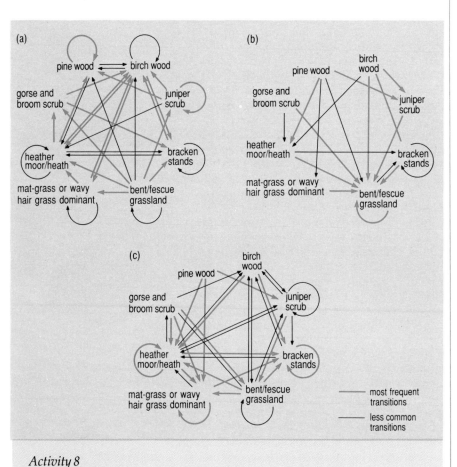

◁ *Figure 4.13*
Successional transitions
between common types
of semi-natural vegetation
under different grazing
pressures on well-drained,
acid mineral soils.
(a) Low grazing pressures
(<1 sheep equivalent per
hectare per year).
(b) High grazing pressures
(>2–3 sheep equivalent per
hectare per year).
(c) Intermediate levels of
grazing (1–2 sheep
equivalent per hectare
per year).

Activity 8

Examine Figure 4.13 and answer the following questions.

Q   What effects do high grazing pressures and frequent burning have on the transition between vegetation types?

A   With the exception of bracken stands, all types of vegetation are succeeded by bent/fescue grassland which eventually becomes dominant. Burning and grazing together prevent regeneration of a species-rich habitat.

Q   What are the main differences in the successional transition between low grazing pressure without burning and intermediate levels of grazing and burning?

A   Low grazing pressure without burning allows pine and birch wood to regenerate, bracken is less dominant, and there are more frequent transitions from mat-grass and bent/fescue grasslands to juniper scrub and birch-wood habitats. Intermediate pressure prevents woodland regeneration and encourages a variety of types including heather, bracken and mixed grasses.

Research has revealed the differential impact on species composition of treating moor-grass-dominated grassland with lime and chemical fertilisers. Under rotational grazing, but after only five years, lime-treated grassland becomes dominated by sheep's fescue, whereas fertiliser-treated land has mainly bent-grasses. Thus, in the case of hill sheep, moderate densities tend to enhance species diversity, while low and high grazing pressure reduce diversity. With no effective upper limit (up to 6 ewes per hectare) on the number of sheep for which HLCA can be paid, there are periodic claims of over-grazing through 'farming for the subsidy'. But while sheep numbers have undoubtedly increased over the last decade (see Table 4.9), there is no consistent evidence of over-grazing.

Table 4.9 also indicates the extent to which beef cattle have declined in importance within the upland farming system. This change in farming practice is thought to be one of the main reasons for the extension of bracken (*Pteridium aquilinum*) into both grassland and heathland. Cattle graze less selectively than sheep, although their trampling effect is thought to be the main mechanism for suppressing the growth of bracken. In addition,

Table 4.9   Changes in breeding ewes and beef cows in Wales, 1974–86

County	Rough grazing as % of total agricultural land	Ewes			Beef cows		
		1974	1986	Change %	1974	1986	Change %
Clwyd	23	452 289	622 078	37.5	23 328	15 803	−32
Dyfed	18	596 911	860 415	44	52 304	38 291	−27
Gwent	16	159 725	200 516	26	10 016	6 981	−30
Gwynedd	48	716 293	926 011	29	41 753	29 107	−30
Mid Glamorgan	40	141 628	170 412	20	8 856	6 404	−28
Powys	38	1 252 806	1 640 040	31	84 456	67 658	−20
South Glamorgan	4	1 946	26 479	1260	1 885	1 510	−20
West Glamorgan	40	6 212	83 529	1245	6 256	4 963	−21
Wales (total)	31	3 401 238	4 529 480	33	228 854	170 717	−25

Source: Welsh Agricultural Statistics, 1974 and 1986.

bracken is no longer cut to the same extent as in the past for livestock bedding. Taylor (1980) has estimated an annual rate of expansion of bracken in Wales of 2072 ha between 1936 and 1966, and 10 360 ha for the United Kingdom. Ecologically, bracken suppresses other plants and tends to grow in association with a limited range of shade-tolerant species. There is also some evidence that bracken acts as a carcinogen in livestock, with a similar effect on humans who consume their milk and dairy products over a long period of time.

5.3   *Intensive cereal farming in the United Kingdom*

The environmental impact of intensive cereal farming can be usefully examined under five headings: field size, chemical pollution, soil structure, pesticides/herbicides and habitat destruction.

The economics of agriculture have moved in favour of farm machinery which requires large fields for maximum operating efficiency. Increases in *field size* reduce the time spent turning machinery at rows ends, raise the speed of equipment across the land and enable wider implements to be employed. The result has been the removal of small woods and hedgerows, a trend particularly evident in the intensive cereal-growing areas of eastern England where hedges are no longer needed to control livestock. In addition, farmers have been relieved of the costs of trimming and managing woodland and hedgerows, while small gains have been made in the area of productive farmland. Concern about the rate of hedgerow removal began to be expressed in the 1970s, although most studies have shown that the highest rates of removal occurred in the 1960s. Between 1945 and 1970, for example, hedgerows were destroyed at a national average rate of 8000 km a year, with rates possibly ten times above the national average in cereal-growing areas. Since the 1960s the rates of hedgerow removal appear to have fallen back to more acceptable but still ecologically damaging levels.

The removal of woods and hedges has three important environmental impacts. First, it reduces habitat diversity. Work by the Nature Conservancy Council has clearly demonstrated a marked reduction in the number of mammals, birds and Lepidoptera in areas where hedges have been removed or replaced by wire fences. The felling of woodland reduces roosting and nesting sites for birds and small mammals, while the removal of hedgerows destroys the habitat corridor that links those sites with foraging areas in the fields. Secondly, hedgerow removal detracts from the visual amenity of the landscape by destroying a characteristic element of the traditional British countryside. Thirdly, a number of studies have shown that wind erosion of the soil is more prevalent in those areas where hedgerows have been removed. Wind velocity is reduced leeward of a hedgerow in proportion to its height and density.

Turning now to *chemical pollution*, we have seen already that the application of fertilisers represents a significant modification of the agroecosystem. Unfortunately, not all of the fertiliser is taken up by the field crops in intensive cereal cultivation: the excess is leached from the soil, especially by winter rainfall, and ultimately enters the water courses, including ponds and lakes. The accumulation of nitrates and phosphates in water bodies creates algal blooms and eutrophication and leads to the collapse of the ecosystem. Figure 4.14 shows the problem to be most severe in central and eastern England, with the Broads of Norfolk and Suffolk being particularly adversely affected. It should be noted, however, that some of the pollution is also caused by sewage outfalls. A rising level of nutrients in

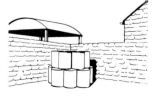

Farmers have been responsible for removing thousands of kilometres of hedgerows, changing the landscape and affecting the ecology of the countryside.

groundwater vulnerable to nitrate contamination

Figure 4.14
The impact of agrochemicals on the environment: fertilisers.

the Broads over the last thirty years has been related to the progressive decline of reed-swamp and the reversion to open water. Under anaerobic water conditions, the plants appear to be susceptible to root damage, while the number of freshwater fish and amphibians has been similarly depleted. In addition, rising nitrate levels have been recorded in groundwater supplies, thereby posing a hazard for human drinking-water.

The impact of arable farming on *soil structure* is also well documented with many researchers concluding that continuous cereal growing can lead to structural damage. The decline in structural stability and macroporosity of the soil can be relatively rapid, a process that is exacerbated by the loss of decomposable organic compounds through crop removal and the burning of cereal stubble. Compaction of the soil surface by machinery can also be

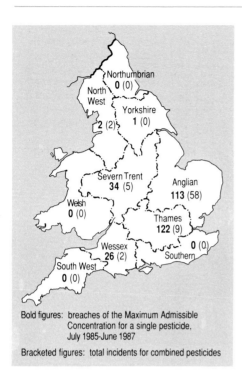

◀ *Figure 4.15*
The impact of agrochemicals on
the environment: pesticides.

Northumbrian
0 (0)
North
West
Yorkshire
2 (2)   **1** (0)

Severn Trent
34 (5)   Anglian
113 (58)
Welsh
0 (0)
Thames
122 (9)
Wessex   **0** (0)
26 (2)   Southern
South West
0 (0)

Bold figures: breaches of the Maximum Admissible
Concentration for a single pesticide,
July 1985-June 1987

Bracketed figures: total incidents for combined pesticides

problematic when tillage takes place under unsuitable soil moisture
conditions. Some researchers point out that, with so many separate machine
operations under cereal farming, the compaction of soil over large parts of
any field is almost inevitable. However, the impact of changes in soil
structure on crop yields, especially through compaction, is difficult to
detect, although it has been of continuing concern over the last two decades.

Fourthly, inorganic *pesticides and herbicides* have played a large part in
modern agriculture. They vary in toxicity, specificity and persistence.
Ideally pesticides should be effective against specific organisms without
having damaging effects on other insects and micro-organisms.
Unfortunately too many of the early pesticides were broad-spectrum
poisons that killed pest and predator insect alike and many were persistent.
More recent organophosphate pesticides are less persistent but more toxic
and specific. Nevertheless, there is growing concern over the side-effects of
toxic residues in human food, while resistances in insect populations require
ever more powerful pesticides. The incorrect application of sprays can also
be problematic, with wind-drift taking toxic chemicals onto adjacent and
unsuitable crops and ecosystems, as well as areas of human settlement. The
use of herbicides to kill weeds in cereal crops is open to the same objections.
More recently, evidence has emerged on the presence of pesticide residues
in drinking-water. Figure 4.15 shows that reported breaches of Maximum
Admissible Concentrations are greatest in the vegetable- and cereal-growing
areas of eastern England.

Finally, lowland *habitats* have not been immune from the processes of
'reclamation' and 'improvement' that we identified in the uplands in
relation to moors and heaths. In the lowland, associated mainly with
intensive cereal farming, woodland and wetland habitats have been
destroyed over the last three decades, the scale of which has only recently
been quantified by bodies such as the Institute for Terrestrial Ecology and

◄   *The Halvergate Marshes: arable farming or intensively managed grass required a lower water table so large ditches were dug in an 'improvement scheme'. However, objections to this led to the Broads Grazing Marsh Conservation Scheme in 1985, a blueprint for the idea of Environmentally Sensitive Areas announced in 1987.*

the Nature Conservancy Council. Their research for the United Kingdom has revealed 40% losses of lowland heaths, 50% losses of lowland fens and up to 50% losses of ancient lowland woods. Rates of loss tend to be most severe in southern and eastern England, with less damage in western and northern regions of the United Kingdom. Just as moorland reclamation on Exmoor became a major issue in the late 1970s, so the wetlands of the Halvergate Marshes assumed a similar role in relation to lowland cereal production in the early 1980s. The marshes, forming a 3000 ha triangle of land between the Lower Bure and Yare rivers in eastern Norfolk, in the heart of the Broads, yield a fertile soil when drained, and this potential became increasingly attractive to the land-owners under the cereal price support system of the Common Agricultural Policy. There was a complex and protracted conflict between the land-owners, conservation pressure groups,

Countryside Commission and Nature Conservancy Council (O'Riordan, 1986) but, as in the Exmoor case, the final outcome yielded the loss of some habitat, on this occasion to draining and ploughing for cereals, while other areas became protected by management agreements and financial subsidies to land-owners to continue traditional livestock grazing (The Broads Grazing Marsh Conservation Scheme).

5.4   Summary

The two cases have underlined the varying environmental impacts of temperate agriculture and caution us against making generalisations on temperate farming systems. In the case of hill sheep farming, stocking densities have been shown to be the critical factor in habitat modification, as well as for the economic well-being of the farming community. In reviewing the evidence on environmental impact we may conclude that the hill sheep farming system in Britain maintains rather than damages the ecological diversity of the upland areas. Indeed other non-farm uses of hill areas appear to have a greater environmental impact, for example forestry, water catchment and the recreational use of hill land. Moreover, in an era of falling profitability for agriculture, including the withdrawal of state subsidies, the alternative uses of hill land are likely to assume a more prominent role, including their impact on the upland environment.

Intensive cereal farming lies at the other extreme of the environmental impact continuum in Britain. The farming system demonstrates a wide range of environmental consequences, many of them undesirable. While the landscape impact is the most dramatic visually, the more insidious consequences of nitrate and agrochemical pollution probably pose greater threats to the long-term stability of the agroecoststem.

6   Conclusion

There is nothing inevitable or beyond influence in the environmental impacts that have been identified: farming systems throughout the world can be developed that are more sensitive to the environment. What determines developments are the economic conditions of agriculture, the structure of state policies on farming, and ultimately the attitudes and behaviour of those who own and farm the land. Of these features, we must recognise the central role played by the state in:

● financing the type of research and development that has produced the new, high output farming technology.

● supplying the price incentives to farmers to adopt that technology

● ultimately failing to adapt farm policies once it became clear that modern farming was having undesirable environmental impacts.

However, individual farmers must also accept a share of the responsibility. Their profit-maximising behaviour, albeit encouraged through subsidies by governments in many countries, has yielded products surplus to domestic demand, at a cost above that prevailing on world markets, and with environmental consequences the scale of which we are only now beginning to appreciate.

Of course, not all impacts yield the same level of severity for the environment. Establishing that level, however, is fraught with difficulty. On the one hand are value judgements on the nature and quality of landscape, and the importance of preserving different types of habitat, including the diversity of flora and fauna. On the other hand there are scientific judgements on the damage to human health of polluting water and food with agrochemicals, including fertilisers. Opinion is by no means unanimous on where the critical levels of pollution lie. But recent years have seen the weight of opinion slowly turning against the excesses of a modernised, industrialised temperate agriculture and remedial policies and developments are slowly taking shape.

A wide range of policy options is available to limit the damaging consequences of modern agriculture and these are discussed in more detail in the next chapter. One option of current interest, however, is low input-output farming, of which organic farming is a variety. This new agriculture would recreate the diversity of natural ecosystems by integrating crops and livestock, would maintain varied crop rotations, eliminate the use of agrochemicals and limit the use of fossil fuels. Critics doubt if such an agriculture could produce the volume of food necessary to feed the urban population, but supporters argue that if the same quantity of research money is expended on low input-output farming as has been committed to intensive agriculture, then such problems would be overcome. To date governments have avoided direct involvement with these issues, but intervention to promote low input-output farming could be the next phase of agricultural policy-making.

As matters stand, however, and looking just at the United Kingdom, the actual approach being applied is to persuade farmers to adopt voluntarily a more sympathetic attitude to the enviroment by planting woodland, caring for hedgerows, reducing the use of agrochemicals, managing ponds and wetlands for their habitats, and continuing traditional farming practices where they contribute to the maintenance of favoured landscapes and habitats. Financial subsidies from the state are available to promote these practices, backed up by the zoning of selected areas for special protection like the Environmentally Sensitive Areas. Overall, though, a voluntary rather than mandatory approach is being taken to resolve the agriculture–environment conflict.

Turning back finally to the world scene where this chapter began, temperate agriculture cannot be divorced in its impact from farming systems in developing countries. On the one hand, the surpluses generated by temperate agriculture provide the food aid that increasingly underpins the supply of agricultural products in many third world countries. This applies both to emergency situations, for example the droughts which periodically afflict parts of Africa, as well as annual food imports. From the perspective of many developing countries, the continuation of food surpluses in temperate agriculture has a higher priority than the resolution of the environmental impacts we have been discussing. On the other hand, the protective farm policies in temperate agriculture exclude some of the agricultural exports of other third world countries – although not animal feeds and oilseeds – and so contribute to their economic problems. As noted in the opening paragraph to this chapter, temperate agriculture probably exemplifies, as well as any other human activity, the conflict between maintaining economic well-being and the quality of the natural environment.

References

BAYLISS-SMITH, T. P. (1982) *The Ecology of Agricultural Systems*, Cambridge, Cambridge University Press.

BOWLER, I. R. (1979) *Government and Agriculture: a spatial perspective*, London, Longman.

CARSON, R. (1963) *Silent Spring*, London, Hamish Hamilton.

DOREL, G. (1987) 'High-tech farming systems in Champagne, France: change in response to agribusiness and international controls', in Turner, B. L. and Brush, S. B. (eds), pp. 405–23.

DUCKHAM, A. N. and MASEFIELD, G. B. (1971) *Farming Systems of the World*, London, Chatto and Windus.

O'RIORDAN, T. (1986) 'Moorland preservation in Exmoor' and 'Ploughing into the Halvergate marshes', pp. 191–208 and 265–99 in Lowe, P. *et al.*, *Countryside Conflicts*, Aldershot, Gower.

PIMENTEL, D. and PIMENTEL, M. (1979) *Food, Energy and Society*, London, Edward Arnold.

SHOARD, M. (1980) *The Theft of the Countryside*, London, Temple Smith.

SILVERTOWN, J. (1990) 'Inhabitants of the biosphere', Ch. 3 in Silvertown, J. and Sarre, P. (eds) *Environment and Society*, London, Hodder and Stoughton/The Open University (Book One of this series).

SIMMONS, I. G. (1989) *Changing Face of the Earth: culture, environment, history*, Oxford,

SPATH, H. J. (1987) 'Dryland wheat farming in the Central Great Plains', in Turner, B. L. and Brush, S. B. (eds), pp. 313–44.

TAYLOR, J. A. (1980) 'Bracken – an increasing problem and a threat to health', *Outlook on Agriculture*, Vol. 10, pp. 290–304.

TURNER, B. L. and BRUSH, S. B. (eds) *Comparative Farming Systems*, New York, Guildford Press.

Further reading

HAINES, M. (1982) *Introduction to Farming Systems*, London, Longman.

SIMMONS, I. G. (1980) 'Ecological-functional approaches to agriculture in geographical contexts', *Geography*, Vol. 65, pp. 305–16.

WOLMAN, M. G. and FOURNIER, F. G. (eds) (1987) *Land Transformation in Agriculture*, Chichester, John Wiley.

1   Introduction

This chapter examines the principal competing demands on the countryside of the United Kingdom and their environmental impacts. It does so for two related reasons. First, the use of rural land became an urgent issue of practical politics in the 1980s as the perceived need for agricultural production diminished and the way was opened for other uses. This issue has also arisen in other European countries and in the United States. Second, policy debates about the use of rural land have had to recognise that separate policies for different sectors – agriculture, forestry, industry and so on – have often failed because of the interaction between sectors. This problem has been a difficult one when only balancing economic motives with social aims; it has become even more complex now that environmental criteria are also being seriously considered. Nevertheless, there have been some attempts at integrated rural management and these are worth evaluating as possible guides to policy improvements in future.

2   The ascendancy of agricultural interests

For most of the post-war period, agriculture has enjoyed a special status as the favoured use of rural land and the most subsidised sector of the economy. This raises two questions: how was this special status achieved, and why has it now come under question? These questions are answered in the next two subsections.

2.1   A forty-year perspective

To provide answers to these questions, it is necessary to go back to the Second World War. Then, after a period of agricultural depression which had existed for most of the inter-war years, a coalition government, committed to the maximum output from home farming, decided to address the likely shape of agriculture once peace returned. A committee under Lord Justice Scott was set up for this purpose and it ultimately put forward plans that were to set agriculture firmly in an expansionist phase.

    The Report of the Scott Committee made recommendations that formed the basis of the 1947 Agriculture Act. This Act guaranteed markets for farmers, a stable and efficient industry, home production levels which would ensure food supplies for national needs, and reasonable incomes to farmers through a system of guaranteed commodity prices. The philosophy contained in this legislation manifested itself through two powerful policy mechanisms. Firstly, a series of financial incentives was made available to improve the infrastructure of farms to allow them to become more 'efficient'. Secondly, to protect these farmers while structural improvements – such as land drainage, field and farm amalgamation schemes, and new and/or improved buildings – were taking place, prices would be supported to allow a reasonable income to farmers. The burden of price support was not to fall on the consumer, but would be paid for from the Exchequer.

During the 1950s and 1960s, however, dependence on price supports grew so that by the time the United Kingdom joined the European Economic Community in 1972, what had been planned as a short-term measure had become the overwhelming proportion of support payments to agriculture. Grants for structural improvements were costing the government only a quarter of that spent on keeping domestic agricultural prices way above those of the world market, mainly through price support.

Throughout this expansionist phase it should be remembered that agricultural interests were not merely the passive beneficiaries of policies which happened to suit government. Under the terms of the 1947 Agricultural Act farmers had been given a seat at the table for the annual negotiation of commodity prices through the National Farmers' Union (NFU). By this alone they had become 'insiders' insofar as they not only had direct access to the Minister of Agriculture, but through him, to Cabinet. The NFU became an increasingly powerful lobby, assisted by the fact that successive governments were well stocked with farmers or land-owners with a vested interest in state support for agriculture. Not only did the NFU have the financial clout which enabled it to put over to local and national politicians a point of view which favoured the continuance of a high level of government assistance, but it also employed full-time liaison officers in the House of Commons and serviced an all-party committee on agriculture. Its public relations department became second to none, issuing thousands of press releases and, in the early 1980s, claiming that over thirty hours of broadcasting each week was devoted to information provided by it. It is not surprising that one commentator concluded in 1980 that 'in the post-war history of agriculture, it is not only the government of the day, but the NFU which has been responsible for guiding and shaping the destiny of British farmers.'

As agriculture in the United Kingdom became subject to the European Common Agricultural Policy (CAP), the structure of agricultural assistance changed little, although the consumer came to bear a much greater proportion of the direct costs of food production through prices in the shops rather than Exchequer support. Commodity prices were now set annually in Brussels, with differential support for farm products. This increasingly led in the direction of monoculture as farmers tended to concentrate on the most profitable products. Structural support was provided through European Directives or policy instructions to member countries. The most important of these covered farm modernisation, early retirement and socio-economic advice. A fourth directive on 'Less Favoured Areas' applied where remoteness, altitude or otherwise poor agricultural conditions posed a problem for farmers (see Figure 5.1).

By the late 1970s the CAP had attracted wide and popular criticism on three main fronts. First, it was hugely expensive, costing at its peak over 75% of the whole European Community budget. For the United Kingdom

Figure 5.1   Less Favoured Areas.
The Less Favoured Areas Directive, introduced in 1945, was extended in 1984 so that it covers 53% of the United Kingdom. Apart from providing more favourable support for agriculture, these areas are now eligible for special assistance for the development of tourism and craft industries.

alone farm support amounted to more than £1100 million by 1980 with support prices averaging 30% of farm incomes. Secondly, it was producing massive food surpluses; butter, beef and cereals 'mountains', wine 'lakes' and so on became accepted European jargon. The third criticism was that all of this very expensive over-production was having a disastrous impact on the environment, an aspect of central concern to this chapter.

Activity 1

Go back over Section 2.1 and make a list of the main economic and political factors that have contributed to the post-war prosperity of agriculture.

2.2   Environmental impacts of agriculture

The Scott Committee had noted that inter-war agricultural depression had led to much rural dereliction and assumed that a more prosperous agriculture would produce a more attractive landscape. Unfortunately, the structural supports offered to farmers provided incentives to remove features such as hedges and marshland. At that time the Committee were not able to foresee the impacts that large-scale mechanisation and the intensive use of chemicals were to have.

After the United Kingdom joined the EEC it became more profitable to produce cereals than livestock. Grants available for farm modernisation and structural change allowed farmers to claim 50% of the costs of drainage and ploughing. As a result, large areas of former grassland and smaller areas of woodland, marshland and heath were converted to intensive cereal production.

Activity 2

Re-read Chapter 4, Section 5.3 to revise the principal environmental impacts of intensive cereal production.

Q   Can you, from your own observation, think of at least one other major impact *not* mentioned in Chapter 4?

A   Certainly another important impact on the rural landscape resulting from changing agricultural practices concerns the visual effect of new farm buildings.

Farm capital grants have encouraged the erection of large farm structures, further enabling the intensification trend of modern farming in livestock rearing as well as cereal farming. Increased production generally has enhanced the demand for a variety of buildings for storage, for example large silage towers and pits, grain silos and barns. The greater use of ever larger machinery requires larger buildings to house them and has made older barns redundant.

As well as increases in the size and number of buildings, there has also been a considerable change in the style of their construction. Buildings represent the largest element of fixed capital on the farm and it is therefore a rational decision to make them as cheap as possible. This has led to an increase in the standardisation and mass production of buildings, with two significant results. Firstly, buildings tend to be larger and more uniform across the countryside and, secondly, they make less use of local materials and traditional vernacular building styles and so are more out of character with the local landscape. But unless such buildings have been constructed within 366 metres of a road, as with all other forms of change in the countryside motivated by agriculture, no planning consent from the local authority has been needed. Indeed, the exemption of agriculture from the provisions of the 1947 Town and Country Planning Act has allowed farmers a freedom to do what they liked with their land not enjoyed by other industrial sectors or members of the community. Finally, where buildings are concerned, farmers have also not been subject to local rates. The incentive has been therefore to put up large new low-cost buildings rather than to repair and adapt the old.

'Nobody will ever build on this land while I'm farming it.'

Most of these environmental impacts have been concentrated in the south and east of England, though they have occurred to a lesser extent everywhere. They amount to a radical change in the visual quality of the landscape, a sharp reduction in the area and diversity of habitats for wildlife and increasingly pose a threat of chemical pollution of food and water. Given these environmental costs, it is particularly sad that agricultural policy has been far from an economic success.

2.3   A declining rural economy

The gross economic inefficiency of agricultural support in the UK has already been hinted at in this chapter. It is this kind of economic impoverishment by agriculture that catches the public eye – consumer food prices are high, surplus agricultural commodities cost hundreds of millions of pounds to store, and the vulnerability of both price and structural support mechanisms to abuse is considerable. In the view of many economic analysts, such a situation is an inevitable consequence of an industry maintained in hothouse conditions and fuelled by public money, but outside the disciplines of market forces. This system of support has led not only to problems for the rural environment, but also to considerable problems in the rural economy itself.

In order to guarantee a reasonable income to farmers, the system of indirect supports through guaranteed prices to farmers was established. Generally, these prices are set so as to allow marginal farmers to stay in business, but invariably this means that farmers who are not marginal are able to earn quite considerable incomes. Indeed, until the late 1980s the City saw such farming prosperity, especially in the south and east of England where it was reflected in high land prices, as a sound investment proposition for pension and other long-term funds.

But what of the agricultural workers? Well, they have done particularly badly out of modern agricultural policy. This is because government grants have been made available for *capital inputs* to land drainage systems, farm machinery, fertilisers and so on, but never to *labour inputs* to agriculture. This has had the effect of making capital relatively much cheaper than labour and as a consequence has caused much labour to be shed and substituted by capital wherever possible. In 1981 there were nearly 100 000 fewer people working in agriculture than in 1971. Moreover, the Transport and General Workers Union has estimated that between 1985 and 1987 there had been a further drop of around 20% in the full-time agricultural labour force. Unfortunately for the farm workers, they have not benefited with corresponding higher wages, a factor which in itself has increased the drift from the land.

These kinds of labour losses have had repercussions in rural society as a whole. At one time, agriculture was the principal employer in the rural economy and many rural communities were dependent on agriculture for their livelihood. As the agricultural workforce has declined there has been a drift from the land and a resultant break-up of the local community in many areas. Tales of declining rural services, such as shops, transport, schools and health care, declining rural incomes, and in the more remote areas an ageing population, have provided the focus of rural community concern through the 1970s and the 1980s. The out-migration of agricultural labour over the last two decades has been counterbalanced in some rural areas by an influx of those who wish to live in the countryside but work in the towns, although their presence has only exacerbated the story of decline. For these are the people with their own transport, only too willing to use their cars to travel to group practice surgeries in the next village, or to shop at the nearest supermarket rather than in the village store. This has given a further twist to the downward spiral of provision of local transport and other local services, on which the less advantaged who live and may still work in the village must rely.

Thus the rural economy has experienced vast capital investment in agriculture and a considerable loss of labour, both effects of agricultural support policies. The workings of the rural economy are little understood, but despite the huge levels of subsidy going into agriculture it seems that the overall contribution of this particular sector to the local economy has been slim: even in agriculturally intensive areas such as rural East Anglia, farm output accounts for less than 10% of the region's Gross Domestic Product, and in more marginal areas, its contribution could be much less than this. Such large inputs of capital could certainly have been used much more efficiently in other sectors of the economy.

In distributional terms, agricultural support policies have thus often had an invidious effect. The huge financial support given to agriculture may provide a reasonable income to some farmers, but does nothing for other workers in the rural economy. This sets up artificial disparities in income in rural areas, where, despite farmers' earnings, wages even today remain well below those in urban areas. These distributional effects are at their worst in the remotest areas, where Less Favoured Area supplementary payments to farmers further emphasise the income differences between them and other workers in the local economy.

2.4   Summary

From the days of the Second World War the agricultural production imperative has spawned a very expensive industrialised sector in the countryside as the overwhelming and relatively unfettered land-user. The attainment of production goals has had its costs in the unfairness and inefficiency within the rural economy and in the quality of the rural landscape and ecosystem. The principal impacts on the rural landscape have been: the ploughing of permanent pasture; agricultural intensification which has been manifest in increased field size, the loss of hedgerows and a generally impoverished ecology; and a whole range of new industrial farm buildings. The causes of such tangible expressions of rural change can be found in the attitudes to agriculture of the first post-war government and its successors and those of the EC. However, of no small importance has been the effectiveness of the agricultural lobby with the general public, in Whitehall and in Brussels, thus maintaining a dominant role for agricultural support policies long after there was an objective rationale for them.

Activity 3

Before moving on to look in much more detail at other land-use interests in the countryside, much of Section 2 can be reviewed by answering the following question.

Q   Who have been the beneficiaries from the agricultural policies outlined here and who have been the losers? Make two lists and then compare yours with those given at the end of the chapter.

3   Conservation on an ebb tide

3.1   Amenity conservation and the countryside

Conservation, if it can be called a land use, has provided the sharpest 'on the ground' challenge to agriculture. Interestingly, policies for the conservation of the countryside found favour with the same wartime government that had been responsible for reconstructing national agricultural policy. Even in the nineteenth century there had been a wide range of conservation movements for the countryside, deriving from a number of intellectual origins, but very broadly speaking their parliamentary successes came in two distinct but related spheres – those of amenity conservation and scientific conservation (discussed in the next section).

Amenity conservationists had been essentially concerned with landscape conservation and for this reason, their objectives had been to ensure greater public access to the countryside. Organisations such as the National Trust, the (then) Commons, Open Spaces and Footpaths Preservation Society and the Council for National Parks did much to ensure that landscape conservation designations such as **National Parks** and Conservation Areas (later to be termed **Areas of Outstanding Natural Beauty (AONBs)**) were incorporated into the 1949 National Parks and Access to the Countryside Act. This was one of a series of laws that included the 1947 Agriculture and Town Planning Acts and indeed the 1946 New Towns Act, that were to provide the thrust for post-war reconstruction.

These land-use designations for amenity conservation were to offer the principal statutory means of protecting the landscape, but they applied only to England, Scotland and Wales. In Northern Ireland moves were made early on to parallel the British legislation, but nothing was done until the Amenity Lands Act, 1965. Even by the end of the 1980s, though, there were no National Parks, in this respect resembling Scotland. The situation in both countries has been perhaps a reflection of the less intense pressures on landscape, compared with England and Wales, as much as that of the powers of the large land-owners! However, the situation is changing with the question of National Parks back on the agenda in Scotland: a report is due from the Countryside Commission for Scotland in 1990. In Northern Ireland there are now eight AONBs, along with 38 in England and Wales, while Scotland has its own equivalent **Areas of Outstanding Scenic Interest (AOSIs)**. These remain the single common feature of landscape protection in all the countries of the United Kingdom, but they have always been without the more complex administrative arrangements afforded to National Parks. Indeed, over and above normal planning constraints, the designation of AONBs has remained little more than a recognition of a need to safeguard such areas.

In addition to National Parks and AONBs, the concept of **Heritage Coasts** was introduced in England and Wales in the 1970s with the same principal purpose – that of protecting high-value landscapes. But in their role of providing a framework for combined voluntary and local authority management of vulnerable coastal areas they were also to be non-statutory. By the 1980s these amenity conservation designations (shown in Figure 5.2), together with those for scientific conservation (which will be considered

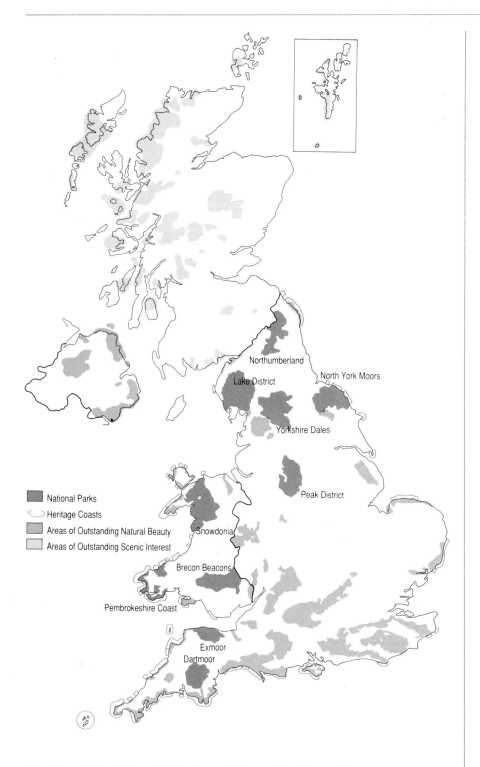

▲ Figure 5.2   National Parks, Areas of Outstanding Natural Beauty in England, Wales and Northern Ireland, Heritage Coasts in England and Wales and Areas of Outstanding Scenic Interest in Scotland, 1989. National Parks cover 13 600 km² or 9.5% of England and Wales; AONBs cover 19 287 km² or 12.8% of England and Wales, and 18% of Northern Ireland and AOSIs cover 13% of Scotland.

below), accounted for nearly a quarter of the total land area in England and Wales – a proportion that in itself can be considered a conservation success.

But how effective have these designations been at protecting the landscape, particularly against the increasing modernisation of agriculture already discussed? In truth, they have had substantial shortcomings in this regard. At the time of the 1949 Act, it was considered that most of the protection of National Parks and AONBs could be adequately carried out with the use of land-use planning control powers introduced in the 1947 Town and Country Planning Act. In effect, until the introduction of management plans in the 1970s and stronger legislation in the 1980s (which will be considered in Section 5) there was little more protection for the landscape in these areas than that provided by the normal development control functions of the local planning authority.

Most important in this respect, of course, was the fact that nearly all of the agriculture – and indeed forestry – was exempt from land-use planning controls, even in National Parks and AONBs, so that landscape protection was not made easier in these designated areas. Such voluntary measures as were introduced for farmers in these areas counted for nothing without financial support, because it was the financial incentives of agricultural policy that were the principal spur to agricultural landscape changes. There was thus one government department, now the Department of the Environment (though it has changed its name several times since the war), trying to conserve our more valued landscapes with very limited physical planning controls and another, the Ministry of Agriculture, Fisheries and Food (MAFF), indirectly dismantling the landscape in the ways outlined.

Ironically, most National Parks are in remoter upland areas which, by the 1970s, were precisely the areas designated by the EC as 'Less Favoured Areas' where livestock headage subsidies and grant aid above the norm was available for farm modernisation. For a time in the 1970s it was even possible to get improvement grants for farms on land that MAFF itself classed as unimprovable! The tide began to turn a little in the 1970s with much argument about the ploughing up of moorland in Exmoor National Park (as was mentioned in Chapter 4, Section 5.2). Between 1954, when the 68 632 hectares of Exmoor were designated, and 1975, 20% of its land was enclosed and subject to 'agricultural improvement'. This led to a government Report, produced by a committee chaired by Lord Porchester, which recommended stronger powers over agricultural activities in National Parks. These powers, which were eventually introduced for areas other than just National Parks, are considered more fully in Section 5.

As for AONBs, it is now commonly recognised that the landscape conservation powers relating to them have been and continue to be somewhat ineffectual. Research has indicated that even the development control function in AONBs is often little different from other areas and other efforts towards landscape conservation are very much at the whim of the constituent local authorities. Although at the end of the 1970s the Countryside Commission, the government's advisory body on landscape conservation and countryside recreation, was debating whether to abolish AONBs altogether, a committee which it had sponsored, chaired by Kenneth Himsworth, reported that the mere fact of their designation had at least helped in the proper ordering of priorities in them. On the strength of this comment, the Commission decided to continue with them and by the end of the 1980s the largest of them all – the North Pennines – was designated. Perhaps the prevailing view about AONB designation is best summed up by the Council for the Protection of Rural England: 'AONBs actually mean very little, but we're awfully glad that we've got them.'

Q   What have been the main weaknesses in terms of landscape
conservation in National Parks and AONBs in the thirty years following
their inception?

A   In both, agriculture and forestry were largely exempt from planning
control and there was no special protection exercised by the Department
of the Environment against the forces promoting agricultural
development through MAFF. If National Parks were designed
positively to promote conservation and enjoyment objectives inside
their administrative structures, for AONBs there were to be no such
arrangements – only a presumption in favour of landscape protection, a
factor which could merely be taken into account in any planning
decision.
    Many pressure groups wanted the 1949 Act to make it mandatory
for the land-use planning function of local authorities in a National Park
to be carried out by a single body known as a joint board, where the Park
covered more than one county. Although there were obvious
advantages in such a cohesive approach, in the end the joint board issue
was left to be decided locally. Only two such joint boards were formed –
for the Lake District and the Peak Park – and these National Parks have
proved to be the most successfully administered.

3.2   Scientific conservation and the countryside

If the amenity conservation provisions for the countryside since the War
have been widely considered to be less than fully effective, **scientific
conservation** had had some noted successes. The key to this was, initially at
least, in the use of the word 'science'. Pressure groups prior to the 1949 Act,
such as the British Correlating Committee representing a range of scientific
interest groups, and the Society for the Promotion of Nature Reserves,
gained much of their momentum from an increasing growth of and interest
in a new strand of the natural sciences in the twentieth century – **ecology**.
This study of complete natural systems, rather than just individual
components of them, led to calls for the conservation of the fauna and flora
of the countryside, and not just its landscape, for reasons of scientific

research. The scientific 'mystique' of this kind of conservation led to most of
the provisions for nature conservation passing through Parliament into the
1949 National Parks and Access to the Countryside Act with hardly any
discussion.

In part, scientific conservation – or **nature conservation**, as it is
commonly termed – was given stronger powers than amenity conservation
although they were to be applied over a much smaller area. The Nature
Conservancy (now Nature Conservancy Council) was to give scientific
advice on the control of fauna and flora and was to have a significant role in
the provision of a national research programme for nature conservation.
Importantly, though, it was also given powers for the purchase and
management of specific areas of land as nature reserves.

Thus, some of the more effective land-use designations, in terms of their
ability to resist agricultural intensification, were introduced – including
National Nature Reserves (NNRs). These were either managed under a
nature reserve agreement with the owner or owned by the Nature
Conservancy and were thus overwhelmingly disposed towards the
conservation and study of our countryside fauna and flora. Other nature
conservation designations also were instituted. Areas considered important
for nature conservation but not of the national significance of NNRs were
introduced as *local nature reserves*, set up by local authorities but managed by
wildlife trusts. More specific sites could be covered by a designation known as
a **Site of Special Scientific Interest**. This was essentially an area about which
the Nature Conservancy could notify the local planning authority of its
scientific worth in the context of development proposals. Again, however,
some of the most damaging operations in SSSIs were to come from agriculture
and forestry, where the local planning authority had little or no control. The
Nature Conservancy had to negotiate as best it could with the Forestry
Commission and the Ministry of Agriculture separately in order to have its
interests better respected.

In terms of land-use control, then, scientific conservationists were given
some quite effective powers in National Nature Reserves in which they have
been able to resist agricultural intensification quite well. Protection of local
nature reserves and SSSIs was less effective up to the beginning of the 1980s,
because their management and ultimately their ownership have required
that scientific conservation has been much more a matter of negotiation.
Indeed, at that time the Nature Conservancy Council reported that some
13% of SSSIs suffered damage to their wildlife interest each year. And
importantly for the competing demands for land in the countryside overall,
all these designations represent only pockets of land in a broader
countryside where the impoverishment of a rural ecology has been taking
place in the manner described in Section 2.3. But in the 1980s changes in
government policy have also shifted the land-use emphasis of scientific or
nature conservation. This is discussed further in Section 5.

3.3   Disparate views of the conservation purpose

Undoubtedly, the fact that agriculture dominated conservation as a
competing demand in the countryside was principally due to the drive to
increase food production aided by a powerful unified agricultural lobby. But
a number of commentators have suggested that the development of the
conservation movement for the countryside has in part been inhibited by the
fact that there are so many disparate views about how and why the
countryside should be conserved. These are often conflicting and as a result

their political force is weakened. Certainly conservation interests have not had any of the 'insider' influence of the kind enjoyed by the NFU and, unlike the farmers' lobby, they do not speak for any specific interest other than society at large.

It has already been mentioned that before 1949 countryside conservation was broadly split into the amenity and scientific camps. But even within these there was a broad spectrum of (overlapping) views. This situation has become even more complex in the years since the Second World War, and countryside conservation has been characterised by a wide range of different pressure groups all championing their own causes. The Council for the Preservation (now Protection) of Rural England, for example, has been concerned with both scientific and amenity conservation and it has been particularly effective, not so much in conservation management, but in political lobbying. The Royal Society for Nature Conservation, on the other hand, has developed an excellent voluntary management framework for scientific conservation in the countryside through the County Wildlife Trusts, but this has been at the expense of its political influence. The Royal Society for the Protection of Birds has a good political profile but has a conservation emphasis that is narrower than some. The National Trust is very much an 'establishment' pressure group, but its early interest in nature conservation was considered by many to be misdirected. Although the 1907 National Trust Act specified that it should acquire and manage sites of special interest to naturalists, it was slow at securing these and did so in a random fashion with little regard to their national importance. The Society for the Promotion of Nature Reserves was set up in 1913 precisely to rectify this omission. Although organisations such as these are quick to form affiliations in arguing a common cause for countryside conservation, their overall profile inevitably remains somewhat fragmented particularly when set against the lobbying powers of the agriculture industry.

The clarity of the countryside conservation purpose has been weakened further by the 'alternative life-styles' revolution of the 1970s which spawned more global environmental groups such as Friends of the Earth and Greenpeace, and the 'green' revolution of the 1980s which has seen environmental issues move to the top of the political agenda. Ironically, the growth in environmentalism that these developments have brought about has done little to raise the profile of countryside conservation, quite simply because very few politicians make any clear link between the conservation of the ozone layer and the diminution of the greenhouse effect on the one hand and the sustenance of the diversified countryside ecosystem on the other. For example, in 1989 at the same time as the government was backing a global reduction in the use of chlorofluorocarbons (CFCs) in refrigerators and so on, it was cutting the Nature Conservancy Council's budget in real terms and, somewhat contentiously, proposing to amalgamate it with the Countryside Commission in Wales and Scotland. These new arrangements would break the mould of forty years' experience relating to the separate existence of these bodies and their predecessors, although the government was now arguing in Part VII of its proposed Environmental Protection Bill for a more sensitive and accountable framework for conservation as it 'continues to rise in importance on the public agenda'. The new combined country agencies would be able, it said, to tailor the delivery of conservation more closely to regional and local needs. This was not how most of the major wildlife and conservation organisations saw it, however, and they expressed considerable reservations, not least because, in their view, the British Isles form a bio-geographical entity which is best served by a co-ordinated scientific approach. Such criticisms were only partly mollified by the decision in November 1989 to set up a joint committee which would handle matters of common interest in England, Scotland and Wales, including scientific standards, and the commissioning and support of research which transcends country boundaries.

Nevertheless, in spite of the claims by government during the progress of the Bill in both Houses of Parliament in 1990 that these proposals – like the 1949 Act – were 'a milestone in the promotion and appreciation of our natural heritage', misgivings continued to be voiced. These largely concerned the likely funding of the combined organisations and the general failure by government to achieve consensus on the proposed reorganisation; the all-important non-government agencies continued to argue that conservation in practice would be considerably weakened by these changes and that Part VII of the Bill should be withdrawn pending proper consultations. Moreover, as the Countryside Commission in England pointed out, not only is the emphasis of the proposed joint committee on nature conservancy rather than wider countryside policy, but it seems that the Commission will not itself have a place as of right on that committee.

Q   Can you identify any links between countryside conservation and global issues?

A   Both are being affected by the industrialisation and intensification of agriculture.

3.4   Summary

The principal designations for amenity conservation have been detailed and their shortcomings examined, concluding that, until the 1970s and 1980s, they offered little more protection than that provided by the 1947 Town and Country Planning Act and even this did not apply to agriculture and forestry. In addition there were the policy conflicts between the Department of the Environment with its landscape protection interests and those of MAFF, often working in the opposite direction. In contrast, scientific conservation has fared better, gaining stronger powers especially in the designation of NNRs which have often been able to resist agricultural intensification. An examination of the conservation lobby has revealed its basic weaknesses compared with that for agriculture; that its interests have suffered as a result is beyond doubt.

4   Increasing pressures from other land uses

Since the War tensions between agriculture and conservation in the countryside have been perhaps the most obvious because of their widespread visible results. But during this period a whole range of other rural land uses has been growing, making the competing demands for the countryside more intense. This section examines a number of these before placing them all into a specific geographical context by assessing competing land-use pressures in a National Park.

4.1   The growth of tourism and leisure

There have been two main types of policy for countryside tourism and
leisure since the War. The first, social policies, have been concerned to
increase the opportunity for the enjoyment of the countryside by the public
at large. The second, land-use policies, have focused on the more legalistic
mechanisms relating to how public access to private land might be achieved.
Despite the first set of policies being the principal thrust for government
action, it is this second set that has been the most controversial since they
have attempted to procure from land-owners access rights to areas that have
invariably been given over to competing land-uses.

Up to the 1949 National Parks and Access to the Countryside Act, there
had been active pressure on the government both to define the network of
public footpaths in England and Wales more clearly and to allow greater
access to open land, particularly in the mountains. Provision was made in
the Act for the proper identification of all footpaths to which the public had a
right of way through the production by each local authority of a Definitive
Map. Although a fine notion, this has been fraught with difficulties and the
work is still not complete! In the Act, provision for access to open land was
not very satisfactory. In the designation of Access Agreements, local
authorities had to negotiate payment to the land-owner in exchange for
access – a system that was never widely adopted. Such a state of affairs
created problems in the 1950s and 1960s, when the popularity of countryside
recreation and tourism began to grow considerably. Increasing car-
ownership, leisure time and paid holidays led many people to fear a

◄   Many pathways in the
countryside are ploughed
up, as in this example, or
remain obstructed or
unmarked, in spite of the
provisions of the 1949
National Parks and Access
to the Countryside Act.
A key preoccupation for the
Countryside Commission in
the 1990s is to see that this
situation is remedied.

'recreation explosion' where the countryside would be flooded with urban populations at play.

During the 1960s the Labour government was keen to further develop public opportunities for access and introduced a whole new range of essentially local authority facilities in the 1968 Countryside Act. Country parks, picnic sites and transit caravan sites were designed to cater for the growing popularity of rural leisure, but local authorities implemented their designation in a rather different spirit. Literally hundreds of country parks and picnic sites were designated during the 1970s, but primarily as a means of *containing* the recreation 'explosion' that they felt might overwhelm National Parks and AONBs, rather than with the main aim of increasing opportunity.

These areas, however, provided yet another set of rural land-use designations, in addition to those for conservation that were considered in the previous section, that allowed some protection from agricultural development. Since the 1970s, though, there have been problems with these designations and the reasons behind them. Firstly, it has never been clearly established that the recreation explosion ever really happened in the way that most leisure planners had feared. Visits to the countryside seem to be much more susceptible to the vagaries of the weather and the day of the week than to indicators of material affluence. Furthermore, there has never been any comprehensive study of whether a large number of visits actually harms the physical and ecological environments of the countryside anyway, although some isolated examples (such as footpath erosion on the Pennine Way – see Plate 10) are evident enough. Generally, most people seem reluctant to stray more than 100 metres or so from their cars.

Secondly, surveys in the 1980s have shown that people do not actually like country parks and picnic sites much – they prefer the 'real' countryside. This has put the pressure from recreation in the countryside squarely back onto the public footpath network, reviving the frictions that have existed for over 200 years between the rambler and the land-owner. The attitude of the land-owner has changed slightly in the later 1980s as rural recreation and particularly tourism have been reassessed for their potential in agricultural diversification, a term used to describe attempts made by farmers to find ways of earning income other than from the production of food commodities which are in surplus. (This is discussed more fully in Section 5.)

The problem of using recreation in particular for diversification, though, is that much countryside recreation is available freely and as of right to the public and it is therefore difficult to generate much farm income from it. Quite naturally, this has led to a keenness for the development of farm tourism rather than just countryside recreation because it is the overnight stay that offers income potential. There are inherent problems here, however, in competing with the cost and the climate of foreign holidays and in developing an economic base that will ever be anything more than seasonal. Besides which, over-provision of accommodation can easily arise, as has already happened in the summer of 1987 in Devon and Cornwall.

Farm diversification, however, is encouraging more active forms of recreation in the countryside, since this is income-generating, and it is in this quickly growing sector that recreation impacts on the rural environment are likely to be the greatest. In the late 1980s, literally hundreds of proposals for golf-courses reached district planning authorities each week. New sites for hang-gliding, clay-pigeon shooting, motor-cycle scrambling and so on are increasingly being set up on farm land and the number of set-piece war games that can be witnessed in the countryside on a weekend is considerable.

4.2 *Expanding timber production*

The expansion of timber production in the United Kingdom has many
parallels with that of agriculture. Although more cyclical, when expansion
has taken place it has been rapid. It has similarly had a number of
detrimental environmental effects which have offended public opinion and
prompted a policy change: in 1988 tax concessions that had attracted the
very wealthy were removed from afforestation schemes. This followed the
controversy created by a scheme for planting one of Britain's few remaining
primaeval landscapes, the Flow Country of Sutherland. The largest
controversy surrounding timber production, however, is its economic
viability.

 The spur to timber expansion has essentially been the perceived need to
hold a strategic reserve of timber. After the First World War timber depletion
was so large that the Forestry Commission was set up under the 1919
Forestry Act to undertake an aggressive programme of planting to double
the national area of the forest estate. A similar programme was instituted
after the Second World War under the 1945 Forestry Act, but as well as
public planting, a complex series of grants and fiscal concessions was
instituted under the 1947 Forestry Act for the private forester, the principles
of which remain with us today.

 By the 1970s and 1980s the argument for expanding timber production
had become a very difficult one. Since the early 1970s the Treasury has
indicated that home timber production is not economic since its capital
investment offers a very low rate of return indeed, calculated to be within
the range of 3 to 5%. This was well below the rate which the Treasury found
acceptable for public investment. An attempt to measure the effectiveness of
investment programmes which takes into account social benefits such as
recreation and employment is made by cost-benefit analysis.

Q   What kind of methodological problems can you envisage arising in
    trying to assess the return on investment from forestry?

A   (a) Trees take a long time to mature. It is very difficult to forecast likely
    timber prices in, say, 50 years' time.
    (b) If strategic or balance-of-payments assumptions are made, it is not
    remotely possible to envisage the likely role of these with respect to
    timber production half a century or so hence.
    (c) Forest planting means new jobs, but it is difficult to calculate the cost
    of their creation, or, indeed, their value in social terms. Such forests are
    often in remote areas where alternative employment is very scarce.
    (d) People use forests for recreation, but some of these attract very few
    and some many hundreds of thousands a year and each visitor may
    spend anything from a few minutes to several hours there. Therefore
    the measurement of recreational benefits of a forest is problematic.
    (e) The capacity of recreation sites to absorb visitors varies greatly. It is
    hard to know just how many can be absorbed by a mature forest
    compared with other recreational sites.

However, many economists do not accept the conclusions of such analysis
for the above reasons and because they say that the scope of the analysis is
too narrow, and that the whole wood-processing industry and its allied
services which are dependent on United Kingdom forest produce should be
taken into account. For example, the net subsidy per job in the industry as a
whole is much less than if only those employed within the forest are
considered. Thus although cost-benefit analysis *seems* to offer some

▲   Commercial timber developments were, until the late 1980s, spurred on by tax concessions for the rich. But they have also proved controversial especially if it can mean the destruction of one of Britain's few remaining primaeval landscapes, the Flow Country of Sutherland. The lower photo shows the land drained and channelled ready for planting.

precision in determining return on investment, its conclusions with respect to forestry are dependent on a whole range of initial assumptions.

Not surprisingly it is the nature of these assumptions that still bedevils reports on forestry. In 1986 the National Audit Office, an independent body set up to review the economic efficiency of public organisations, questioned the real worth of some of the Forestry Commission's claims about the public benefits of forestry. These included employment creation and recreation potential, as well as balance-of-payments and strategic supply arguments. A year later, the House of Commons Public Accounts Committee, the all-party watch-dog on public expenditure, claimed that too many of the Forestry Commission's activities remained unquantified. While conceding that a low rate of return by forestry might be justified on job creation grounds – especially in remote areas – its reasons for making such a contention needed much better supporting evidence.

It is, as with agriculture, however, the landscape and ecological impacts of modern forestry practice that have attracted the most criticism of this second-largest user of rural land. Conifers are fast-growing trees and offer a reasonably quick return on investment by forestry standards. But the size of the plantations required to maximise profits, their geometric boundaries, and the regimented rows they contain, can be a significant eyesore. Some of the more recent attempts to screen these huge blocks of timber with deciduous planting have been considered to be little more than crudely cosmetic. In ecological terms, too, such large-scale monoculture drastically reduces the species diversity of an area, particularly amongst insects, and efficient woodland management reduces the number of decaying and rotting trees upon which much wildlife depends. Coniferous plantations can also lead to soil acidification, thus adding to the effects of acid rain. Finally, some have argued that large-scale timber production could lead to an increased demand for more inland water storage reservoirs because forests, relative to pasture land, inhibit surface run-off by about 25%.

◁ *Regimented conifers, a Forestry Commission practice that has given way in the 1980s to a less geometric approach and a reversion to more a traditional form of woodland planting, also shown in this example.*

4.3   Water collection in the countryside

The most apparent effect of water collection is the large river-regulating reservoirs which drown large tracts of farmland and dwellings and also, in some extreme cases, entire communities. Such reservoirs may mean the loss of fertile agricultural lowlands, as in the case of Rutland Water in Leicestershire, but more commonly they flood the valley bottoms of upland areas. This is devastating for the local economy since valley bottoms are not only the most agriculturally productive areas but also where settlements and communications networks predominate.

This impact could be minimised by using alternative sources of water collection such as underground aquifers or by employing sea-water desalination plant, but river-regulating reservoirs have traditionally been the cheapest means of storing water and have the added advantage of allowing downstream flood control. Any kind of water collection can obviously only be justified if the water is actually needed. However, it has increasingly been argued that in many cases river valleys should not be flooded either because the water is not actually in demand or because it would be more cost-effective to manage water consumption through the use of meters.

It has also been suggested that, in a water industry dominated by engineers, promotion and prestige are more easily associated with large new reservoir construction projects than with the development of demand management policies. In addition, there has always been a tendency by the water sector to produce too much water because the consequences of shortages are severe, but those of surpluses are negligible. This is because water has historically been cheap to store and distribute and the way that people pay for it – through rates rather than related to consumption – hides any wastage. In addition, the way in which planning permission for reservoirs is obtained always puts national need criteria above those of the locality. Thus local opposition on agricultural and conservation grounds can be quite forcefully overridden by claims of a national need for water.

Between the 1960s and the 1980s proposals for the construction of new reservoirs in rural areas have been hotly contested because the need for their water has never been satisfactorily proven. Certainly, this was the case over the development of the Kielder Reservoir in Northumberland. Kielder was to become the largest reservoir in Europe built with large contributions from the European Commission's Regional Fund and justified by the requirements of a growing regional economy during the late 1960s and early 1970s. Subsequent recession made Kielder into the reservoir that nobody actually wanted. Many people have concluded, with the benefit of hindsight, that the money would have been much better spent on renewing the water pipeline infrastructure of the region, which, originally Victorian, has now reached the end of its useful life. Thus in 1989 more than a quarter of the total drinkable water consumption in the region could be accounted for through leakages, a figure close to the national average for such losses.

The advantages of reservoir water collection as a rural land use lie chiefly in the water-based recreation facilities that they offer. These constitute one of the fastest-growing sports sectors of the late 1980s and provide important 'honeypots' to allow people to congregate in the countryside in relatively large numbers. Nevertheless their construction is, as in the case of Kielder, usually resisted by the public on environmental grounds. If the new water companies, following water privatisation in 1989, still favour reservoirs as a means of increasing supply, it is because of the high cost of the repair of the distribution system compared with the development of a reservoir and the personal proclivities of water engineers.

However, if the problem of new water storage sites becomes too acute because of strong opposition, one alternative for them will be the aggressive pursuance of policies of demand management.

4.4   *Mineral extraction in the countryside*

For much of this century, iron ore and coal were, in volume, the largest of the extractive industries. Having been long established, they, along with tin-mining, had created an urban countryside where they had been won. The mining villages of County Durham, the Welsh valleys and, for tin, the Cornish coast, had long developed into distinctive physical and social entities in the countryside. In the post-war context their environmental impact became first one of dereliction and decay, and then later one of reclamation and restoration, sometimes back to the agriculture that had preceded them.

In a more localised way, specific minerals have had a very significant impact on particular countryside locations in the post-war period. The winning of fluorspar and the problems associated with waste disposal in the Peak District, the potash mining in the North York Moors National Park, the quarrying of slate and mining for gold in Snowdonia and the extraction of china clay in Cornwall are all good examples of this. (See Plate 11.)

But since the War it is perhaps the increased extraction of building materials that has had the most pervasive effects on the countryside environment at large. The exploitation of sands and gravels for the construction industry has been widespread, for their workings can be found in many of the lower reaches of river valleys in Britain. The demand for them has grown phenomenally in response to increased infrastructural, housing and industrial requirements in a period of post-war reconstruction and economic growth. As shall be seen in much greater detail in Book Three of this series (Blunden and Reddish (eds), 1991), the impact of aggregates extraction on the countryside is significant because of its broad geographical spread and falls into two main phases – the extraction phase and the after-use phase. Fairly soon after the Second World War, legislation was introduced to tighten environmental controls over both of these phases. The 1951 Minerals Act introduced in particular an obligation on the part of the minerals companies to restore mineral workings to an acceptable state for after-use. But this statute was not backdated and so all mineral workings that were started before 1951 – and most of these have been abandoned only in the 1970s and 1980s – had no such requirements placed upon them. The environmental deterioration in these areas remains a significant problem in the countryside today.

The problems of the minerals sector, particularly in terms of its environmental effects on the countryside, were examined closely in the 1970s by three investigating teams set up by the Department of the Environment, largely as a counterbalance to new legislation (Minerals Exploration Act, 1971) aimed at providing financial help in the costly exercise of finding and developing fresh mineral resources. Two of these reports called for a more effective planning controls system for minerals, and the national co-ordination of aggregates exploitation in order to reduce environmental impact. The third put forward specific proposals to diminish the environmental impact of all minerals extraction other than aggregate materials.

Despite the valuable work carried out by the three teams, little has changed legislatively to improve the environmental impact of minerals

extraction in the countryside. The 1981 Town and Country Planning
(Minerals) Act has extended the 1951 Act's minerals after-use requirements
to include what is now termed 'aftercare', whereby the minerals companies
must now sustain an on-going management regime after minerals have
been worked out, rather than just a once-and-for-all restoration programme.
But this has done little to help local authority planning departments (usually
in county councils) with control over permission to extract minerals in the
first place. Although planning permission is required for minerals
extraction, if it is refused by a county council, minerals companies may
appeal to the Secretary of State for the Environment. The problem here is
that the Secretary of State may use different criteria for judging the
application from those used by the county. Whereas the county will try to
balance environmental considerations against local minerals needs, the
Secretary of State may balance them against national needs and find in
favour of an application that could not be justified in terms of local needs
alone. Thus a decision about minerals extraction and the impact such a
working can have on the countryside may be taken out of the hands of the
local planning authority altogether.

   Nevertheless it remains an impact that can be considerable. The whole
of the development of the sand and gravel workings now occupied by the
Cotswold Water Park in the Thames Valley in Wiltshire and Gloucestershire,
for example, which has completely changed the face of many hundreds of
hectares of agricultural land, was exploited most intensively as the result of
the national need to build the M4 motorway and to develop Swindon. But
unlike this area many of the 'holes in the ground' have no after-use
requirements placed on them at all since they were begun before 1951.

   Whether the effect of minerals extraction on the countryside of the
United Kingdom is likely to diminish or increase is a complex question
which you will be better placed to answer after your study of the next
volume in this series. Certainly the demand for minerals will continue to rise
and if alternative approaches to their extraction and their use, especially
aggregates, are not adopted, then areas of the countryside that so far have
remained unexploited in this way will become affected.

4.5   Military training and other national needs

If the control over minerals development in the countryside suffers from the
problem that national need can often overrule local interest, this is also true
of a number of other large-scale land uses. Principal amongst these is
national defence. Throughout the countryside there are areas set aside for
military training, perhaps the best known being Salisbury Plain and large
parts of Northumberland and Dartmoor National Parks. Such areas are
scattered throughout the countryside particularly in its wilder, more
attractive parts and on the coastline – precisely those areas that are most
popular for the purposes of rural leisure, as Figure 5.3 indicates. Indeed, the
National Parks have suffered especially from the demands of the Ministry of
Defence: while Dartmoor and the Pembrokeshire Coast have around 5% of
their land area owned or leased by the MoD, in Northumberland the figure
rises to 22%. Although low-flying aircraft can create disturbance over a wide
area, perhaps more serious are the physical dangers that training exercises
on firing ranges may cause for the straying rambler. Use by the MoD can
cause great archaeological damage and also removes the possibility of most
other rural land uses, particularly of a more productive kind. However,
military training can have its positive side since evidence suggests that the

◀   *Figure 5.3*
Major military training areas in
Britain. Principal training areas are
associated with a wide range of
training facilities together with
permanent camps and bases;
intermediate training areas have
more than 40 hectares devoted to
live firing and/or dry and adventure
training; specialist training areas
concentrate on single combat units,
for example tank training at
Castlemartin.

restriction of public access and many forms of agricultural activity which such a use imposes can favour the maintenance of great ecological diversity.

In addition to military training there are other large-scale intrusions into the landscape concerned with defence. Undoubtedly the best-known of these is the Fylingdales early warning system in the North York Moors National Park, which comprises three huge 'golf-balls' sitting at the top of an open moorland landscape, currently being replaced (without planning permission) by a large pylon-like structure. More commonly, large radiotelescopes – massive satellite dishes – are to be found in many, often flat, parts of the countryside where they can be seen for miles.

Over these and many other intrusions in the rural landscape (including those discussed above) the government has the final say, often through Acts of Parliament, public inquiries or even Royal Commissions. Thus, ultimately, it was central government that made the decision to allow the building of a huge oil terminal in the Pembrokeshire Coast National Park and a nuclear power station at Trawsfynydd in Snowdonia National Park.

The building of nuclear power stations at numerous coastal locations – including Sellafield, Sizewell and Berkeley – since the War has, at the end of the day, always been a central government decision, for they have been considered not only controversial as visual intrusions into the landscape but also environmental hazards. These, along with nuclear waste reprocessing and weapons plants, can affect adjacent rural land-users. The effects of radio-active discharges on livestock and plant life even at low levels have been known for some time, but more recently there seemed to be evidence of increased child cancer around such installations. However, it now seems likely that this is due to the exposure of workers within the plants, leading to the development of serious health problems in their offspring.

Even in terms of 'soft' energy options, in the 1990s decisions will have to be made about a number of proposed 'wind energy' farms to be sited again in remoter, more beautiful (but windier) parts of the countryside, such as the North Pennines, where the size and density of windmills could provide a significant visual disamenity.

Fylingdales Early
Warning System – an
example of an intrusive
development in a National
Park – North York Moors.
A new system is currently
being installed, but not one
which represents a visual
improvement.

Although designed
not to break the skyline,
Trawsfynydd nuclear power
station remains a massive
intrusion into Snowdonia
National Park.

And it is central government that makes decisions, too, about large-
scale infrastructure developments which may have impacts on the
countryside. These can be as diverse as the siting of the Okehampton
by-pass in Devon inside the Dartmoor National Park boundary, and the
most appropriate route for the channel tunnel link. Here, trade-offs are
constantly being sought between economic expediency and the
environmental impact on the countryside. Beyond roads, the effects of
developments such as a third London airport and a Severn barrage cause
perennial debates about this environmental/economic trade-off.

◁   Figure 5.4
New country towns in
southern England.
Planning applications for
whole new settlements in
the countryside are on the
increase in the wake of a
relaxation in planning
controls, but they are
proving highly controversial
in those areas where they
are proposed.

1	Fradley Hythe	25	Takeley	49	Great Lea	73	Mawsley
2	Bittesby	26	Brenthall Park	50	Upper Donnington	74	Cransley Lodge
3	Stretton Magna	27	Braintree	51	Dunstan Park, Thatcham	75	Far Gollian
4	Gowthorpe	28	White Court West	52	Arborfield	76	Nobotle
5	Mangreen Hall Farm	29	Bathside Bay	53	Ardley	77	Upper Faxton
6	Dickerborough	30	Northwick Village Project	54	Barnard Gate	78	Sulby (2)
7	Guyhirn	31	Tilingham Hall	55	South Newington	79	Newnham Grange
8	Westmere/Wilburton (2)	32	Chafford Hundred	56	Stone Bassett	80	Hatton Rock
9	Waterfenton	33	Vigo	57	Cliveden	81	Tysoe Vale Farm
10	Denny/Denny Abbey	34	Leybourne	58	Marsworth	82	Thornhill
11	Scotland Park	35	Woodchurch	59	Chiltern Acres	83	Hardwick Farm
12	Crow Green	36	Ashford	60	Shenley	84	Middlehurst
13	Swansley Wood	37	Bishops Forstal	61	Wellfield Park	85	Long Marston (2)
14	Great Common Farm	38	Worsham	62	Chaul End	86	Kingston Grange
15	Belham Hill	39	Stone Cross	63	Stewartby	87	Lighthorne Heath
16	Bourn Airfield (2)	40	Southwater	64	Roxton	88	Nelson Quays
17	Highfields	41	Midhurst Common	65	Marston Park	89	Beanhall
18	Nine Mile Hill	42	Whiteley	66	Elstow	90	Mere Green
19	Hare Park	43	Dibden Bay	67	Milton Glebe	91	Shurnock Court
20	Allington	44	Micheldever	68	Chawston/Wyboston	92	Strensham on Avon
21	Red Lodge	45	Nightingales Park	69	Thornberry	93	Westington
22	Stansted	46	Eversley	70	Burton Wold	94	Poulton
23	Easton Park	47	Foxley Wood	71	Stoke Griffin	95	Grange
24	Felsted	48	Spencers Wood	72	Mawsley on the Green	96	Three Legged Cross

Finally, in terms of large-scale developments, there is the ever-present
threat to the countryside from new towns and new villages, leaving aside
constant applications for individual rural dwellings. Thus the post-war new
town developments at Milton Keynes, Livingston, Runcorn, Antrim and so
on have eaten up many hectares of the lowland countryside of the United
Kingdom. But while these and other urban types of development in the
countryside have been perceived as having considerably escalated the loss
of rural land between 1957 and 1971, they have only affected some 2% of the
total land area. More recently, in the wake of a relaxation of planning

◁   *Figure 5.5*
Designing a new
community. Waterfenton
in Cambridgeshire, one of
the many proposed new
country towns. This artist's
impression shows the
proposed new centre.

constraints in rural areas from 1987, a new phenomenon has appeared in
south-east England – the purpose-built country town to be constructed on
greenfield sites, each occupying between 360 and 400 hectares: see Figures
5.4 and 5.5. The developers contend that they would reduce the pressures
for infill, urban sprawl and piecemeal development in the countryside, as
well as providing a high-quality built environment. However, they have
been vociferously opposed by those living in the areas affected. Indeed
these proposals have evoked more heated argument than the development
of the (much larger) new towns ever did.

4.6   Summarising land-use pressures in valued landscapes: a case study

So far this chapter has examined how the drive to increase food output after
the Second World War did much to damage the landscape, ecology and
indeed the economy of the countryside. Although much of this
development was directly at the expense of rural conservation in a number
of forms, the competing demands of other countryside land-users – leisure,
forestry, water, minerals, other large-scale developments and so on – have
created a complex web of land-use policies and land-use interactions, all
with their particular environmental consequences. This subsection will look
at one specific example to give an indication of how these complexities are
manifest in a single area and to summarise many of the points made in this
section. Later, the chapter will examine more closely some novel attempts to
overcome these complexities.

As with much of the countryside of the United Kingdom, the Peak National
Park is predominantly an agricultural area where, because of its physical
characteristics, livestock production has been pre-eminent since the War.
More recently there have been increasing pressures to plough up land for
cereals production. Until the 1980s the National Park Authority could do
little formally to prevent this because of the exemption of most of agriculture

*'We're very lucky, when you think about it,
working in such beautiful surroundings.'*

from planning controls. Incentives to intensify both cereals and livestock
production were enhanced in the 1970s by the designation of much of the
National Park as a 'Less Favoured Area' with higher grant-aid availability for
modernisation. A first clear tension in this area, then, lies in having an
expanding agricultural industry in a National Park, the statutory objectives
of which are to conserve the landscape of the area, as well as to provide
opportunities for public enjoyment. In 1987 changes in government policy at
least made it mandatory for alterations in the use of land for agricultural
purposes or for an extension of woodland to be the subject of consultation
with the National Park authorities, an extension of the notification
provisions contained in the 1981 Wildlife and Countryside Act that we
consider further in Section 5.1 below.

On the public enjoyment front, the National Park also faces land-use
problems too. It was in the Park area that the conflicts between recreationists
and land-owners refusing to allow access to their land came to a head in 1932
when 800 ramblers from Manchester organised a mass trespass on Kinder
Scout. It was as a result of this that the 1949 National Parks and Access to the
Countryside Act introduced Access Agreements. Nearly all of these Access
Agreements have been designated within the Peak National Park and bring
a range of associated management duties as well as costs.

These alone have not resolved recreation pressures in the Park,
however, and a whole new series of recreation management experiments –
public transport, park-and-ride schemes, cycle hire schemes and the
development of interpretation centres – have all had a role to play in
balancing visitor numbers with the quality of the recreation experience in
the Park. Nowhere is this balance more delicate than in those areas
dedicated to nature conservation. In several National Nature Reserves
particular care has to be taken with the management of public access lest the
effects destroy the very scientific worth of the Reserves themselves.

In the Derwent Valley area of the Peak District, the National Park authority and the National Trust have combined with forestry and water interests to resolve the problems caused by tourist pressure on the area. (Above) planting schemes have been undertaken to improve the area; (below) keeping out cars has greatly enhanced its recreational appeal and made its conservation much easier.

Conservation and recreation, however, provide only the tip of the iceberg in rural land-use conflicts in the Peak National Park. As an upland area at the upstream end of the Severn–Trent water system and close to large industrial populations, historically there have been great pressures within the Park for the construction of water storage reservoirs. Subsequent to their construction, certain of these such as the Ladybower and Derwent, have generated their own recreation problems, while during the construction of the Derwent reservoir a whole village (after which the reservoir was named) was drowned. In close association with water developments have been those of forestry. Again, the terrain and soil quality of the area have made the Park susceptible to large-scale coniferous timber expansion with no recourse to planning controls on the part of the Park Authority.

It has perhaps been over or in connection with the extraction of minerals, however, that land-use conflicts in the Peak National Park have been most intense. In addition to the mining of fluorspar, pressure to extract limestone for both the construction and the chemicals industries has been very great indeed. Although applications for minerals extraction have been resisted with some successes by the Peak Park Joint Planning Board, a large number of quarries are worked and associated activities such as cement works provide significant intrusions into the landscape. Even where development has been diverted outside the Park, it has been of sufficient scale, such as the Tunstead ICI quarry, still to have a significant visual impact from within the Park. (See Plate 11.)

Thus reconciling rural land-use conflicts is a paramount purpose of the work of the Peak National Park Authority. Although this often entails significant compromises, sometimes to the National Park objectives themselves, it has also brought forth new initiatives. One of these will be considered more closely, in the field of integrated rural development, in Section 6 below.

Activity 4

The exercise just carried out in relation to the Peak National Park has strong similarities, if in a more limited way, with the approach to Cumbria in Chapter 1 of Book One (Silvertown and Sarre (eds), 1990). You should therefore now be ready to consider part or all of a National Park or an AONB that you know well and try to sort out the different land-use demands made upon it, and then consider the complex web of interactions that exist between these. You might find it useful to do this as a flow diagram.

Check your answer with the example given at the end of the chapter. The diagram there gives you a simplified version of such an exercise, but for a lowland area – the Norfolk Broads – to provide a counterbalance to the upland setting used above.

5   *Agricultural diversification: conservation on a flow tide?*

5.1   *New conservation controls in the countryside*

By the late 1970s the damage caused to the countryside by unfettered agricultural expansion had become untenable. The Porchester Report (referred to in Chapter 4 and in Section 3.1) formally proposed new measures for the control of agriculture in high-value landscapes. Both the scientific and amenity conservation bodies put their weight behind these proposals. By the 1980s, budgetary crises with the Common Agricultural Policy and continuing food surpluses led to formal proposals in Europe for the curbing of food output. But in the United Kingdom it was new conservation measures against the environmental damage caused by agriculture that began to bite even before policies to curb food over-production started to take effect. The issue of solutions to check food over-production will therefore be returned to in the following section.

By 1981 the Wildlife and Countryside Act had been passed requiring farmers to notify local authorities of intentions to undertake potentially damaging agricultural operations: objections could lead an authority into negotiating a management agreement with the farmer to desist from such activities. However, in such a case a farmer would be entitled to compensation payments equivalent to the value of output forgone as a result of not carrying out improvements, or in extreme cases could result in the purchase of the land.

Safeguards against damaging operations in National Parks and SSSIs were also introduced in the Act. The latter required SSSIs to be renotified by the Nature Conservancy Council. This meant that the 30 000 or so owners and occupiers of such sites, designated originally under the 1949 National Parks and Access to the Countryside Act, had to be given full details of the site and the kind of operations which, if carried out there, could damage it. The same information also had to be passed on to the local authority, the water authority and the Secretary of State for the Environment.

The sheer cost of these management agreements, particularly when there was no certainty that a farmer would have ever carried out the operations he had threatened, was the subject of much criticism. In an attempt to overcome this in one particularly valuable wetland area that was under threat of drainage, Halvergate Marshes in the Norfolk Broads, the Countryside Commission proposed in 1985 rather than compensation payments, a set of payments for the positive management of agricultural land, but in an environmentally sensitive way. This was known as the 'Broads Grazing Marsh Conservation Scheme'. From these beginnings, **Environmentally Sensitive Areas (ESAs)** emerged and are to be found throughout Europe. Indeed, they have been formally enshrined in United Kingdom legislation in the 1986 Agriculture Act.

Some other loopholes of the 1981 Wildlife and Countryside Act were closed in a 1985 Wildlife and Countryside (Amendment) Act, particularly in relation to notification procedures for both management agreements and SSSIs, but the principal conservation successes in relation to agriculture have been in relation to ESAs. These were to cover areas whose national environmental significance was threatened by agricultural change, but which could be conserved through the adoption or maintenance of particular forms of farming practice. The areas were to represent a discrete and coherent unit of environmental interest, to permit the economical administration of appropriate conservation aids.

Two rounds of ESAs were designated, in mid 1986 and mid 1987: see Figure 5.6. The schemes are voluntary and require the farmer to adhere to particular management regimes in exchange for financial assistance. The particular management system varies from area to area but may include, for example, restrictions on fertiliser use and reductions in stocking densities. The use of chemicals is also commonly discouraged, and traditional features of the landscape retained and maintained. Clearly, much of the purpose of ESA management is to redress directly the worst ravages of agricultural intensification summarised earlier in this chapter.

By mid 1988, over 1400 farmers had applied to join the first round of the scheme, putting forward some 78% of the land eligible for it. (The government's budget for ESAs at that time was running at about £12 million

◀   *Figure 5.6*
The ESAs of England and
Wales. Those designated
by 1989 have increased
the variety of our protected
landscapes and provide
a much more effective
approach to conservation.

a year.) As a result, the ESA scheme has been considered a clear step forward in mitigating the worst ravages of agricultural practice in a climate of expansion. But at the end of the day, these areas, important as they are for conserving landscapes of high quality, cover only a very small part of agricultural land in the United Kingdom and more comprehensive policies for conservation will eventually be required. As already noted, conservation causes generally have been helped by various policies that have been introduced in the 1980s, to curb food over-production. It is to these that consideration is now briefly given.

◀   *The Somerset Levels – an example of an Environmentally Sensitive Area and one landscape of high quality that could easily have been destroyed without ESA status, now recognised by the European Community as a means of reconciling agriculture with conservation.*

5.2   Food over-production solutions

There is a logic that suggests that if much of the damaging impact of agriculture can be attributed to agricultural expansion, then curbing expansion will have an ameliorating effect on the environment. This has been the case in varying degrees, and this section reviews a number of policies that have been instituted or proposed since the start of the 1980s which were designed to curb food over-production, paying particular attention to their actual or likely environmental impact and effects on the rural economy.

The European Commission and most economists readily agree that since it is the high prices of agricultural commodities that encourage farmers to produce more than is required, with attendant environmental consequences, then reducing these prices affords the only long-term solution to the food surplus problem. For political reasons and for the long-term stability of the agriculture industry, this has not yet been instituted on any wide scale. It is feared that farmers would quickly go out of business, particularly those who have borrowed large sums of money, bringing about agricultural depression and possible food shortages. Besides, it is also worth remembering that the CAP, with its system of price support, has been a key feature of the EC and was designed by the original signatories of the Treaty of Rome as a means of stemming rural depopulation.

It is therefore only possible to speculate on the likely environmental and economic impacts of price reductions. Taken on their own, they may encourage further intensification in certain areas as farmers seek to sustain their gross incomes in a regime of falling prices. In other areas, farmers may find that the marginal costs of additional production may be greater than output values and thus reduce output levels. These choices in turn will depend on the cost of inputs. Thus, price restraint policies could have quite an unpredictable effect on the environment and land use in the countryside, although they are in fact unlikely to be introduced in isolation from other support policies for agriculture such as the Environmentally Sensitive Area scheme discussed above.

It is therefore instructive to look at the impacts of other kinds of restraint measures that are either being introduced or contemplated since it is in tandem with these that price restraint policies are likely to operate. In 1984 quotas were imposed on milk production in the United Kingdom as part of a European Commission policy to reduce output. This simply set a limit on the amount of milk that a farmer could produce before being penalised by levies. In principle, they could also be used to put a ceiling on the amount that a farmer could produce that would qualify for the kinds of price support measures discussed in Section 2 of this chapter. This is less painful than price reductions since the latter reduces the level of subsidy on all, rather than only marginal levels of, output.

The introduction of quotas provoked a quick response from farmers who culled cows and reduced their use of high-protein feed concentrates to get their levels of production down. Some farmers, with heavy borrowing commitments to finance plant modernisation or extensive herd replacement schemes, went out of business. Other farmers wishing to reduce overheads and maintain profitability have purchased milk quotas from those changing the nature of their agricultural enterprise or going out of business. In many cases, dairy farm net incomes have actually risen as a result of this, so the effects on the rural economy within agriculture at least have not been completely adverse. They do, however, restrain the most efficient producers. For these reasons and the bureaucratic inefficiencies and loopholes that have been experienced in the implementation of milk quotas, they are unlikely to be extended to other sectors.

Environmentally, too, the effect of quotas is uncertain, but it may not be large. On the one hand, it may lead to lower input, lower output farming with the result that the landscape may appear as less intensively cultivated. On the other hand, it could drive certain farmers out of dairying altogether and into more intensive enterprises such as cereals.

A second means of reducing output is to place adjustable taxes on all outputs of a certain kind. These are called **co-responsibility levies** and were introduced into the United Kingdom for wheat in 1986. These levies are designed not only to reduce production levels, but are also considered to be useful in helping to pay for the storage of wheat surpluses. In practice, co-responsibility levies are little different in their effects to a cut in the prices that farmers receive, except that smaller producers can be exempted from the levy. Environmental and economic impacts are therefore likely to be similar if somewhat smaller than those of a reduction in prices.

Where co-responsibility levies have been introduced in Europe they have generally been very expensive to administer and monitor, and in the main have been too small in size to have any effect on output levels. They thus tend to be considered rather cosmetic as a means of reducing food surpluses. Two further means of curbing food over-production are likely to have greater impacts on both the rural environment and the rural economy than those considered so far. These are extensification and 'set-aside'.

Extensification is a broad notion concerned to lower the intensity of output in agriculture, essentially by reducing the inputs. Clearly, lower inputs to agriculture, as have been seen in the case of introduction of milk quotas, will lead to a less industrial farm landscape without any necessary loss in net farm incomes.

Extensification as proposed can take a number of different forms. It could, for example, entail a reduction in farm inputs such as the fertiliser nitrogen. In fact, a number of people have proposed the introduction of nitrogen taxes as a simple way of reducing output. This is also a very flexible means of controlling production, since output is very sensitive to nitrogen levels and varying the tax would correspondingly vary output. Nitrogen quotas also have been proposed and these would have a similar though more selective effect. Reducing farm modernisation subsidies to capital equipment would also reduce the amount of machinery going into agricultural production.

In the context of extensification, the movement towards organic farming is gaining momentum as part of a general but quite fundamental change in attitudes by the public to food consumption and the environment. This relies on 'natural' inputs to agriculture which remove not only large amounts of nitrogenous fertiliser from the production process, but also pesticides and other manufactured chemicals. Although this appears to reduce the cost of inputs per hectare, this is offset by the increased input to the cultivation process in order to reduce the problem of weeds. Outputs per hectare also fall. But there is a corresponding market premium for organically grown foods so that ultimately revenues per hectare need not be any lower than in conventional farming.

Extensification would be likely to have clear environmental benefits to the countryside. Landscapes would be less industrial in appearance and more akin to the 'patchwork quilt' of the nineteenth century. Some of the principal benefits, however, would come with an enriched rural ecology. Reductions in all forms of manufactured chemicals would go a long way towards reversing the ecological impoverishment process that was charted in Section 2 of this chapter. The rural economy may also experience benefits. With a reduction in capital inputs to agriculture there may well be an increase in labour inputs as a substitute. Indeed, some research has suggested that if organic farming became the prevailing food system in the United Kingdom it could create an extra 1.3 million jobs directly in agriculture. The trickle-down effect on the rural economy of such an increase in rural employment would be considerable. However, contrasting evidence from some organic practitioners indicates that human and mechanical inputs can remain much the same as for other more orthodox systems of production.

Set-aside is an over-production solution concerned specifically with taking land out of agriculture. To remove food surpluses in the United Kingdom at present output levels per hectare it might be necessary to have to take up to 2 million hectares of farmland out of production. This policy was introduced under the 1986 Agriculture Act, where farmers were given compensation payments per unit area for taking a minimum of 20% of their land out of production. This has been severely criticised on two main fronts. Firstly, it is irrational to take agricultural land out of production when it has clearly been the input of *capital* that has been the cause of food over-production. Put simply, set-aside removes the wrong factor of production. Secondly, while a farmer may take 20% of his or her land out of production, he or she is still eligible for capital grants to further intensify production on the remaining 80% of his or her land. Thus the farmer might well end up producing the same amount of food, while receiving compensation payments for setting land aside.

The impact of set-aside on the rural economy is slight since it creates no jobs and need affect farm incomes little. Environmentally, there are pockets of land that are now no longer intensively farmed, but with no positive management these are quickly taking on the appearance of derelict land. This has become such a problem that in 1989 the Countryside Commission introduced an experimental scheme in East Anglia that provided payments for the positive management of set-aside land in some non-food-producing use, such as development for recreation.

Activity 5

Tabulate the impacts of the solutions to food over-production discussed in this section with the proposed solution on the left and adjacent to it on the right, favourable environmental impacts and unfavourable environmental impacts.

Your table should show four solutions. Each one will have a favourable environmental impact but *two* will also show possibilities for unfavourable environmental outcomes.

Q   How can the unfavourable impacts and the problems of food surpluses be most *directly* resolved?

A   By cuts in the prices of the agricultural commodities in question.

Q   So why isn't this done?

A   The fear that farmers will go under with ensuing agricultural depression, and the possibility of food shortages. Rural depopulation which might follow could prove unacceptable to the original Treaty of Rome signatories. Drastic commodity price reductions are therefore unlikely to be embraced by many of our Community partners except as a last resort.

The prospect of large areas of surplus land in the countryside deriving from attempts to find solutions to the over-production of food is, of course, central to this chapter. What should be done with it? Does such a policy mean that the competing demands on the countryside of the United Kingdom are likely to diminish? Well, not exactly. At the same time as the government has been developing policies to stem food over-production, it has been introducing policies to help farmers diversify out of agriculture altogether. These have been policies attempting to establish 'alternative land uses in rural economy' which is precisely the name, shortened to **ALURE**, of the policy package. The environmental and land-use implications of ALURE are now briefly examined.

5.3   *Alternative land uses for the countryside*

As well as introducing Environmentally Sensitive Areas, the 1986 Agriculture Act based on the ALURE package introduced a number of measures for diversifying the rural economy. One of these was generally to encourage non-farm developments on agricultural land which was also given force by a Department of Environment Circular of 1987, *Development Involving Agricultural Land*. This was aimed at relaxing planning controls over agricultural land in all areas but Green Belts and National Parks and led, quite quickly, to a spate of planning applications for houses, golf-courses and even whole country towns (as was mentioned in Section 4). As a general policy theme, this relaxation of development controls has probably been the most significant measure in recent years that has increased competing demands on the countryside – and understandably has caused much consternation amongst environmental pressure groups and, in specific areas, around for instance the proposed sites of Foxley Wood and Stone Bassett, amongst a wider public.

A 'Farm Woodland Scheme' provided a second strand to the ALURE package. In the early 1980s the Forestry Commission had already introduced a Broadleaved Woodland Scheme to provide planting and management grants for non-coniferous woodland schemes. The Farm Woodland Scheme was introduced by the MAFF in 1986 to supplement this, particularly as a means of encouraging farmers to take land out of food production, either as part of or in addition to the set-aside scheme. In the longer term the environmental benefits of such a scheme could be positive, but the uptake of the Farm Woodland Scheme has been very low so far, since it entails farmers tying up their land in timber growing for unacceptably long periods of time.

The ALURE package also provided grants to aid diversification of the farm business, and feasibility studies for alternative business, but they have to be of certain specified types. The potential for diversification, however, falls into four broad areas, the first of which is tourism and recreation. Although these have been exploited to a degree as was noted above, there is always the uncertainty here of not knowing when the market might become saturated in any particular area, and capturing income from recreation is always a problem.

Adding value to farm products represents a second process of diversification. This entails processing foods, marketing specific food qualities or developing 'pick your own' enterprises. These kinds of activity offer some potential since traditional rural imagery provides a potent marketing tool. Diversifying into alternative crops and livestock represents a third way of broadening the farm enterprise. These might include breeding goats or snails, or rearing sheep for milk, or deer for venison, or growing unusual crops such as borage or evening primrose. Organic farming can be considered as part of this area of diversification, although in most respects it is a return to a mixed method of farming using crop rotation and involving the keeping of animals.

Finally, farms may develop ancillary resources on the farm. The potential of this is enhanced by the liberalisation of planning controls in that farm buildings might now be more readily used for homes, craft industries

◄ *Barns and other redundant farm buildings of character are being converted for other uses, in this case a silk-screen printers. These tend to be more acceptable to planners than developments which might offer more direct benefit to the local community.*

or tourist accommodation. But in addition areas such as woodlands or
wetlands might be used for game, for timber or water-based recreation.

Generally, in the 1980s, then, the sovereignty of agriculture as a rural
land use has been brought into question. Under a remit to promote more
widely the economic and social interests of rural areas as a whole,
agriculture ministers under the 1986 Agriculture Act now have an explicit
duty for the conservation and enhancement of the natural beauty and
amenity of the countryside. Solutions to food over-production as well as
measures to diversify the rural economy will change the balance of
competing demands on the countryside, to make it more diverse in both its
environmental and economic base. These new measures, however, have
been implemented too recently for their long-term effects on the countryside
economy and environment to be clear yet. As Table 5.1 shows, at present the
sums of money devoted to diversification are minute compared to the £1800
million spent on supporting food production in 1987.

Not surprisingly, these measures have been subject to much debate and
criticism, most notably in a 1987 Countryside Commission report produced
by its Countryside Policy Review Panel *New Opportunities for the Countryside*.
In its proposals for wide-ranging changes to agriculture, forestry, recreation
and conservation, it takes issue with government. To begin with it
considered that the ALURE target of removing about one million hectares
from the production of surplus agricultural commodities was inadequate
and should be doubled. As for financial incentives to develop new forms of
enterprise, although it felt that if the £5 million expenditure on farm
diversification and the development of new marketing skills amongst
farmers seemed adequate, the government should be spending at least that
sum to assist with the conversion of redundant farm buildings to new uses.
The targets for new farm woodlands to be achieved over a three-year period

Table 5.1   *Financial allocations to diversification*

	£ million
ALURE package proposals made in April 1987	
Rural diversification under ALURE	25
Diversifying into woodland (Farm Woodlands Scheme)	13 (for 33 000 ha)
On-farm diversification	3
Farm products marketing	2
Proposals made in November 1987 for additional funds	
Covering all ALURE schemes	1
Set-aside and extensification	
Proposals made in November 1987 for 1988/90 for extensification and set-aside	16
Conservation Annual allocations	
Original ESAs (6)	12
New ESAs (6)	7
NCC estimate of SSSI management agreement costs	15–20

(as shown in Table 5.1) were short of the mark, with the Review Panel looking for over 200 000 ha at an expenditure of £40 million. The Review Panel also considered that the six proposed new ESAs needed to be increased to between 30 and 40 at an outlay of around £40 million. The total cost of a package which would be effective, according to the Countryside Commission's report, would be £320 million, over seven times that of the ALURE package.

It would seem that government had seriously underestimated the cost and the extent of its new measures aimed at diversifying the rural economy, at least as far as the Countryside Commission were concerned.

5.4   Summary

The 1980s saw a number of attempts to bring agriculture into a more harmonious relationship with conservation, at least in the most vulnerable of landscapes, especially through ESAs. But the key to the problem overall has been to find ways of cutting agricultural production, particularly of those commodities in surplus and which cannot be marketed. Schemes used to this end have included milk quotas and cereal production levies, extensification, set-aside, farm diversification and a range of alternative uses for rural land. However, the role of government in activating such a programme has been criticised by its chief advisory agency on the countryside, the Countryside Commission.

6   The future

As well as the changes based on the agriculture industry that have come about in the 1980s, a number of other characteristics of rural areas have emerged, particularly in terms of changes to the rural community and its relationship with the land. This final section of the chapter briefly reviews two of these and speculates on how rural communities might develop into the 1990s.

6.1   Integrated rural development

So far this chapter has considered all of the competing demands for the countryside separately. This is a perfectly acceptable way of doing things, since, in the United Kingdom, each of the land-using sectors tends to be organised and administered separately. But the very fact that most rural activity is carried out in an unco-ordinated way is one of the principal causes of land-use conflict in the countryside.

Because of this, one type of initiative that has attracted much interest during the 1980s has been the development of a more holistic approach to the planning of the countryside, which has become known as **integrated rural development (IRD)**. Such approaches had been tried in England in the

1960s, with the introduction of Rural Development Boards, but at that time government ministries jealously guarded their own sectoral interests and as a result only one was formed, for the North Pennines, and this was short-lived. In the 1980s, however, the European Commission helped support a series of experiments in IRD, the chief characteristics of which are summarised in Box 5.1. However, one of the best known IRD experiments was in the Peak National Park centred on the villages of Longnor and Monyash. Here the Peak National Park Joint Planning Board set up the experiment in an attempt to ease some of the problems that were outlined in Section 4 above.

In this experiment, arrangements were made to remove to a large degree the usual sectoral policies and funding arrangements for a small rural area, and encourage a number of agencies to work together and help to fund a common set of policies. Thus policies of MAFF, the (then) Development Commission, the Countryside Commission, the Nature Conservancy Council and so on were co-ordinated, but so too were approaches to financing projects. This led to some interesting innovations in both community projects and environmental schemes well before the current over-production and diversification measures had come to fruition. Thus, rather than the normal MAFF payments to farmers to increase production in a marginal agricultural area, a consensus policy was devised that allowed, for example, environmental payments for the reconstruction and restoration of dry-stone walls and the growth of wild flowers in meadows. In community terms, too, small industrial developments were initiated and community facilities enhanced.

Although an experimental scheme, this 'tale of two villages', as it was called, has generated some useful practices that are being adopted Europe-wide. IRD is felt particularly to be useful in remoter rural areas and other areas that are economically marginal where in the early years of the European

---

Box 5.1   Integrated Rural Development

Policies for the countryside have long been devised on a sectoral basis. In other words, they are separately designed to specifically serve the interests of agriculture, forestry, recreation, conservation and so on. Although they may be applied locally, the fact that they are originated by central government means that they are 'top down' in their approach. Integrated rural development seeks to stand much of this more traditional way of thinking on its head to positive effect.

Integrated rural development (IRD) as a concept can be summarised in three key words – *individuality*, *involvement* and *interdependence*.

'Individuality' means looking at rural areas as they are and recognising in their individuality a source of economic strength, social identity and environmental character. Different parts of the country are manifestly unalike. If public policies tend to treat rural areas as if they were the same, administrative convenience may be served, but there is a danger of masking or even destroying the individual identity of these different areas.

'Involvement' means trying to involve local communities in thinking about their own future and in working out and putting into practice their own ideas for improving that future. Such work can concentrate on solving problems, but people are encouraged to think positively – to improve their economic position, their social life or their environment.

'Interdependence' means looking at individual rural areas as a whole. Rural areas do not consist of a set of absolutely distinct interests. Society wants rural areas to provide food and a whole range of other resources to meet its needs. It also wants it to offer an attractive environment for recreation, opportunities for the conservation of wildlife and reasonable living conditions for a significant proportion of the population. The achievement of any one of these objectives can affect others for good or ill. IRD aims to eliminate any actions that may produce harmful side-effects. More positively, it tries to devise measures that encourage actions which create benefits for social, economic and environmental interests simultaneously.

◄ *Longnor and Monyash in the Peak National Park have been the subject of the best-known integrated rural development experiment of the 1980s. (Above) Longnor workshops (microplant) and (below) the new village hall in Monyash.*

Community concern for rural development involved only structural measures under the Less Favoured Areas Directive. Because of this a number of lessons from the whole of the European Commission IRD experiments are being adopted in a special agricultural package to assist poorer Mediterranean areas, known as the 'Integrated Mediterranean Programme'.

6.2   The enterprise economy and the urban countryside

Remoter rural areas may therefore be nurtured into economic growth through a system of integrating and co-ordinating competing demands on the countryside of the United Kingdom. But the pressures and the prospects

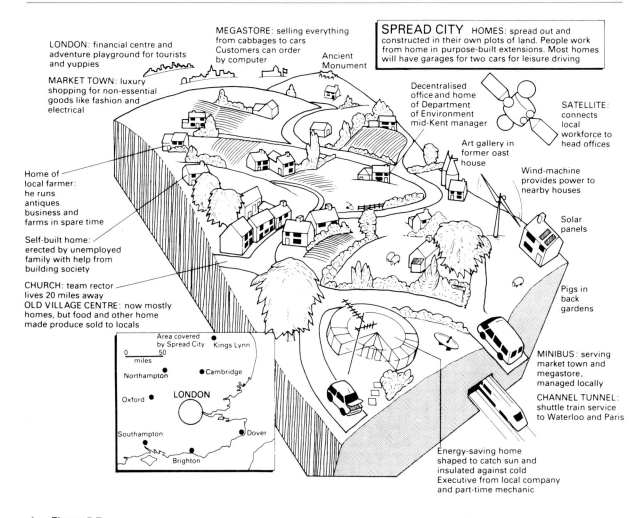

LONDON: financial centre and adventure playground for tourists and yuppies

MARKET TOWN: luxury shopping for non-essential goods like fashion and electrical

MEGASTORE: selling everything from cabbages to cars Customers can order by computer

Ancient Monument

SPREAD CITY   HOMES: spread out and constructed in their own plots of land. People work from home in purpose-built extensions. Most homes will have garages for two cars for leisure driving

Decentralised office and home of Department of Environment mid-Kent manager

SATELLITE: connects local workforce to head offices

Art gallery in former oast house

Wind-machine provides power to nearby houses

Home of local farmer: he runs antiques business and farms in spare time

Self-built home: erected by unemployed family with help from building society

Solar panels

CHURCH: team rector lives 20 miles away
OLD VILLAGE CENTRE: now mostly homes, but food and other home made produce sold to locals

Pigs in back gardens

Area covered by Spread City   Kings Lynn
0   50
miles
Northampton   Cambridge
Oxford   LONDON
Southampton   Dover
Brighton

MINIBUS: serving market town and megastore, managed locally

CHANNEL TUNNEL: shuttle train service to Waterloo and Paris

Energy-saving home shaped to catch sun and insulated against cold Executive from local company and part-time mechanic

▲   Figure 5.7
Spread City – a vision of the future? By early in the twenty-first century will we have a semi-urbanised countryside similar to that shown in this diagram, stretching from Cambridge to Bournemouth and from Oxford to Dover?

for the future of communities and land uses in lowland areas may be very different. Here, particularly with the relaxation of planning controls under the 1987 Circular *Development Involving Agricultural Land*, much more pressure for development for both housing and high-tech industry is becoming apparent and this is leading to many areas taking on the appearance of an urban countryside.

The likely development in this direction has been termed 'Spread City', shown in Figure 5.7. This means that essentially most of south-east England will have an urban mentality and lifestyle. Most shopping, whether you live in a town or not, will be done in out-of-town megastores. Village shops will sell only antiques and luxury items. Alternative technology will lead to smaller more sustainable 'homesteads' and many people will work from home or from 'tele-cottages' as they have been called. Here, computers, telephones, fax machines and eventually satellite 'interactive' television will obviate the need to meet face to face to do business. As Box 5.2 explains, it could be the way forward for non-commuting rural communities away from large metropolitan areas.

<hr>

Box 5.2   The Electronic Village: a vision for the future?

Accessibility – whether to education or jobs – is increasingly becoming a problem for some country people. But one solution could be a growing network of village projects, in the United Kingdom and across the world, that are linked by the latest communications technology.

The concept of the 'tele-cottage' was launched in 1985 in a small village in a remote area near Sweden's Norwegian border. Vemdalen, a winter ski resort and forestry area, had only limited employment opportunities and a falling population. But the tele-cottage, the concept of a Swedish businessman, has changed all this. The tele-cottage is equipped with fifteen personal computers and word-processors, telex, fax and teletext equipment and satellite television receivers, all financed by local and central government and locally raised funds.

In it:

- children and adults have opportunities to learn new technologies

- formal education and self-study in computer uses relevant to business and private needs can take place without the need to travel to distant colleges

- tradespeople can try out computer programs and be trained in skills such as book-keeping, and they can use telex, fax and electronic mail service facilities

- access is possible to international databases, broadcasts and other users of electronic communications

- people can find a social meeting place since the cottages are equipped with a lounge and kitchen

- local people can work for employers many miles away via the computer technology without travel costs or wasted time.

Thirty-five tele-cottages exist in Sweden and there are others under way in Norway, Finland, Austria, France, Ireland and West Germany. In the United Kingdom the first tele-cottage was opened on 16 December 1989 at Warslow, near Leek in Staffordshire, funded by the County Council and the Rural Development Commission. British Telecom is now sponsoring the scheme and has joined forces with the Highlands and Islands Development Board to establish tele-cottages in Islay, Stornaway, Orkney, Shetland and Argyll.

6.3   Rural welfare

Given the strong possibility of this kind of 'Spread City' vision in less remote areas, it is now incumbent on government and its agencies to extract the benefits from such developments, and minimise the drawbacks. One of the prevailing features of the past ten years of 'market economics' policies has been the lack of any really significant policies to enhance rural welfare. 'Spread City' could be a welcome vision for some, but remains a vision of affluence. In parts of lowland Britain, many rural-dwellers have either drifted or been displaced to the town since the War and the cost of country property has led to an incoming, single-class rural society (as was noted in Section 2.4). If such a trend continues there may ultimately be no need for policies of rural welfare, since all the less well-off will have left.

But for people now working as opposed to only living in the countryside, wages are still lower and job opportunities fewer than in the towns. In the remoter areas unemployment can be high or employment, at best, seasonal, and underemployment can be a particular problem for women. In areas with high house prices, this can lead to significant rural deprivation and further out-migration. This situation is already leading to shortages of labour for rural work and an unbalanced economy. So much so, that in some parts of south-east England, villagers have to 'bus' people in from the nearest town to do house-cleaning and gardening jobs.

As the dependence on the countryside for work diminishes and the less affluent move out, the downward spiralling effect on services that was referred to earlier must continue. Village shops will close, and public transport diminish and so on, because the orientation of the affluent country-dweller is towards the town or its peripheral megastore for shopping and this is invariably reached by private car.

There is thus a policy challenge into the 1990s, not only to bring the land uses of the countryside into greater environmental harmony at a time of food surpluses, but also to ensure a balanced community in the countryside to avoid affluent ghettoing and the danger that the countryside could end up as a place of private affluence but public deprivation.

References

BLUNDEN, J. and REDDISH, A. (eds) (1991) *Energy, Resources and Environment*, London, Hodder and Stoughton/The Open University (Book Three of this series).

SARRE, P. (1990) 'Environmental issues in Cumbria', Chapter 1 in Silvertown, J. and Sarre, P. (eds) *Environment and Society*, London, Hodder and Stoughton/The Open University (Book One of this series).

Further reading

BLUNDEN, J. R. and CURRY, N. (eds) (1985) *The Changing Countryside*, produced by The Open University in association with the Countryside Commission, London, Croom Helm.

BLUNDEN, J. R. and CURRY, N. (eds) (1989) *A Future for Our Countryside* (2nd edn), Oxford, Blackwell.

MACEWEN, A. and MACEWEN, M. (1987) *Greenprints for the Countryside? The story of Britain's national parks*, London, Allen and Unwin.

NEWBY, H. (1985) *Green and Pleasant Land? Social change in rural England* (2nd edn), London, Wildwood House.

Answer to Activities

Activity 3

Beneficiaries have been:

(a) the public who, before entry to the EEC, enjoyed 'cheap' food subsidised by Exchequer (deficiency) payments and stable levels of production;

(b) large cereal producers who became wealthy as a result of preferential price support for their output;

(c) upland farmers who were able to stay in business as result of Less Favoured Areas and Farm Modernisation Directives;

(d) land-owners, who have seen land values rise faster than inflation partly as a result of agricultural price support;

(e) farm machinery, fertiliser and pesticide manufacturers taking advantage of the replacement of labour by capital and the move to monoculture systems.

Losers have been:

(a) the public, who after the United Kingdom joined the EEC saw a transition from 'cheap' to 'expensive' food, with inflated prices now falling directly on the consumer, to the disadvantage of the least well-off;

(b) agricultural workers, many of whom have had to leave the land and, for those who stayed, low wages compared with industrial rates;

(c) upland stock farmers, compared with others in the agricultural sector, since their levels of support were generally less favourable;

(d) the wider rural community, since agricultural policy has paid little heed to the non-farming population, the increasing affluence of farmers often existing side by side with growing rural deprivation;

(e) the conservationist, with a reduction in the variety of flora and fauna, especially in lowland England.

Activity 4

28 000 hectares in extent, and lying astride the boundaries of Norfolk and Suffolk, the Broads is a delicately balanced system of shallow, reed-lined lakes (or broads), slow-moving wide rivers, marsh-grazing lands and fens. But in this area a number of conflicting demands – from recreation, agriculture, liquid waste disposal and the changing socio-economic character of the area in general – can be seen to have interacted with consequences for its wildlife and landscape.

For example, looking at the diagram, the discharge of sewage effluent containing phosphorus into the river system, combined with nitrogenous

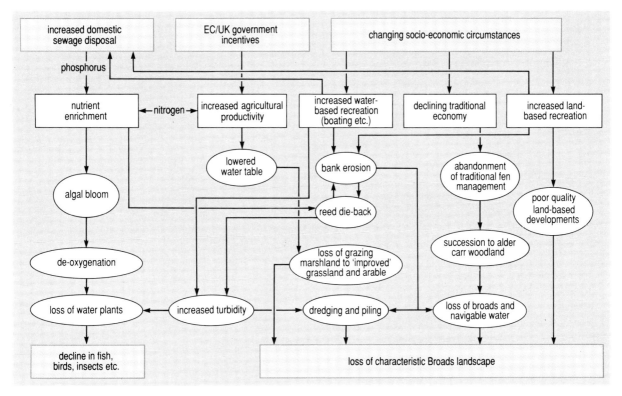

▲   *The Norfolk Broads: a web of interactions*

fertiliser run-off from the surrounding fields, has created a nutrient-rich medium. The algal content of the waters as a result has increased massively, leading to oxygen loss, damage to plant life and, in turn, a decline in the diversity of flora and fauna. Also, the greater use of powered pleasure-craft on the waterways (which feeds back into the need for more local sewage disposal) has churned up the mud, again with adverse effects on the reed-beds, and thus has added to the problems for wildlife. Without reeds to support the banks of the broads and rivers, these have had to be artificially secured with piles, thus diminishing the traditional character of the area.

You can follow other interactive pathways through the diagram for yourself. But note that 'traditional economy' in the context of fen management involves the harvesting of reeds as material for thatching. Failure to do this eventually allows the growth of woody plant species which ultimately invade the open broads.

◄ *Reedmarsh and windpumps – a typical Broads landscape. The harvesting of reeds is not only part of the traditional economy of the Broads – they are used for thatching – but it is also an important element in the preservation of wildlife habitats.*

1   Introduction

The previous chapter ended by looking at the pressures on rural areas near British cities. This chapter explores the urban environment, more generally in the first world and then at the inner-city areas in Britain. The focus is on the causes of the 'urban problems' which allegedly make large cities unattractive living environments. However, to understand these contemporary problems it is necessary to set them in a historical context. This includes both the factual history of the development of great cities, which links back to Chapter 1, and a debate with a much longer span about the relative merits of the city and the country.

Reactions to the city and to urban life have long been sharply polarised. On the one hand, there are those who equate the word city with its Latin root 'civitas' and its derivative 'civilisation' and look back to the city-states of Athens and Rome as the seat of contemporary western civilisation. Indeed, almost all ancient civilisations including the Sumerian, the Indo-Gangetic and the Egyptian were based around some form of urban settlement. The ancient Greeks and Romans viewed cities as centres of culture and civilisation (despite the undoubted environmental problems of Rome) and this positive view of cities was also common during the Middle Ages when European city-states were centres of wealth, trade, culture and learning. Because serfs could become 'freemen' after living in a city for a year it was said that *'Stadtluft macht frei'*, literally 'city air makes free'. This view of cities was given its most eloquent expression by Samuel Johnson who commented in the mid eighteenth century: 'When a man is tired of London, he is tired of life; for there is in London all that life can afford.'

On the other hand, there are those who view cities and urban life as 'nasty, brutish and short'. Cities are seen as dirty, run-down and decaying, offering precious little civilisation and many dangers and disadvantages. There is a case that this view came to prominence in Britain from the early nineteenth century onwards with the advent of widespread urban industrialism, a point which is discussed in Section 2. In this respect, the timing of Dr Johnson's comment about London is interesting. Would he have said the same a hundred years later? His view is obviously not shared by the hundreds of thousands of people who have moved out of London in the last few decades. One of them, a well-known journalist, sets out why he is tired of London in Box 6.1.

Activity 1

Read the article by Kellner and answer the following questions:

Q1 In what way are the problems Kellner describes 'environmental'?

Q2 Are there different types of problem involved?

Q3 What kind of explanations does he offer?

Compare your answers with those given at the end of the chapter.

Kellner's article is a typical expression of a common contemporary belief that cities have inherent problems which reach their worst form in the inner city. Like most commonsense accounts of urban or inner-city problems, it involves many strands – physical, social and behavioural – and is unclear about what causes what. Explanations are easier to find for the physical problems, but very much more difficult for the social and behavioural ones which take a variety of different forms.

First, people in cities are frequently said to behave differently from people in small towns or rural areas. They are believed to be impersonal, rude, aggressive and unfriendly, and the bigger the city, the worse the behaviour. The reputation of New Yorkers and Parisians is legendary in this sphere, and myths abound about the foolishness of asking New York police

---

Box 6.1   Peter Kellner: A capital example of British rot

Only when I moved to Cambridgeshire last year did I realise quite how shabby London had become. Like most Londoners I had grown used to its filth, its fumes, its hazards and its humidity. Now, as an intermittent commuter, I wonder why anyone – certainly anyone with children – would choose to live in London out of preference rather than out of necessity.

An accumulation of news stories has confirmed my fierce new prejudice against city life. Recent reports of chronic teacher shortages in Tower Hamlets – where children have to stay at home because there is nobody to teach them – are only the latest. For example:

●   Teacher shortages are by no means confined to London, but the city's recruitment problems are worse than elsewhere. Teachers are being sought in Ireland, Scotland, Germany and Australia. The National Association of Head Teachers has advised its members in inner London to send pupils home if they do not have enough staff to go round [. . .]

●   London's hospitals are suffering the same kind of stress as its schools, and for many of the same reasons: nurses and junior doctors are faced with frightening housing and/or transport costs, and have difficulty making ends meet. Their talents are in demand throughout the country. Cash incomes elsewhere are slightly lower, but living costs are significantly less, so they enjoy greater spending power and a superior quality of life. For those who stay, morale has been sapped by a succession of closures – such as when the Brompton Hospital in Fulham had to close half its paediatric intensive care unit [. . .]

●   London's fabric is rotting. Inadequate investment, training and staffing have already contributed to the King's Cross and Clapham Junction disasters. At a more routine level, human beings are forced to travel on the Underground in conditions that would be banned if we were animals [. . .] Investment [. . .] has failed to match demand.

●   One problem that some London Transport staff must tackle is rats. Some have been issued with sticks to ward them off platforms. One estimate suggests that London's rat population has grown by 50 per cent in the last few years. Barnet Council has warned residents to keep out of the borough's rivers and streams lest they catch Weil's disease, a potentially fatal disease spread by rats' urine. One Lambeth pest controller reports that '98 per cent of the rat cases we deal with involve sewers which have crumbled' [. . .]

●   London now resembles the kind of American city that gave rise to Tom Lehrer's advice: 'Don't drink the water and don't breathe the air.' Even the pigs notice: some who arrived at Hyde Park in May for a farming festival refused to drink London's recycled, chemical-infested water, as it was not as fresh as the Welsh spring water they were used to. In Epping Forest, a recent study by Bob Johnston, a plant physiologist from Oxford Polytechnic, found 45 per cent of the trees dead or dying from air pollution.

●   Humans are affected, too. The highly publicised outbreaks of legionnaires' disease mark the extreme end of an ominous scale. According to Patrick O'Sullivan, professor of architectural science at the University of Wales, a rapidly growing number of people are falling victim to 'sick building syndrome', which is partly the result of air-conditioning that fails to filter out pollutants in the atmosphere.

●   Although other cities have their hell holes, London as a whole is more dangerous than any other conurbation. Londoners are more likely to be

for directions – 'Go and buy a street directory, bud'. People in small towns and villages, by contrast, are widely believed to be polite and helpful. The implicit suggestion is that there is something about the size, environment or social structure of cities which affects social behaviour. As one writer put it:

> When I first came to New York it seemed like a nightmare. As soon as I got off the train at Grand Central I was caught up in pushing, shoving crowds on 42nd Street. Sometimes people bumped into me without apology; what really frightened me was to see two people literally engaged in combat for possession of a cab. Why were they so rushed? Even drunks on the street were bypassed without a glance. People didn't seem to care about each other at all.   (quoted in Milgram, 1970, p.1461)

assaulted, burgled, or run over than anyone else in mainland Britain, and the capital's villains are less likely to be caught. One compelling index of risk is provided by insurance companies. By moving to Cambridgeshire, my car insurance premium has been halved and my home contents insurance cut by two-thirds. My insurance company has nine rates for home contents insurance. The two highest rates cover 136 postal districts. Ninety of these are in London.

That catalogue of London hazards is incomplete. It does not include the background, low-level squalor that statistics and news reports pass by: increased begging, vagrancy, rubbish in the streets, uncleaned pavements, the stress, the smells, the noise.

Nor, I admit, does it include the attractions of London, although sometimes these are over-rated. It is possible to make too much of the fact that London's orchestras match any in Lower Saxony, that its theatres show more Alan Ayckbourn plays than any other city in the world, and that its football matches occasionally end in fewer than 10 arrests.

Perhaps Londoners accept too much too readily. If they all swapped homes with Parisians for a week, I have little doubt that they would demand the same low fares, efficient tube system and daily street cleaning. Instead a slower, but eventually more telling, reaction is taking place. People like me are rejecting today's London by settling elsewhere.

In the 1950s, more than eight million people lived in greater London. By the 1970s its population was declining rapidly, by 88 000 a year. During the recession of the early Thatcher years, London's population stabilised at 6.8 million: evacuees were matched by new arrivals looking for work. Now the exodus has started again. The latest figures from the Government's census office show that London's population fell by 30 000 last year.

My family accounted for five of them. We settled in a village and quickly discovered the tangible meaning of the phrase 'quality of life'. The children go out in safety to play with their friends. Our windows are free of grime and our walls free of graffiti. People talk to each other in the post office.

Traffic fumes are absent. Crack is unknown, truancy rare. The schools, hospital and health centre we use are as full of confidence as the Government's mean and disruptive policies allow. In last month's heatwave, when London was unbearable, our village was merely hot.

We are not – yet – typical. Most people who leave London move to the outer suburbs or new towns. Many travel back to the capital daily to work: hence the enormous increase in commuter journeys on British Rail and the continuing congestion in the centre of London.

It is a process reminiscent of the one that started some years earlier in New York. The pressure on the city's resources continues – in some respects, increases – but fewer and fewer people live locally to finance them. Local taxes rise and public services crack up [. . .]

Left to itself and market forces, this process has an inescapable logic. The trends are already visible. London is becoming polarised between those who are trapped and those who can buy their way out of trouble. Weekend cottages, private schools, health insurance, security guards, taxis and water filters are all available to those who can afford them. Everyone else must make do, or leave.

Those most able to leave, however, are precisely those whom London most needs – trained people with portable skills such as teaching or nursing. Unskilled people have fewer chances to find work and affordable housing elsewhere. It ought to shock, but not to surprise, that London combines pockets of some of Britain's greatest wealth with some of its worst unemployment; and within walking distance of each other [. . .]

Source: *The Independent*, 7 August 1989

Secondly, cities are commonly associated with the prevalence of a wide variety of social pathologies. Incidence of crime, divorce, mental illness and drug use are alleged to be greater in cities than in small towns or rural areas, where people are believed to be more upright, law-abiding and socially integrated. On the face of it, there seems to be evidence for some of these beliefs. The murder rate in Washington, DC, a city of 750 000 (excluding the surrounding suburbs), is now 1000 a year, a large proportion of which are drug-related killings; there, young black males, the victims of most killings, face a 1 in 10 chance of violent death or injury before they are twenty-five (*The Economist*, 1989). Nor are such problems confined to US cities, though they are particularly severe there because of the large, unemployed underclass and ready availability of firearms. In Liverpool, Glasgow and other British cities there are widespread concerns over the incidence of hard drug use. Such 'evidence' is partial and selective and we would need a much more rigorous empirical analysis to draw any conclusions, but the central core of beliefs is still strong: cities have more social problems than towns or villages.

The third belief goes beyond the mere identification of social problems in cities or their alleged higher incidence, to suggest that there may be something about urban environments which *causes* social problems. Particular parts of cities, especially the inner cities and some peripheral council estates, often possess run-down environments and contain concentrations of poverty, unemployment and poor housing. These areas are often linked with problems of social breakdown and disorder. The urban riots or disturbances in the United States in the 1960s and in Britain in the 1980s were almost all concentrated in the inner cities. This sometimes leads to the view that social problems are caused *by* the inner cities or something in or about them. As Peter Wilshire and Rosemary Righter put it in a colour supplement report in the mid 1970s:

> Britain's cities are rotting at the core. Even in such traditionally pleasant spots as Exeter and Edinburgh the symptoms are beginning to show. Boarded up businesses and derelict sites; slum pockets and vandalised high-rise blocks; shrinking job opportunities; lengthening unemployment queues; rising welfare bills. The change has been swift and dramatic. It was first realized ten years ago that some inner-city districts were becoming chronic *generators* of deprivation and poverty . . . What has gone wrong?   (emphasis added)

What is being asserted here goes beyond the previous two beliefs, in that it is suggested that inner urban areas do not merely have concentrations of social problems, but may actually cause them. There is a related belief, that certain built forms, particularly high-rise or deck-access housing, are a cause of social problems such as delinquency, assault and burglary or that they provide an ideal environment for such things to occur. By contrast, semi-detached suburbia is often seen as a haven of order and tranquillity. This form of **physical environmental determinism** was given expression by Winston Churchill who said: 'We make our buildings, and then our buildings make us'.

There has been no evidence provided to back up any of the statements in this chapter so far. They are simply generalizations about the range of popular views about the role of the urban environment in shaping or influencing human behaviour. But you will probably recognise some of them, and agree that they raise a number of important issues concerning the environment in which most of us – nearly 80% in Britain – live.

Throughout the chapter the focus of attention is on the question of whether cities, parts of cities or specific urban environments are the *cause* of some sorts of human behaviour or social problems. I stress the word *cause* because there is a big difference between the argument that certain behaviours or problems are merely concentrated in cities or specific environments within them and the argument that they are the cause of these problems. This is the difference between **statistical correlation** and **causality**. As these terms are extremely important but may be unfamiliar to you, they are briefly explained in Box 6.2 using house prices as an example.

Q   Can you think of any recent beliefs or arguments about urban problems which suggest different causal relationships between people and their built environment?

A   Some examples are:

  ● The 'cycle of deprivation': this argument, which influenced some Cabinet ministers, was that inadequate parents brought up inadequate children, who tended to live in substandard areas and become inadequate parents. The causation is social.

  ● The notion of 'sink estates': this suggested that public housing areas could go into a vicious cycle of decline where physically poorer areas would be allocated more disruptive families, who would fail to keep up their homes and vandalise public spaces, driving away more respectable residents and increasing the concentration of rough residents. Here social processes exaggerate initially small physical differences.

Box 6.2   Correlation and causation

In the United States house prices are generally higher in the south and west of the country than they are in the north and east. Research has been done which examined the variation in house prices between different urban areas in the US and tried to relate house price differences to a number of other variables to see if there was any statistical relationship between the two (Stutz and Kartman, 1982). The statistically most important variable linked with house price differences was, believe it or not, diurnal (or daily) temperature variation: high median house prices were generally linked with cities with a high diurnal temperature variation and vice versa. That is to say, house price and temperature variations were *statistically correlated*. Does this mean that the two were causally related? In other words, did one cause the other? We can immediately rule out any idea that house prices are a cause of temperature variations, but is it possible that temperature variations cause house price variations?

Q   Can you think of any causal relationship(s) that link temperature range and house prices?

My answer is given below, but before you read on, pause and try to answer the question. You will find this a valuable exercise in developing your analytical abilities.

A   There is no possible *direct* link, but there is perhaps an *indirect* one through the well-documented role of population migration from the cold north-east of the US to the warm south and south-west (known as the Sun-belt), with demand for houses being higher in the south-west than it is in the north-east. Also, because the south-west is generally more economically prosperous than the north-east and has higher average incomes, this will force up house prices. But, as you can see, this is a long way from postulating a direct link between house prices and temperature variation.

Unfortunately causation and correlation are often confused, and this is particularly so where cities are concerned. Because some problems are concentrated in cities, it is easy to jump to the conclusion that they are caused by cities.

The existence of different 'commonsense' explanations for similar or related urban problems is extremely important because policies to solve problems are likely to fail unless they address the real causes. If the physical environment causes the social problems, rebuilding may be an appropriate solution, but if the causes are social, rebuilding will be futile. The first step towards solving urban environmental problems must be to unravel their causes, and this will be the principal concern of this chapter.

The simple example in Box 6.2 not only illustrates the difference between correlation and causation, but also provides an important clue to how causes can be disentangled. In part, this is a matter of logical analysis of the possible mechanisms which might link the phenomena in question, which should be followed by a search for evidence that those mechanisms actually occur. But in many cases it is easier to seek for underlying causes in a complex like 'the inner-city problem' by studying change through time: logically, causes must occur before effects. Unfortunately this simple principle sometimes meets the difficulty that, as the concept of a sink estate suggested, the cause-and-effect relationship may be cyclical, so this strategy becomes similar to asking 'which comes first, the chicken or the egg?' Often, however, historical analysis can help us to disentangle complex causal relations.

For this chapter, historical analysis has two further advantages. First, it allows us to connect contemporary urban problems to Chapter 1 and the analysis of industrialisation and population change: this puts the urban problem into a global and historical perspective that is more relevant to other environmental issues than a myopic analysis of current British cities would be. The second advantage of a historical analysis is that it allows us to draw on some of the earlier theorists who began to probe the causes of urban problems and see their analyses in relation to the times in which they lived.

The attempt to unravel the causes of urban problems in the developed world through historical and theoretical analysis is carried out in Sections 2 and 3. Section 4 then returns to the contemporary inner-city problem, with two aims: to carry out the same kind of theoretical analysis of causal relationships at work today and then to evaluate the successes and failures of recent policies, both in practical terms and as 'experiments' in which certain changes were made and experience showed whether these were changes to root causes or to symptoms.

2 Do urban environments influence attitudes and behaviour?

As the introduction showed, there is a body of popular opinion that holds that living in cities generates changes in behaviour and thereby a variety of social problems. Because these views first emerged in the late nineteenth and early twentieth centuries, it is important to place the debate in its historical context, principally the rise of rapid, large-scale urbanisation in Europe and North America at that time. The rise of the industrial city was a radical break with the previous rural society, and poets, writers and social scientists tried to describe and analyse urban life from the early nineteenth century onwards. The dominant reaction was one of shock and horror, and this reaction has arguably influenced our views of cities ever since. These reactions will be outlined shortly. First, however, it is appropriate to briefly describe the scale and impact of rapid urban growth. (You may wish to refer back to Chapter 1 at this point.)

2.1   The nineteenth-century growth of the urban population

In 1800 Britain was still a largely rural and agricultural society, though already playing an important part in world trade. Of a population of 10.6 million, only 20% lived in towns of over 10 000 and half of them lived in London which had a population of one million – the largest city in the world. Liverpool, Manchester and Birmingham had all grown rapidly to populations of 60–75 000, but they were exceptions: only ten other towns had populations of over 10 000. By 1901 Britain, however, had been dramatically transformed into the world's first urbanised society. Some 25 million, or 77%, of the population now lived in the much larger towns and cities: Birmingham and Manchester had both grown to over 500 000 people and London had grown to 6.5 million. In some previously rural areas the increase was even more impressive: Middlesbrough, for example, had grown from just 25 people to 91 000 during the nineteenth century. A new class of industrial cities had sprung up where none had existed before. The rate of population growth in Manchester in the early decades of the nineteenth century was particularly remarkable: it grew at 30% a decade and has been termed 'the shock city of the 1840s'.

This rapid growth of the urban population was partly the result of high birth rates in the cities, but given the very high death rates the key to urban growth was the high rate of rural to urban migration. Urban population growth was not matched by equivalent levels of new building, and because of the poor urban transport system and the absence of large-scale suburbanisation, the result was an extremely dense, ill-equipped and tightly packed form of development. The level of overcrowding in the central and inner areas of London, Liverpool, Manchester, Glasgow and Birmingham was scarcely believable by contemporary western standards. Houses were divided and sub-divided, the back courtyards were built on and cellar dwellings were created. Whole families were forced by poverty to live in one room. The parallels are more with third world cities than with contemporary western ones.

The empirical evidence for high population densities and high levels of overcrowding in nineteenth-century cities is well documented. According to the 1891 census, 20% of the population of London lived in overcrowded conditions, defined as more than two persons per room, in tenements of less than five rooms; in the central areas 30–40% lived in such conditions. If those living at two per room are included in overcrowding statistics (the measure used by Charles Booth in his pioneering investigations), then the proportion rises to between 36 and 60% of the population in the central areas of London. Similar figures have been documented for Liverpool where many people lived in the infamous 'cellar dwellings', Glasgow where overcrowded tenement blocks dominated, and cities such as Nottingham where 'back-to-backs' were commonplace.

◄ *The tenements of Glasgow.*

2.2   The nineteenth-century urban environment and ill-health

There is no doubt that the nineteenth-century urban environment, particularly the very poorly built, damp and overcrowded working-class housing which frequently lacked water and basic sanitation, had marked detrimental effects on health and death rates. In her book, *Cruel Habitations*, Enid Gauldie notes that:

> The shortage of accommodation sent town rents for decent housing beyond the pockets of the labourer, and cellars, shacks and sub-divided rooms were all that were left for him [sic]. Unpaved and undrained streets degenerated everywhere in quagmires. Refuse piled up. Water ran dry. Roofs leaked rain, floors rotted, walls bulged and the back courts overflowed with sewerage.   (1974, p. 73)

The results were predictable. In his Report, *Sanitary Conditions of the Labouring Population* (1842), Edwin Chadwick, a pioneer of urban public health reform, showed that average life expectancy of labourers in Liverpool was 15 years compared to 35 years for professionals and the gentry. Much of the difference stemmed from the fact that 62% of labourers' children died before the age of 5. Common causes of death were pneumonia, typhus and cholera, but as typhus was louse-carried and attacked dirty people living in bad conditions, the middle classes were not concerned: it seemed only just. It was not until the cholera epidemic of 1848 which crossed class and income groups with impunity that the establishment pressure for sanitary reform grew. Chadwick's pioneering work bore fruit in the 1848 Public Health Act.

   Although concrete achievement was not very great, with the government refusing to introduce any element of compulsion into legislation, local authorities were given the power (not a duty) to appoint public health officers. In addition Local Boards of Health *could* be established

◀   A famous engraving by Gustave Doré showing the dense development of London.

if either the local authority or 10% of ratepayers requested it, or if the average death rate over seven years exceeded 23 per thousand. The Local Boards could also be given the power to provide a continuous pure water supply if they requested it. Improvements were slow, but as Gauldie observes: 'It was a great achievement to have *public* health as a concept recognised on the statute books. Individualism was the dominant philosophy' (1974, p. 133). The Act was even less effective where housing was concerned because although it laid down that no new houses were to be built without adequate drains or a sufficient water-closet, privy or ash-pit, the conditions were too imprecise to be enforceable and the means of enforcing them were not built into the Act.

The pressure for effective legislation was growing, however, and in 1866 the Sanitary Act was passed, masterminded by John Simon, the Medical Officer for the General Board of Health. The Act gave wide powers to councils to control overcrowding and to designate some dwellings as 'unfit for human habitation'. These powers were also strengthened in the Sanitary Law Amendment Act 1874 which gave councils the power to make regulations regarding ventilation of rooms, the paving and drainage of premises and segregation of the sexes. Finally, the Public Health Act 1890 allowed councils to ensure that WCs were supplied with adequate water for flushing, and to control building structures, room heights, minimum street widths and the like. The foundations were in place to ensure a minimum level of housing and sanitary provision for the twentieth century.

It is clear that the nineteenth-century urban environment, like the urban environment in the third world today, had a very detrimental effect on health and mortality, but what of social behaviour in general? The following sections examine some of the nineteenth- and early twentieth-century analyses of urban social behaviour in an attempt to see how far this was seen as a product of cities or of modern society in general.

2.3   Nineteenth-century writing and the experience of urban life

> The English are town birds through and through. Yet they don't know how to build a city, how to think of one, or how to live in one.
> (D. H. Lawrence)

Not surprisingly, the rapid growth of the large cities and the social conditions within them, led many contemporary observers to try to describe and analyse the new urban world they encountered. The literary reaction was one of bafflement and revulsion against what were seen as new forms of social behaviour found in cities, particularly the anonymity and isolation of social life. The work of Dickens abounds with descriptions of the new urban life, and in 'Residence in London' William Wordsworth wrote of:

> How men lived
> Even next-door neighbours, as we say, yet still
> Strangers, nor knowing each the other's name.
> O Friend! one feeling was there which belonged
> To this great city, by exclusive right:
> How often, in the overflowing streets,
> Have I gone forwards with the crowd, and said
> Unto myself, 'The face of every one
> That passes me by is a mystery!'

Raymond Williams in his major book, *The Country and the City* (1973), suggests that these lines were the first expression of what subsequently became the dominant urban experience – strangeness, isolation, loss of connection and of self-identity in the anonymous crowd. Nor were these sentiments confined to poets and novelists. In *The Condition of the Working Class in England in 1844*, Friedrich Engels, the industrialist and collaborator of Karl Marx, wrote:

> The very turmoil of the streets has something repulsive, against which human nature rebels. The hundreds of thousands of all classes and all ranks crowding past each other, are they not all human beings with the same qualities and powers, and with the same interest in being happy? And (yet) they crowd by one another as though they had nothing in common, nothing to do with one another, and their only agreement is the tacit one, that each keep to his own side of the pavement, so as not to delay the opposing streams of the crowd, while it occurs to no man to honour another with so much as a glance. The brutal indifference, the unfeeling isolation of each in his private interests becomes the more repellent and offensive, the more these individuals are crowded together, within a limited space. And, however much one may be aware that *this isolation of the individual, this narrow self-seeking is the fundamental principle of our society everywhere, it is nowhere so shamelessly barefaced, so self-conscious as just here in the crowding of the great city*. The dissolution of mankind into monads, of which each one has a separate principle, the world of atoms, is here carried to its utmost extremes.   (pp. 57–8; emphasis added)

This argument developed the perceptual confusion and ambivalence which Wordsworth and others identified into a wider analysis of the human condition within **urban and industrial capitalism**. It should be added that though Engels saw this condition as 'the fundamental principle of our society everywhere', he also saw it as being particularly manifest in the great cities, where it was 'carried to its utmost extreme'. This is a very important point to which I will return in Section 3. What Engels seems to suggest is that there are two levels of causality. The first and most important one is linked to the advent of industrial society in general, and the second is associated with urban concentration which intensifies the first.

In his writing, Engels concentrated on the poverty and squalor of working-class existence in the new industrial cities. But while other writers recognised this, they were often more concerned with the threat posed by the rise of a new urban proletariat. In 1842 in *Notes of a Tour in the Manufacturing Districts of Lancashire*, Cooke Taylor had this to say of Manchester:

> As a stranger passes through the masses of human beings which have been accumulated round the mills and print-works in this and the neighbouring towns, he cannot contemplate those 'crowded hives' without feelings of anxiety and apprehension almost amounting to dismay.   (p. 6)

◀   *A traffic jam in Ludgate Hill: 'The very turmoil of the streets . . .'*

Similar views were expressed sixty years later by Masterman in *The English City*:

> To some observers the change excites only a lament over a past that is
> forever gone. They mourn the vanishing of a vigorous jolly life, the . . .
> secure and confident life of 'Merrie England'. To others, again, the
> change is one charged with a menace to the future. They dread the
> fermenting in the populous cities, of some new, all-powerful
> explosive, destined one day to shatter into ruin all their social order.
> In these massed millions of an obscure life, dimly understood and ever
> increasing in magnitude, they behold a danger to security and all
> pleasant things.   (1904, p. 61)

What is clear from these quotations is that the industrial town was linked to
the working class and was feared because the working class was seen as
frightening. This fear reinforced existing deep-rooted, anti-urban
sentiments in Britain which were linked to the dominance of the land-
owning interests. But, if the fear of the urban working class reinforced
anti-urbanism in Britain (Glass, 1955), it also led to a fear that urban living
caused the mental and physical decline of the working class. The theory of
urban degeneration which was put forward in the late nineteenth century in
Britain is discussed below.

2.4   Late nineteenth-century theories of urban degeneration

> The child of the townsman is bred too fine, is too great an exaggeration
> of himself, excitable and painfully precocious in its childhood,
> neurotic, dyspeptic, pale and undersized in its adult state, if it ever
> reaches it.   (Dr J. P. Freeman-Williams (1890) *The Effect of Town Life on
> the General Health*, p. 5)

Gareth Stedman Jones, on whose book *Outcast London* (1971) this section is
based, states that the theory of hereditary urban degeneration received
widespread support from a number of eminent statisticians in the 1880s and
1890s. In 1893 Longstaff wrote in the *Journal of the Royal Statistical Society*
that:

> . . . the narrow chest, the pale face, the weak eyes, the bad teeth, of the
> town-bred child are but too often apparent. It is easy to take an
> exaggerated view . . . but the broad facts are evident enough; long life
> in the towns is accompanied by more or less degeneration of
> race.   (quoted in Stedman Jones, 1971, p. 128)

It was widely believed in the late nineteenth century that country
immigrants were innately sturdier and superior to the town-bred. And there
was statistical evidence that appeared to support this. Commenting on the
failure of 15-year-old London boys to reach the required standards of height
and girth, the Metropolitan Poor Law Inspector stated in 1871 that: 'it is well
established that no town bred boys of the *poorer classes*, especially those
reared in London, ever except in very rare instances, attain . . . (4'10½" and
29" chest) at the age of 15. A stunted growth is the characteristic of the race'
(quoted in Stedman Jones, 1971, p. 129; emphasis added). Llewellyn Smith
argued that there was an inverse relation between poverty and immigration,

▲   *Dudley Street, Seven Dials. Another engraving by Doré, showing the inadequate living conditions and overcrowding of the poor in London.*

and it was no accident that the East End had the highest rates of infant mortality:

> It is the result of conditions of life in great towns, and especially in the greatest town of all, that muscular strength and energy gradually get used up; the second generation of Londoner is of lower physique and has less power of persistent work than the first, and the third generation (where it exists) is of lower than the second.
> (1902, pp. 110–11)

Llewellyn Smith backed his argument with extensive statistical data which showed a positive correlation between level of poverty and the proportion of London-born in different areas: the higher the proportion of London-born, the greater the level of poverty.

Activity 2

Can you think of any other causal relationships which might link poverty and the proportion of London-born?

Stedman Jones argues that while there was a general correlation between the two sets of data, the percentage in poverty increasing roughly in line with the percentage born in London, this does not show that poverty was *caused* by urban life, as Smith believed. He inferred causation from correlation, and 'assumed the very causal link he was purporting to prove'.

Stedman Jones argues that the explanation for the high incidence
of poverty among the London-born was not urban degeneration but 'the
traumatic impact of the Industrial Revolution upon the older industries of
London' which were labour-intensive and were badly hit by provincial
factory competition. To the extent that the London-born working classes
were shorter and less well-built than provincial migrants, it reflects the
impact of poverty on health. Certainly, the theorists of urban degeneration
never suggested that middle- and upper-class Londoners were degenerate
compared to their rural counterparts! Yet if the theory of _urban_ degeneration
were true, as opposed to the theory of class- and industry-based poverty, we
should expect this to be the case. Stedman Jones suggests that the theory of
urban degeneration was not an explanation of London poverty but a
reflection of middle-class fears of the new urban working class of the type
outlined above. While it was undoubtedly true that the urban working
classes were physically stunted, this was a result of industrialism and
poverty, not urban life itself. And as living conditions have improved over
the last hundred years, so has the physical condition of the working class.
The effects of poverty and industrialism were confused with those of urban
living. This confusion was to be replicated many times in the subsequent
years, and not just in Britain.

3   _Theoretical analyses of urban life and behaviour_

Although rapid urban growth and overcrowding manifested itself first in
Britain – the world's first urbanised country – they spread across Europe and
parts of North America through the late nineteenth and early twentieth
centuries. The growth was particularly marked in New York and Chicago, a
result of rapid migration from Europe into North America. Irish, Poles,
Italians, Germans all poured in. The growth of cities led to late nineteenth-
and early twentieth-century European and American social scientists trying
to analyse the new realities of contemporary urban life. The sections which
follow will look at the writing of Simmel, Park and Wirth with respect to the
role of cities and society in affecting behaviour.

3.1   _Georg Simmel: 'The metropolis and mental life'_

Leaving aside Engels' early observations, one of the first social scientists to
attempt to pin down the alleged effects of urban living on individuals was
the German psychologist Georg Simmel, in his famous essay, 'The
metropolis and mental life', written in 1901. In this essay Simmel addressed
the question of 'the inner meaning of modern life' and how 'the personality
accommodates itself in the adjustments to external forces' generated in large
cities. His starting-point was psychological, and he asserted that: 'The
psychological basis of the metropolitan type of individuality consists in the

intensification of nervous stimulation which results from the swift and uninterrupted change of outer and inner stimuli' (emphasis added).

Referring to the psychological conditions which the metropolis creates he stated that:

> With each crossing of the street, with the tempo and multiplicity of economic, occupational and social life, *the city sets up* a deep contrast with small town and rural life with reference to the sensory foundations of psychic life. The metropolis exacts from man [sic] as a discriminating creature a different amount of consciousness than does rural life. Here the rhythm of life and sensory mental imagery flow more slowly, more habitually and more evenly. Thus the metropolitan man develops an organ which protects him against the threatening currents and discrepancies of his external environment which would uproot him. He reacts with his head instead of his heart.   (emphasis added)

This, and the emphasis given to impersonal economic exchange which reduces all things to the question of 'how much', explains, according to Simmel, why relations between metropolitan individuals are anonymous, impersonal, distant, matter-of-fact and calculating. As he puts it:

> *The money economy dominates the metropolis*: it has displaced the last survivals of domestic production and the direct barter of goods . . . The matter of fact attitude is obviously intimately interrelated with the money economy, which is dominant in the metropolis, that nobody can say whether the intellectualist mentality first promoted the money economy or whether the latter dominated the former.   (emphasis added)

He also argued that with the aggregation of so many people, the variety and complexity of affairs and relationships in the modern metropolis, and the need to integrate these, that without 'the most punctual integration of all activities and mutual relations into a stable and impersonal time schedule', the structure would break down into total chaos. The result of all these tendencies and pressures is, says Simmel, impersonality and indifference. Simmel argued that 'the individualisation of mental and psychic traits which *the city occasions is in proportion to its size*'. Finally, he suggested that a specifically metropolitan trait is the tendency of some to adopt 'extravagances of mannerism, caprice and preciousness'. He suggested that the meaning of these behaviours lies not in their particular content, but in the need to assert one's own individuality and sense of being different in an impersonal metropolis. Hence perhaps the extravagant exhibitionism of the contemporary Mohican hair-styled urban punk, the 'gothic', or the City yuppies and their conspicuous mobile phones!

More recent research on the way people adapt to sensory overload (Milgram, 1970) suggests that Simmel was correct to draw attention to the intensification of nervous stimulation associated with the modern metropolis. But, while this intensification and various adaptions to it are perhaps most clearly marked in cities, there remains the crucial question of whether they are specific to the city or whether they are characteristic of modern life in general and merely concentrated in cities, as Engels suggested. If the latter is correct, it may be that it is *not* cities which cause such changes in behaviour, but the character of modern industrial society. Such behaviour may be particularly concentrated in cities but not caused by cities alone. Indeed Simmel comes close to saying this on several occasions where he refers to the links between the contemporary money economy and the city. Although Simmel suggests that it is the metropolis which causes the increase in nervous stimulation, he makes many references to the rise of rationality and sophistication in the modern money economy. Did he therefore confuse cause and effect? The city may manifest and concentrate certain characteristics but does it necessarily cause them? This is now discussed in relation to the ideas of Park and Wirth.

3.2 *Park and the Chicago School of urban sociology*

It was mentioned above that Chicago was one of the most rapidly growing cities in North America in the late nineteenth and early twentieth centuries. Not surprisingly, it gave rise to a body of writing and research which tried to grapple with 'the city'. This subsection will briefly consider one of the most important products of the Chicago School, Robert Park's essay entitled 'The City: suggestions for the investigation of human behavior in the urban environment', published in 1925.

Park's interest was in the new forms of human behaviour found in cities, and he argued that:

> [T]he growth of cities has been accompanied by the substitution of indirect 'secondary' for direct, face-to-face, 'primary' relations in the association of individuals in the community. It is probably the breaking down of local attachments and the weakening of the restraints and inhibitions of the primary group, *under the influence of the urban environment*, which are largely responsible for the increase of vice and crime in great cities.   (pp. 23–5; emphasis added)

Park saw the replacement of primary by secondary relations and the breakdown of traditional social controls in the city as direct causes of urban social problems. The urban social environment exercised an influence on behaviour. But Park, like Simmel, also saw that the city was closely linked to the advent of modern industrial society and the market economy. He stated that it was 'the market which brought the modern city into existence', and he commented that:

> Modern methods of urban transportation and communication – the electric railway, the automobile, the telephone and the radio – have silently and rapidly changed in recent years the social and industrial organisation of the modern city . . . These changes in the industrial organisation and in the distribution of population have been accompanied by corresponding changes in the habits, sentiments, and character of the urban population.   (p. 23)

It would therefore appear that Park, like Simmel, realised that the urban environment could not be considered in isolation from the changes in the wider industrial society. It may have an influence on human behaviour, but how independent was this of the effect of industrial society? Was it that the dominant cause of the breakdown of existing social controls in the city was a result of the rise of modern society and industrialism, and that such changes were merely particularly manifest or concentrated in cities, as Engels suggested? Unfortunately, neither Park nor Simmel answered this question. The focus of their attention was on the city, even though they saw that the city was not independent of wider social changes.

3.3   Louis Wirth: urbanism as a way of life

In 1938 the Chicago sociologist Louis Wirth published his famous essay 'Urbanism as a way of life'. His starting-point, like others before him, was to attempt to analyse the dramatic changes in social organisation and behaviour which seemed to result from large-scale urbanisation. As he noted in the introduction to his essay:

> Just as the beginning of Western civilisation is marked by the permanent settlement of formerly nomadic peoples in the Mediterranean basin, so *the beginning of what is distinctively modern in our civilisation is best signalled by the growth of great cities*.   (emphasis added)

But how should the city be defined? Wirth stated that because his concern was with the 'peculiar characteristics of the city as a particular form of human association, a sociologically significant definition of the city seeks to select those aspects of urbanism which mark it as a distinctive mode of group life'. He rejected definitions based purely on size, physical boundaries or density, occupational composition or political organisation. And, because he wanted a definition which included the central characteristics which cities have in common, but which allowed analysis of their variations, he argued that: 'For sociological purposes a city may be defined as a relatively large, dense, and permanent settlement of socially heterogeneous individuals.' The central task for the urban sociologist 'is to discover the forms of social action and organisation that typically emerge' in such areas as a result of their size, density and social heterogeneity. Wirth said that because urban social life bears the imprint of an earlier folk society, the characteristic modes of settlement of which were the farm and the village, we should not expect to find abrupt and discontinuous variations between urban and rural types of personality or social life. Instead, he argued that the city and the country may be regarded as two poles or ideal-types, in relation to which different settlements can be characterised:

> [U]rbanism will assume its most characteristic and extreme form in the measure to which in which the conditions with which it is congruent are present. Thus, *the larger, the more densely populated, and more heterogeneous a community, the more accentuated the characteristics associated with urbanism will be*.   (emphasis added)

On the basis of his definition Wirth formulated three important sociological propositions regarding urbanism as a way of life. He argued first that increasing population limits the possibility of people knowing others personally. Wirth argued that interaction of people under conditions which makes contact as full personalities impossible leads to the **segmentalisation** of human relationships: 'The city is characterised by secondary rather than primary contacts [which are] impersonal, superficial, transitory, and segmental.' Wirth argues that the superficial, anonymous, transitory character of urban-social relations makes intelligible the blasé outlook, the sophistication and rationality of the city-dweller. And he suggests that although city-dwellers are free from the constricting social controls of small group society, they have lost the spontaneous self-expression and participation that comes from living in an integrated society. Hence urban life is often rootless and manipulative in character and acquaintances are seen as a means for the achievement of one's own ends.

   Secondly, Wirth suggested that density 'reinforces the effect of numbers in diversifying men and their activities and in increasing the complexity of social structure'. While physical contacts become closer, social contacts are often distant and people are identified in terms of their roles or functions not personalities: 'The close living and working together of individuals who have no sentimental or emotional ties foster a spirit of competition, aggrandisement, and mutual exploitation'.

Thirdly, Wirth suggested that social heterogeneity is important in that it breaks down the rigidity of social distinctions. The greater variety of individuals means that they can mix and acquire membership of widely divergent social groups, each of which functions only with reference to a part of the whole person. Thus, there is acceptance of transitoriness, instability and insecurity as a norm. Wirth also added that: 'Overwhelmingly the city dweller is not a home-owner, and since a transitory habitat does not generate binding traditions and sentiments, only rarely is he truly a neighbour'.

Activity 3

Make your own assessment of the validity of Wirth's theory of urbanism as a way of life. Does his analysis of urban life and urban social relations match your experience or perceptions? If so, how? If not, why? Does his analysis of urban social life apply equally to different areas of cities? Even if Wirth's characterisation of urban social life and personality seems accurate, does it stem from size, density or heterogeneity or from something else?

Now compare your assessment with that in the section below.

3.4   Herbert Gans: an empirical critique of Wirth

The first major critique of Wirth was produced by Herbert Gans in 1962. Gans made two fundamental criticisms: the first was that Wirth was analysing urban–industrial society rather than the city; the second was that Wirth's characterisation applied only to the residents of the inner-city and then only in part. He went on to argue that Wirth's analysis of the city had to be questioned on three counts:

> First, the conclusions derived from a study of the inner city cannot be generalised to the entire urban area. Second, there is not yet enough evidence to prove, nor admittedly to deny, that number, density and heterogeneity result in the social consequences which Wirth proposes. Finally, even if the causal relationship could be verified, it can be shown that a significant proportion of the city's inhabitants were, and are, isolated from these consequences by social structures and cultural patterns which they either brought to the city or developed by living in it.

While a substantial proportion of the inner-city population was, and is, made up of heterogeneous individuals, Gans argued that a large proportion of the population consists mainly of relatively homogeneous groups who are shielded from the suggested consequences of number, size and heterogeneity.

Gans, an American sociologist working in Boston, suggested that there are five main types of inner-city residents. These are:

(a) the 'cosmopolites'

(b) the unmarried or childless

(c) the 'ethnic villagers'

(d) the deprived

(e) the 'trapped and downwardly mobile'.

The cosmopolites include students, artists, writers, musicians and other intellectuals and professionals. They live in the inner city to be near the cultural facilities that are concentrated in city centres. They are often unmarried or childless or have childcare facilities if they are well off. The single or childless, says Gans, often live in the inner city for a short period until they marry or have a family, though some permanently unmarried may remain in the inner city for most of their lives. The 'ethnic villagers' are the inner-city ethnic groups who live in some ways in the way they did when they were peasants in European or third world villages and they often isolate themselves from significant contact with city facilities apart from workplaces. Gans states:

> Their way of life differs sharply from Wirth's urbanism in its emphasis on kinship and the primary group, the lack of anonymity and secondary group contacts, the weakness of formal organisations, and suspicion of anything and anyone outside their neighbourhoods.

Gans argues that the first two groups live in the inner city by choice, and the third partly out of necessity and partly because of tradition. The last two groups, however, are in the inner city because they have no other choice. The deprived are poor, and often black, and they have to take the poor housing and run-down neighbourhood to which the housing market relegates them. The trapped are often left high and dry by neighbourhood deterioration and the downwardly mobile are in a similar position and are old and poor. These five types, says Gans, all live in dense, heterogeneous surroundings but,

> . . . they have such diverse ways of life it is hard to see how density and heterogeneity could exert a common influence. Moreover all but the last two types are isolated or detached from the . . . social consequences which Wirth described . . . The deprived and the trapped do seem to be affected by some of the consequences of number, density and heterogeneity. The deprived suffer considerably from overcrowding but this is a consequence of low income, racial discrimination, and other handicaps, and *cannot be considered an inevitable result of the ecological make-up of the city*.   (p. 102; emphasis added)

Gans concluded that:

> Wirth's description of the urban way of life fits best the transient areas of the inner city. Such areas are typically heterogeneous in population . . . Under conditions of transience and heterogeneity, people interact only in terms of the segmental roles necessary for obtaining services. Their social relationships thus display anonymity, impersonality and superficiality.

This fit, says Gans, is not surprising as Wirth and the other Chicago sociologists did most of their empirical work in the inner city which, at that time, consisted of slums recently invaded by waves of European immigrants and rooming-house and skid row districts – all marked by very high levels of

migration. Gans went on to argue that surburban life bears little
resemblance to Wirth's urbanism:

> As anyone who has lived in these neighbourhoods knows, there is
> little anonymity, impersonality or privacy. In fact, American cities
> have sometimes been described as collections of small towns . . .
> Postwar suburbia represents the most contemporary version of the
> quasi-primary way of life.   (p. 105)

3.5   *Capitalism as a cause of urbanism*

Gans also argued that Wirth was analysing urban–industrial society rather
than the city, and comparing it to pre-industrial societies. A similar criticism
was made by Manuel Castells, a prominent Marxist sociologist, who argued
that the characteristics of urbanism are a product of modern capitalist society
and not of cities per se. As Pickvance (1974), a British translator and
interpreter of Castells, observes:

> Much criticism of Wirth's thesis has been narrowly empirical, to the
> effect that in particular localities Wirth's description of urbanism does
> not hold true. Such criticism often ignores the fact that Wirth was
> presenting the urbanism theory primarily as a tendency, rather than as
> a description applicable in all its details to actual settlements. A much
> more fundamental criticism can be directed against the primary
> assumption of Wirth's thesis: namely, the assumption that it is the *city*
> which produces a certain type of culture. In the early period of
> industrialisation a new way of life did appear first and foremost in
> cities. But to say that the city was the cause of this way of life is to
> commit the error of spurious correlation. Against this, *Castells provides
> an alternative causal analysis: that urbanism is the cultural translation of
> capitalist industrialisation into modern society*.   (p. 208; emphases added)

Castells argued that the anonymous, impersonal and transitory social
relations identified by Wirth *do* exist, but that the cause is *not* the size,
density or heterogeneity of cities or any aspect of cities per se, but the
economic and social relations existing under modern capitalist
industrialism. Castells points to the key role of capitalist industrialism, not
urbanism, as a way of life. The physical and social characteristics of large
contemporary cities are the production of capitalist industrialism rather than
of urbanism per se. There is a strong case for this argument, not least
because the large cities which had attracted the attention of Simmel, Park
and Wirth were themselves primarily the product of capitalist urban–
industrialism. As was shown in section 2.1, the rapid growth of cities in the
nineteenth and early twentieth centuries occurred as a result of the
migration of population to work in the mills and factories of the new
industrial centres.

  In this respect there is considerable similarity between Castells' position
and Simmel's view that what is crucial to understanding the metropolis is
the money economy, and the dominance of money values over more
traditional social values. Indeed, given the importance Simmel attached to
the money economy in his analysis of urbanism it can be argued that, like
Wirth, he got the causal relations confused, and attributed to the modern
metropolis what he should have attributed to the money economy and the
capitalist mode of production. In this interpretation the causal relations
between settlement types and the social characteristics of cities are spurious.

Both are the product of capitalist industrialism. This is shown diagrammatically in Figure 6.1. But Wirth anticipated and explicitly denied this criticism arguing that industrialism and urbanism are separate phenomena:

> It is particularly important to call attention to the danger of confusing urbanism with industrialism and modern capitalism. The rise of cities in the modern world is undoubtedly not independent of the emergence of modern power-driven machine technology, mass production, and capitalist enterprise. But different as the cities of earlier epochs may have been by virtue of their development in a preindustrial and precapitalist order from the great cities of today, they were, nevertheless, cities.

What we have, then, are two alternative theoretical explanations of the same phenomenon. One which attributes the cause of social relations allegedly found in cities (and everywhere in modern society) to capitalist urban–industrialism and mass society, and the alternative which attributes their cause to settlement forms. For Wirth settlement forms have absolute causal autonomy, whereas for Castells capitalism has causal autonomy, and settlement form simply gives rise to spurious correlations. These two alternatives are shown in Figure 6.1.

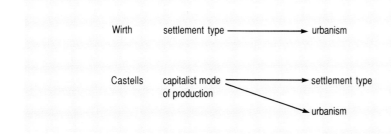

◀   Figure 6.1
Alternative conceptions of
the causes of 'urbanism'.

It can be argued that by rejecting the idea that settlement type played any role in the development of the ways of life which Wirth identified, in favour of the determining role of capitalist industrialism, Castells threw out the baby with the bathwater. In his view settlement type plays no role in shaping behaviour. Instead, settlement forms are themselves the product of the mode of production. But Pickvance points out that there is an alternative conception of causality. Accepting that urbanism and settlement type are both determined by capitalism does not in fact exclude a causal link between spatial form and urbanism. His diagrammatic representation of the alternative is shown in Figure 6.2. As Pickvance points out, however, for

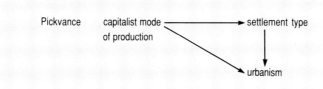

◀   Figure 6.2

settlement type to exercise an independent effect on the social relations of urbanism, rather than being an intervening variable, it is a necessary but not sufficient condition that settlement types have relative autonomy from the mode of production. He argues that they do, and that the mode of production does not totally determine settlement types or spatial forms. Instead these are variable across space and time.

> *Activity 4*
>
> Castells argued that it was capitalist urban–industrialism that was important, not settlement type. Can you see any flaws in this stress on capitalist urbanisation?
>
> Consider this question before going on to the next section.

3.6   Capitalism or industrialism as causes of urbanism?

The discussion in the last section has been in terms of 'capitalism versus urbanism', but there is an argument that this is unnecessarily restrictive. While Marxists like Castells attribute the determining causality to the capitalist mode of production, there are some **technological determinists** or **convergence theorists** who argue that it is not capitalism which has produced modern society and its associated behaviours and social forms, but industrialism, whether capitalist or socialist. They argue that similar processes and phenomena are found in the industrialised, state socialist societies of the Soviet Union and eastern Europe. Thus, while earlier urban theorists may have focused too much on urbanism and settlement type, it can be argued that Castells focused too narrowly on capitalism, to the neglect of industrialism and mass society.

   Technological convergence theory argues that the social structure of industrial–urban societies adjusts to the needs of the economy. The technical and organisational requirements of mass industrial production lead to similarities in occupational and organisational structures, in urban form and social behaviour. The advocates of this thesis argue that political ideology is of limited importance, and that similar structures will emerge under state socialism and western capitalism. The logic of industrialism requires specific economic, social and spatial forms as prerequisites for efficient functioning and results in growing convergence between industrial–urban societies. The most explicit development of the convergence thesis was by Clark Kerr and his associates in their book, *Industrialism and Industrial Man*, published in 1962.

   The convergence thesis stimulated research in a number of areas including occupational stratification and class inequality, state intervention in social welfare, housing policy and the like. Some analysts, such as Ray Pahl, argued that the similarities in outcomes between east and west in terms of urban problems and inequalities pointed to the existence of common processes which operate under both capitalism and socialism. One of his radical suggestions was that it was not capitalist or socialist modes of production which explain urban problems, but rather the *level* of production. Technology may be more responsible for urban problems than political and economic organisation. Proponents of this view would point to the evidence which emerged in the early 1990s from eastern Europe showing the high levels of urban and environmental pollution which exist in these countries. Hawley (1971) has put forward a similar view regarding urban and regional organisation:

> The regions and nations of the world are being absorbed into an expanding world economy. As one society from another has yielded to the superior economic and political power of an industrialized market economy, it has been thrust along a path towards drastic internal reorganization . . . *Participation in the world economy has demanded of every society the adoption of a new technological regime*, a reorientation of resources, a fundamental reconstruction and alignment of social units, and a broad scale redistribution of its population . . . Although urbanization begins in very different cultural contexts . . . the land soon begins to reproduce phases and patterns that occurred in other times and places.   (pp. 311–12; emphasis added)

The convergence thesis is superficially attractive and rather plausible. But other authors have pointed to its problems. One of the major weaknesses is the tendency to look for similarities of outcome and attribute them to similar processes. The high-rise blocks in eastern and western European cities can be seen to derive from the same need to house as many people as possible as quickly and as cheaply as possible. But while some causes are very similar, others are very different. Ivan Szelenyi, a leading Hungarian urban sociologist, now living in California, argued in his book *Urban Inequalities Under State Socialism* (1983) that the middle class was strongly represented in the best housing in Hungarian cities. But this was clearly not a result of a market system of housing allocation as in the west. On the contrary, he argued, it was the result of a system of administrative allocation which favoured the middle classes who could work the system. More recent work on Hungary and other eastern bloc countries has confirmed that this is widespread and that the 'new class' of officials and party bureaucrats tend to benefit from administrative allocation, just as these kinds of people do in market systems. The key finding, however, is that while the inequalities may appear similar to those in the west, they are produced by different mechanisms. A very similar point can be made regarding the proliferation of high-rise state housing on the periphery of most eastern bloc cities. They are similar to those found in Glasgow and Liverpool, but they are there for rather different reasons and serve a different purpose. The stress on industrialised building systems was common to both east and west, but there was no problem over land acquisition or high inner-city land values in eastern Europe. Whereas in the west high-rise blocks were generally built to replace inner-city slums, in the east they were to house a large number of people drawn into the cities as a result of socialist industrialisation. And it is fair to say that the eastern bloc countries do *not* have an inner-city problem similar to that found in many western cities. Because the cities of eastern Europe did not undergo rapid industrialisation in the nineteenth century, many social problems in eastern cities are concentrated in the new peripheral estates built to house the influx of industrial workers post-1945.

It would seem, therefore, that it may not be adequate to replace capitalism by industrialism in Castells' formulation, and simply assume that urban problems and processes are similar in east and west. Economic and political organisation may be an independent variable along with industrialism and settlement type. There are also considerable theoretical problems with the related idea put forward by Hawley above which implies that there is a single path along which all countries are moving at different stages. This sort of analysis which Bertrand De Jouvenel, the French futurist, has termed 'the railway track', suggests that modernisation takes place along one track, and different countries are at different positions along the line. This is the 'what the US does today, the UK will do in 10 years' time' mode of thought, and it is extremely superficial. Viewed in these terms, eastern Europe is simply a forty-year-long railway siding which has now rejoined the main line!

3.7   Conclusions

If the logical possibility of a relationship between settlement type and behaviour exists, as Pickvance suggests, does it have any empirical basis? Engels, Simmel, Park and Wirth all argue that it did. They suggested that while anonymity, impersonality and segmented social relations are all characteristic of modern industrial societies to some extent, they are particularly manifested in cities, particularly in the inner areas. As Engels noted over 150 years ago, while 'this isolation of the individual, this narrow self-seeking is the fundamental principle of our society everywhere, it is nowhere so shamelessly barefaced . . . as in the crowding of the great city'.

The problem, however, is that the evidence is not always clear and that, even where it is, other interpretations can be offered. Although a number of researchers have examined urban–rural differences on a variety of indicators such as crime and illegitimacy rates, social interaction patterns, educational levels, mental illness and the like, it is difficult to draw firm conclusions from the results. Although crime rates are much higher in cities than in rural areas, it can be argued that this is because there are more opportunities for crime in cities than there are in rural areas, rather than a result of differences in outlook or behaviour. Similarly, although there is some evidence that rates of mental illness are higher in urban than in rural areas, this can be partly attributed to the movement of mentally ill people to cities rather than to anything inherent in cities. In his extensive and comprehensive review of the literature on this question which analysed hundreds of different studies, Fischer argued that 'the data, where they exist, are inadequate and contradictory' (1972, p. 227) and stated that: 'Whether, and in what ways cities affect social relationships is still . . . an open question' (p. 228). Many studies confused moving to a city with the effects of being in a city and others confused urbanism and industrialism. Fischer concludes that:

> Urbanization as a historical process, usually occurs concurrently and interactively with other powerful processes: industrialization bureaucratization, Westernization, and democratization. But, no analytical understanding of it will be achieved until sociologists cease to use these terms interchangeably and begin to disentangle them from each other . . . Furthermore, the effects of urbanization as a social change process must be distinguished from the effects of urbanism as a settlement type.   (p. 227)

The case for the city influencing attitudes and behaviour must therefore remain unproven, though lingering suspicions exist, and I would support Pickvance's argument that although the social and economic structures exercise a crucial influence on various forms of behaviour, settlement form can exercise an independent effect. This is difficult to detect empirically, however.

You may ask in the light of this conclusion what value there is in analysing the views of early urban theorists at such length. My answer is that, although the theorists differ in how they formulate their explanation and the role they accord to the physical structure of cities in causing behavioural and social problems, they *all* point to the causal influence of the wider society. While they construe that society differently, as capitalism, industrialism or the money economy, their attention to these wider influences is sufficient to make it extremely unlikely that a purely physical set of policies will solve urban problems. Instead, the solution of urban problems may require more radical social change.

4   Urban social problems and the inner cities

During the last twenty-five years the older inner-city areas of Britain and other countries have come to be seen as the locus of a number of social problems. This section will examine the extent to which these problems are characteristic of the inner cities or whether they have a wider distribution. It will also explore the extent to which such problems are concentrated in the inner cities and thus are problems *of* the inner cities. In other words, is there something about the inner cities which causes such problems or are they simply a problem of concentration? You should re-read the quote in the introduction from Righter and Wilshire regarding the alleged causal role of the inner cities. First, however, the nature of 'inner-city problems' or problems in the inner cities needs to be defined and a number of questions relating to this issue considered.

Q   Make a list of some of the major problems found in the inner cities or frequently associated with them. Do not look at my list until you have drawn up your own!

A   What problems did you identify? Did you pick out some of the following: unemployment, poor housing, a concentration of less skilled workers, poverty, poor or decaying physical environment, racial tension, crime, low educational attainment, social unrest, industrial decline? Almost all have been identified at various times as key characteristics of the inner cities.

Q   Do you think that these characteristics are found exclusively in inner cities or are they particularly concentrated there?

A   They are particularly concentrated in the inner cities rather than exclusive to them. The inner cities do not have a monopoly of social problems although they may have more than their fair share. On the contrary, almost all the problems listed are found widely across much of Britain: for example, there are more poor people living outside the inner cities than within them. Figure 6.3 provides information on each of eight English inner-city areas on several 1981 census indicators. It also gives national rates for England and Wales. You will notice that while the incidence of these indicators is generally higher in the inner cities than the national average, they are also variable between different inner-city areas. The inner cities are not totally homogeneous.

Q   If social problems such as low incomes and unemployment are not exclusive to the inner cities, can you think of other areas where they sometimes tend to be concentrated?

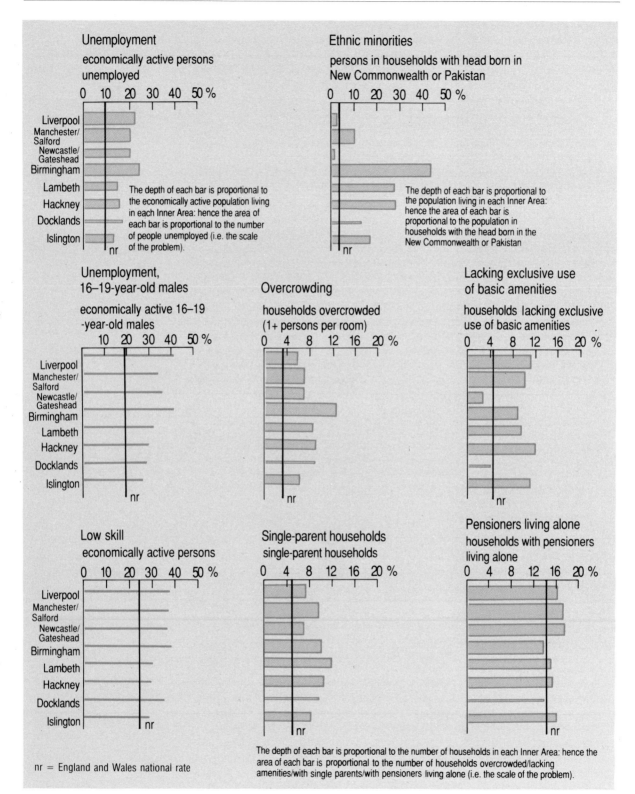

▲ Figure 6.3
Information on eight 1981 Census indicators for the eight English inner-city partnerships plus the national average.

A There is evidence that the incidence of certain problems such as unemployment and low incomes is extremely high in some peripheral council estates such as those in Liverpool, Glasgow, Edinburgh and Newcastle. In some of the estates around Glasgow, male unemployment rates in the early 1980s exceeded 50%. There are also high levels of unemployment in many of the older industrial regions and in some isolated towns and villages.

Activity 5

At this point you should read Box 6.3 which is an extract from the Department of the Environment's (1979) White Paper, *Policy for the Inner Cities*. This provides an official overview of the nature of the problem.

Write a short 100–200 word summary in your own words of the nature of the inner-city problem as outlined in the White Paper. You may find it useful to organise this under the three headings of economic decline, physical decay and social disadvantage. This activity will help you to grasp and remember the main points more clearly.

As you will have gathered from the extract, and as you saw in the discussion of the Kellner article, there is no single inner-city problem. Instead, there are a number of *interrelated* problems, notably those of a declining economic and industrial base, major job losses and consequent high rates of unemployment, a high incidence of poverty, housing stress, differential migration and population decline, and a concentration of the less skilled and economically inactive, as well as pervasive problems of poor-quality housing in drab or decaying surroundings. As the White Paper puts it:

> Many of the inner areas surrounding the centres of our cities suffer, in a marked way and to an unacceptable extent, from economic decline, physical decay and adverse social conditions.

The words 'marked' and 'unacceptable extent' are revealing, for the White Paper also pointed out that whilst the inner areas are characterised by the *scale* and *intensity* of their problems and the rapidity of the population and employment decline, substantial concentrations of unemployment, poor housing and decay are also found in small cities and older industrial areas. Such problems are often acute on some peripheral council estates around the big cities and, as was seen in Chapter 5, are not unknown in rural areas either. 'Inner-city' problems are thus not confined to the inner cities.

This is a crucial point which raises an important question. If so-called 'inner-city problems' are not confined to the inner cities, in what sense can they be said to be inner-city problems? Are they problems 'of' or 'in' the inner cities? The answer is in two parts. First, as the White Paper indicated, the inner cities are distinguished not by the unique occurrence of certain problems but by the concentration and intensity of overlapping problems. To this extent it is misleading to speak of inner-city problems as though they were somehow unique or caused by inner cities themselves. But this is only half the answer because it is also necessary to explain why certain problems are concentrated in the inner cities. The concentrations are not random or accidental and it may be that there are some characteristics of the inner cities which play a role in the concentration of such problems. Also it is necessary

---

Box 6.3   Department of the Environment: Policy for the Inner Cities

The nature of the problem

Many of the inner areas surrounding the centres of our cities suffer, in a marked way and to an unacceptable extent, from economic decline, physical decay and adverse social conditions. The Inner Area Studies of parts of Liverpool, Birmingham and Lambeth – major studies over four years – and the West Central Scotland Study in relation to Glasgow, have underlined the erosion of the inner area economy and the shortage of private investment which might assist the process of regeneration. They have demonstrated the prevalence of poverty, poor environment and bad housing conditions, and they have analysed the response of Government. They have also illustrated the differences which exist between the cities they studied – Lambeth suffering still from high population density and congestion; Glasgow and Liverpool now experiencing a lack of demand which is manifest in large areas of vacant land; Birmingham's situation somewhere between, facing a serious industrial setback and still subject to strong housing pressures.

6   Inner area problems are a feature of many of our older towns but they are at their most serious in the major cities. In smaller cities and older industrial areas there are substantial areas of decay, bad housing, poor employment and social problems. Deprivation exists too in some pre- and post-war council estates, sometimes on the edge of the big cities. There is undoubtedly a need to tackle the problems of urban deprivation wherever they occur. But there must be a particular emphasis on the inner areas of some of the big cities because of the scale and intensity of their problems and the rapidity of rundown in population and employment.

Economic decline

7   The decline in the economic fortunes of the inner areas often lies at the heart of the problem. Compared with their own conurbations, the inner areas of the big cities suffer from higher unemployment at all stages of the economic cycle. In inner areas generally there has developed a mismatch between the skills of the people and the kinds of job available. In some cities such as Glasgow and Liverpool, there is a general lack of demand for labour which affects the whole conurbation but is particularly severe in the inner areas.

8   The inner areas have long had more than the national proportions of unskilled and semi-skilled

workers, the groups among whom unemployment is highest. In 1971, for example, unskilled and semi-skilled men accounted for 38% of the labour force in inner Birmingham, 35% in inner Manchester and 34% in inner Glasgow, compared with 23% nationally. The loss from the cities of a higher proportion of skilled than less skilled workers has made unemployment worse. Between 1966–71 only 15% of net migrants from Birmingham comprised semi-skilled and unskilled workers; from Manchester it was only 16%. Most of those who left were skilled and managerial people.

9   At the same time, there has been a loss of jobs in the traditional industries – the older service industries like the docks and the railways – and in manufacturing industries. A large number of firms have closed, many of them small firms. Sometimes this has been brought about by redevelopment, when the firms have not found new premises in the area or have decided to go out of business for other reasons. Some firms have moved out of the inner cities to find better sites. But generally, the movement of firms has been a contributory factor, not a major cause of decline. In some areas, the main cause of job losses has been the closure of large manufacturing firms and, more generally, the shrinkage in employment in large firms.

10   There has not been enough investment in new manufacturing industry to counterbalance these job losses. Major new enterprises have tended to prefer peripheral locations to the inner city. The growth of new service industries and office jobs has benefited the inner cities broadly in line with the national trend, but the jobs created have been different and have not made up for the loss of manual jobs.

Physical decay

11   The most characteristic single feature of the inner city is the age of its housing. Despite the extensive redevelopment and clearance of slum property since the war, there still remains a great deal of poor-quality housing lacking basic amenities, not in good repair and set in a drab environment.

12   In some cities the processes of clearance and redevelopment have got badly out of step. The bulldozers have done their work, but the rebuilding has lagged behind. Sometimes this has been caused by changes of plan as more people left the cities than expected. In other instances it has resulted from reductions in the allocation of resources, central and local. Whatever the explanation, there is a wide

◀   *The redundant docks of Canary Wharf before redevelopment.*

See also Plate 12.

extent of vacant land in some inner areas, mainly in public ownership; and there is much under-used land and property, with shops boarded up and sites and buildings neglected. The opportunities afforded by redevelopment to create public open space have not been taken.

13   This shabby environment, the lack of amenities, the high density remaining in some parts and the poor condition of the older housing in the inner areas contrast sharply with better conditions elsewhere. They combine together to make these areas unattractive, both to many of the people who live there and to new investment in business, industry and housing.

Social disadvantage

14   The inner areas of cities have a higher concentration of poor people. Partly this reflects high unemployment, but in addition the level of earnings often tends to be lower. The Inner Area Studies have shown the importance of work for married women in enabling families to move out of poverty. For those who are incapacitated, for the old, and for the unemployed, income support is very important. Whilst there cannot be any question of higher scales of benefit for people living in the inner areas, it is desirable to encourage the maximum take up of rent and rate reliefs and discretionary benefits where people are entitled to them.

15   The innermost areas in and around the city centre itself, tend to serve as a refuge for those least able to cope in society, amongst them the homeless and those with personal problems such as alcoholism or drug addiction. Over a wider range of the inner city there are often substantial numbers of people with social needs requiring help and support.

16   Too many inner area children reach the school leaving age with insufficient skills in reading, writing and handling figures to hold down satisfying jobs. Where jobs are scarce, some may feel that their education has been irrelevant to the real prospects they face; others find it difficult to identify with the purposes of the school. These attitudes may find expression in truancy and various other behaviour problems.

17   The Inner Area Studies have shown that there is a collective deprivation in some inner areas which affects all the residents, even though individually the majority of people may have satisfactory homes and worthwhile jobs. It arises from a pervasive sense of decay and neglect which affects the whole area, through the decline of community spirit, through an often low standard of neighbourhood facilities, and through greater exposure to crime and vandalism which is a real form of deprivation, above all to old people. All this may make it harder for people to maintain their personal standards and to encourage high standards in their children. Sometimes people from particular inner areas experience extra difficulty in getting a job or a mortgage. This collective deprivation amounts to more than the sum of all the individual disadvantages with which people have to contend. It is an important argument for tackling inner city deprivation on an area basis, and for discriminating in favour of the inner areas in the working out of public policies and programmes.

to ask whether this concentration of problems may give rise in turn to other problems which are unique to the inner cities. One way to try to answer these questions is to examine in turn various aspects of the problem. Let us start with economic decline.

4.1   *Economic decline and the inner cities*

It is sometimes argued by those on the political right that the concentration of unemployment in the inner cities and in peripheral council estates is a result of indolence, fecklessness or general loss of will to work among the inhabitants. According to this view there are jobs for those who want them; the problem is one of lack of motivation. It is no doubt true that there are some people who do not want to work and prefer to live on social security.

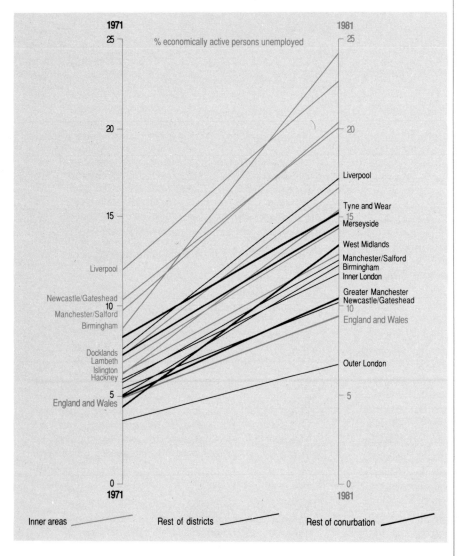

▲   *Figure 6.4   Changes in rates of unemployment of economically active persons between 1971 and 1981.*

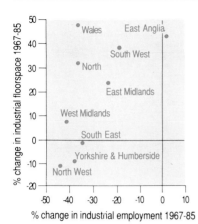

◀   *Figure 6.5*
Unemployment rate,
United Kingdom,
1970–1987.

But the main problem with this argument is how it explains the persistent geographical variations in unemployment between regions, or the sudden rise of unemployment across the country, but particularly in the northern industrial areas, in the early 1980s. Figure 6.4 shows the marked regional variations in unemployment and Figure 6.5 shows the sharp rise in unemployment from 1979 onwards. Do we believe that people in the north or in the inner cities have a weaker will to work than those in the south, or that there was a sudden rise in indolence and fecklessness from 1979 until 1985, when unemployment began to fall again? Both of these hypotheses are very unlikely, to put it mildly. What causal mechanisms can be put forward to account for these geographical or temporal differences in the will to work?

Given that the level of registered unemployment – itself a very problematic measure – is a reflection of the relationship between the supply of available jobs and the supply of potential workers, it is much more likely that the high levels of unemployment in the north and the inner cities and the increase in unemployment from 1979 to 1985 are reflections of differences in the supply of jobs and the demand for labour than a reflection of differences in the attitude of workers to work. This may seem apparent to you – particularly if you are, or have been, involuntarily unemployed – but it is important to deal with the individualistic argument that unemployment is a result of individual characteristics before looking at variations in economic conditions.

The DoE White Paper refers to the loss of jobs with the closure of traditional industrial firms and the shrinkage in employment in the inner cities. There is a very large body of research evidence in support of this view and Figures 6.6 (a) and (b) show the scale of the rapid decline in manufacturing employment in the large cities and the northern industrial regions from 1967 to 1985. These losses have been most severe in the inner cities where large swathes of manufacturing industry have simply closed down and disappeared since the early 1970s. But this is a description of what has happened rather than an explanation.

Q   Why do you think manufacturing industry declined in the inner cities? Make a list of possible reasons.

A   There is a variety of reasons, most of which are related to the characteristics of manufacturing industry in the inner cities or to the physical characteristics of their factories rather than to the general environmental character of the inner cities. Some of these factors are listed below.

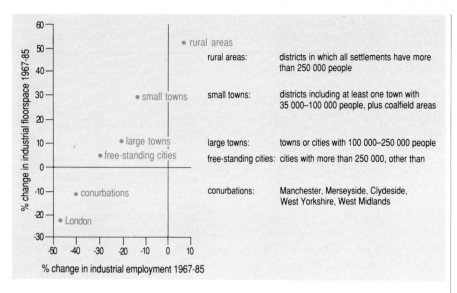

rural areas: districts in which all settlements have more than 250 000 people

small towns: districts including at least one town with 35 000–100 000 people, plus coalfield areas

large towns: towns or cities with 100 000–250 000 people

free-standing cities: cities with more than 250 000, other than

conurbations: Manchester, Merseyside, Clydeside, West Yorkshire, West Midlands

(a)   By type of settlement.

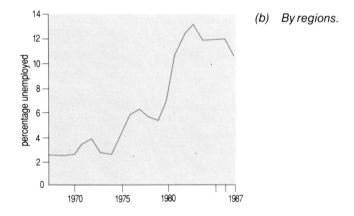

(b)   By regions.

◄   *Figure 6.6*
Changes in manufacturing employment and industrial premises.

1   *Accessibility*. In the nineteenth century, before the advent of the lorry and the car, many factories were located in the inner city to be close to the city centre and railway stations where accessibility was at a maximum for both movement of goods and labour. With the advent of the lorry, the growth of cities and the increase in congestion, there are many advantages in being located on the periphery of the urban area or near motorways. In other words the old locational advantages have disappeared and sometimes become disadvantages.

2   *Changes in production techniques*. Many of the nineteenth-century factories were multi-storey. These are now old and out-dated, and unable to be easily adapted to new conveyor-line production techniques. The production costs in such factories are often far higher than new, purpose-built, single-storey, continuous flow-line factories and they simply cannot compete in cost terms. But rebuilding in the inner city can be difficult and expensive, partly because of the close proximity of buildings and problems

of assembling large enough sites, and partly because of high land costs. New building therefore takes place on greenfield sites in the urban periphery or beyond, where land and building costs are lower. Companies can also often generate large sums if they relocate production and sell their inner-city site for office or housing development.

3   *Labour costs and unionisation*. There is evidence that inner cities are more heavily unionised and labour costs are higher than in suburbs or small towns where it is easier to get cheaper, non-unionised, often female labour. In addition, it is sometimes argued that the right labour skills are not available in the inner cities and that firms can get labour more easily in suburban locations.

4   *Planning controls and rates*. It is sometimes argued that firms have been forced out of the inner cities by the imposition of new planning controls on small factories and workshops and as a result of local authority clearance and redevelopment schemes designed to improve the inner-city environment. In addition, it was argued in the 1980s that small firms were being forced out of the inner cities by high-spending Labour local authorities, high business rates (now replaced by the standard business rate) and a negative attitude to enterprise. While there is some evidence that planning policies and clearance schemes did result in the loss of some firms and jobs, a Cambridge University study in the late 1980s found no evidence that high rates were a significant factor in forcing firms out of the inner cities. And while in the 1970s some Labour inner-city councils may arguably have been anti-enterprise, in the 1980s many have employed business development officers or units to attract and retain employers.

5   *Environmental reasons*. It is sometimes argued that firms are attracted to suburban or rural locations simply because they are more environmentally attractive. There is some evidence for this but it is unlikely that firms would move for environmental reason alone unless the new location offered advantages of accessibility, land or labour costs, or financial incentives as well. Environmental reasons are unlikely to be crucial in isolation from lower production costs or higher profitability.

6   *Industrial structure*. One school of thought suggested that the inner cities lost more manufacturing employment than other areas of the country because they had an adverse industrial structure. This structure, it was argued, was dominated by older, non-growth industries which were more prone to falling demand and job losses. Available evidence does not support this, however (Robson, 1988).

7   *Industrial restructuring*. One argument which found support in the late 1970s and 1980s was that inner cities had suffered badly from manufacturing job losses not simply because of their age or location or facilities, but because their higher relative costs made them particularly prone to closure or rationalisation as a result of falling demand and falling profits. Compared to locations in cheap labour/land areas or in some third world countries, the inner cities are relatively disadvantaged and have either lost out competitively or have been closed down by multi-national firms seeking to reduce or relocate capacity.

It is clear that there is a variety of reasons to explain the loss of inner-city jobs during the 1970s and '80s. Some of them are clearly related to the specific environmental characteristics of the inner city, but the characteristics in question are linked more to the location and historical development of the inner city and to current economic disadvantages relative to other areas.

In the nineteenth century the inner cities were the industrial powerhouse of Britain. The fact that they are no longer is partly a reflection of their earlier success, their ageing and outdated facilities and the changing distribution of population and accessibility in late twentieth-century Britain. The focus of economic growth has moved elsewhere.

4.2   *Physical decay*

There is no doubt that many inner cities are beset by a poor and run-down physical environment. As the White Paper noted:

> The most characteristic single feature of the inner city is the age of its housing. Despite the extensive redevelopment and clearance of slum property since the war, there still remains a great deal of poor quality housing lacking basic amenities, not in good repair and set in a drab environment. In some cities the processes of clearance and redevelopment have got badly out of step.

But these environmental attributes of the inner city are not ones of location per se. They are partly a product of the development process. Most inner-city areas were, almost by definition, built in the mid to late nineteenth century when cities were expanding. The housing is therefore a hundred years old or more. But the age of housing is not an automatic guarantee of a poor environment, as you will realise. Mayfair, Bayswater, South Kensington and Hampstead in London were developed in the eighteenth or nineteenth century and they are highly expensive, desirable residential areas – partly *because* of the age and type of housing. The same is true of parts of Edgbaston in Birmingham, Clifton in Bristol and the New Town in Edinburgh. So there is no necessary correspondence between the location or age of housing and a run-down physical environment. On the contrary, age and an inner-city location characterise some of the most attractive and desirable residential areas in Britain.

Q   Why do you think that many inner-city areas are characterised by poor housing and a run-down physical environment? Make a list of reasons.

A   The answer lies in the nature of the housing and its subsequent history. The areas of poor run-down housing were for the most part built for the working classes in the late nineteenth century. They were often shoddily built and poorly equipped then, and they have declined rapidly since. This physical decline was assisted by the fact that the residents of these areas were generally poor and neither they nor the landlords were in a position to maintain the houses to a high level. Where housing built originally for the middle classes is concerned it has sometimes deteriorated, but this is usually a result of the original type of residents moving out and being replaced by poorer residents, possibly with the houses being subdivided. Where the housing is more recent – post-war council redevelopment – the design and construction have often been defective as a result of the 1960s and '70s' drive to build as many units as possible, as quickly as possible. Taken in conjunction with government subsidies which favoured high-rise and deck-access housing, and pressure to redevelop the inner city at high densities, the result was often the creation of new slums for the working classes to replace the old slums. There is nothing wrong with high-rise housing blocks in principle. Some of the most expensive and exclusive housing in London and New York is in high-rise blocks – the Barbican and Chelsea Harbour in London and Trump Tower in New York. The Barbican was in fact initially built as council housing by the City of London Corporation and has only recently been sold. The issue is more to do with for whom housing was built, the quality of design, construction, maintenance and security, than with high-rise or high densities per se.

The general conclusion I would draw is that poor-quality housing is generally poor quality because it was built cheaply for working-class residents or because good-quality, middle-class housing was filtered down to working-class residents unable to maintain it by virtue of their income. Housing age, location and building type have very little to do with the process of slum creation.

4.3   Social disadvantages

One of the problems referred to by the White Paper was that of 'labour mismatch' – mismatch between the skills of the people and the kinds of jobs available. To the extent that this is true, it raises questions about the reasons for the concentration of less skilled workers in the inner cities.

Q   Why do you think that semi- and unskilled workers are concentrated in the inner cities and some peripheral council estates? Make a list of possible reasons.

A   Several reasons can be put forward to explain this concentration. First, manufacturing industry was traditionally concentrated in the inner cities and poor passenger transport meant that working people had to live close to their work. This was the most important reason historically (Stedman Jones, 1971). Second, a process of selective middle-class suburbanisation began in the mid to late nineteenth century. The middle classes were able to afford better housing on what was then the urban periphery, away from the noise and pollution of the inner city and they could afford the cost of transport. Third, the housing built in the inner cities was often for the working classes, and the middle classes were unlikely to want to live there. Fourth, the building of owner-occupied suburbs in the inter-war and post-war years reinforced the tendency for those who could to move out. As the White Paper notes: 'Between 1966–71 only 15% of net migrants from Birmingham comprised semi-skilled and unskilled workers; from Manchester it was only 16%. Most of those who left were skilled and managerial people.' There is a considerable body of evidence to support this, and selective out-migration is still a major force for urban social change. The main difference today is that the middle classes are now moving away from the large cities altogether to small towns and villages. The result is rapid urban population decline and differential social change. To this extent, the tenure structure of the housing market has a key role, in that there is less mobility out of the council sector than out of owner-occupation and private renting. To some extent, the less skilled and lower paid are trapped in the inner cities, unable to escape to the surrounding owner-occupied suburbs and commuter villages.

Not surprisingly, this concentration of the less skilled and low-paid generates other social problems. The poor performance of many inner-city schools is partly a product of their class composition and the creation of a set of attitudes which do not see advantage in educational qualifications. This is reinforced by the high rates of teacher turnover in the inner cities. As a result of this concentration of social disadvantage in the inner cities, it is possible to postulate the existence of a process of **circular and cumulative causation** by which the concentration of certain problems may give rise to other problems. To this extent it is possible to argue that the inner cities can generate social problems although the root causes lie in differential processes of change in the economic and urban system as a whole rather than in the inner cities in isolation. They are part and parcel of a wider process of uneven development. As paragraph 17 of the White Paper noted:

> . . . [T]here is a collective deprivation in some inner areas which affects all the residents, even though individually the majority of people may have satisfactory homes and worthwhile jobs. It arises from a pervasive sense of decay and neglect which affects the whole area . . . This collective deprivation amounts to more than the sum of all the individual disadvantages with which people have to contend. It is an important argument for tackling inner city deprivation on an area basis . . .

The White Paper is correct that this is an important argument for tackling inner-city deprivation on an area basis, although if the root causes of economic decline and social change lay outside the inner cities it is arguable that area-based policies may only succeed in ameliorating symptoms of decline. But, to the extent that there is a collective social disadvantage in the inner cities this will reinforce the cycle of deprivation which may have its roots elsewhere. To this extent the inner-city environment can generate social problems. But, as I hope has been made clear, the environment is economic and social as much as or more than it is physical.

Activity 6

In the light of the explanations outlined in Section 3, compare the causes given for inner-city decline by Kellner in Box 6.1 with those of the White Paper in Box 6.3. Compare your answer with the one given at the end of the chapter.

4.4   *Policies for the inner cities*

The more impatient among you may be saying 'It's all very well to spend several thousand words dissecting the inner-city problem, but what has been done about it and what should be done about it?' This is an important question, but, as you will appreciate, it is pointless acting without first trying to diagnose the nature of the problem and its causes. Why the government White Paper *Policy for the Inner Cities* was so important was that it recognised that most problems found in the inner cities were the result of forces outside the control of the residents. This is true of economic decline, physical decay and social disadvantage. This is important because the government's previous Community Development Programme, established in the early 1970s, was based on the view that inner-city problems were isolated and local and were primarily problems of breakdown of community spirit and failure of service delivery and co-ordination by central and local government. As a result, the initial policy emphasis of the government's Urban Programme was on community development, the co-ordination of local services and the provision of facilities to improve the social fabric of the inner cities. The problem was seen primarily in social rather than economic terms.

This may seem rather shortsighted in hindsight, but it was not until the CDP research teams challenged this diagnosis, and the Department of Environment's inner-city research studies (1977) identified the key role of manufacturing industry closures and employment decline in the inner cities, that it was realised that many urban economic, social and environmental problems were part and parcel of a wider pattern of economic change which was creating unemployment, urban dereliction and social marginalisation. This shift went further in the mid 1980s with publication of a number of major studies of economic change in the large conurbations. As a result, academic and government perceptions of the causes of inner-city problems became increasingly economic in focus and the policy emphasis shifted accordingly. As Robson (1988) has put it:

> Over the past decade . . . a consensus view has emerged. It sees the problems as being fundamentally economic ones, that unemployment and its associated poverty have provided the seed-bed out of which dereliction, disinvestment, and the social malaise of cities have sprung . . . Social explanations have largely disappeared as prompts to the roots of urban malaise.   (pp. 60–1)

Not surprisingly, the policies pursued by central government have also changed, and there has been a growing stress on the economic regeneration of the inner cities although this has been shaped by the Conservatives' determination that the market and not the state should play a key role in solving the problems. Major programmes of state spending have been rejected in favour of initiatives designed to encourage private capital back into the inner cities. Some of the main ones are listed below.

The Conservative government during the 1980s relied on several policies for economic regeneration. The first was **Enterprise Zones (EZs)** of which 23 were established in inner-city areas between 1981 and 1984. The rationale of Enterprise Zones, which were conceived by Peter Hall, Professor of Geography at Reading University, was to try to foster the kind of economic growth found in Hong Kong, Singapore and elsewhere where controls and taxes on industry were limited and where enterprise could flourish free from government red tape. Industries which located in Enterprise Zones (averaging about 850 hectares in size) were given a ten-year tax holiday from rates and certain business taxes and planning controls, and government statistical requirements were limited. Controversy surrounded EZs from the start, however, and in 1989 the government announced the termination of the scheme on the grounds that other measures were more cost-effective. The principal problem was that a large proportion of firms locating in EZs were not new but were simply moving from nearby to take advantage of the tax breaks on offer. As a result, they were generating very little new employment when the job losses at the old plant were taken into account. One of the clearest examples of this involved the new newspaper-printing plants in the Isle of Dogs EZ in Docklands. They simply moved from Fleet Street, where they sold their old buildings for development, introduced new printing technologies in new automated plants and shed large numbers of jobs. One result was the Wapping industrial dispute in 1988 when redundant newspaper workers picketed *The Times'* new plant. Another criticism of the EZs was that lower production costs were effectively capitalised into higher rents, with up to 60% of financial benefits going into the pockets of landlords.

The second major plank in the Conservatives' inner-city policy was the public–private partnerships designed to encourage private investment on the back of relatively small sums of public money. These replaced the previous central–local government partnerships which were seen as excessively bureaucratic and they included the Urban Development Grant, introduced in 1982, and the Urban Renewal Grant, introduced in 1987. Both schemes were designed to encourage private developers to invest in inner-city regeneration, with pump-priming money from central government designed to lower acquisition and preparation costs of sites and make development profitable to the private sector.

The third major initiative by the Conservative government was the establishment of **Urban Development Corporations (UDCs)**. The objective was to regenerate selected inner-city areas, such as old docks, using central government seed money to improve the infrastructure and attract private investment back into the area. Because their success was seen as being reliant on private sector investment and because the Conservative government believed that Labour-controlled, inner-city authorities were too bureaucratic to get things done and were hostile to enterprise and profits, the UDCs with independent planning and financial powers were imposed from above on local authorities. UDCs are not elected bodies and are not accountable to the local electorate. How far these views were correct can never be proved, but the London Docklands Development Corporation (LDDC), the first and largest UDC, was strongly opposed by the local councils who argued they were being replaced by an undemocratic body. However, more recent UDCs have been welcomed with open arms. Political disagreement aside, the LDDC has been very successful in overseeing the regeneration of Docklands as a major centre of financial services and luxury housing. How successful it has been in terms of providing jobs and homes for local people is another question entirely. Docklands has been transformed from a working-class community to an up-market, yuppie residential area and many local people have been displaced. This transformation has been achieved with the aid of very large sums of central government subsidy to LDDC, and it can be questioned whether Docklands would have 'succeeded' to the extent it has if it had been located anywhere but close to central London.

This is an important question because UDCs have subsequently been set up in an attempt to regenerate key parts of other cities such as Liverpool, Cardiff, Middlesbrough docks and the Lower Don Valley in Sheffield, the historical centre of the local steel industry. In the cases of Liverpool and Cardiff, the intention seems to be the revitalisation of the docks as a post-industrial cultural centre, complete with wind-surfing, cafés and museums. While this may work in terms of attracting people back in, it is questionable whether many jobs will be created. But possibly the role of the UDCs is in their demonstration effect rather than in direct job creation. They may encourage industry and employment into the inner cities, and break down the image of decay and dereliction. Only time will tell whether or not they will be successful or whether they prove an expensive flop.

Glasgow has been remarkably successful of late in promoting a new image of itself as a post-industrial cultural centre. In 1988 it held a successful garden festival in the old docks, following previous festivals in Liverpool (1984) and Stoke on Trent (1986) (on the old steel works site). Further festivals in Gateshead (1990) and South Wales (1992) will result in the landscaped sites then being handed over to private developers. In 1990 Glasgow was named Cultural Capital of Europe for the year. This attention to the image of the inner cities is very laudable, and Glasgow appears to be

▲   The redevelopment of London's Docklands.

attracting many international visitors. But is this enough to counteract the loss of tens of thousands of jobs in steel and shipbuilding over the last few years? Can a new future be built on garden festivals, and a remaking of the image of the nineteenth-century industrial inner cities as environments for living in, or is this no more than a contemporary equivalent of Roman circuses? Perhaps both economic and 'image' policies are needed to regenerate the inner cities. Only time will tell. What is certain is that government inner-city policy during the 1980s has increasingly been based on a view that the environmental and social problems concentrated in the inner cities have their roots in wider processes of economic and social change which extend far beyond the inner cities themselves. The urban problem is now seen in much wider terms than it was twenty years ago. To this extent, the argument that cities cannot be analysed in isolation is now accepted.

Activity 7

Evaluate the prospects for the UDCs in the light of the analysis of the causes of urban problems in this chapter.

Compare your answer with the one at the end of the chapter.

5   Summary and conclusions

This chapter has devoted most attention to the problems of the urban social environment rather than to physical problems such as air and water pollution. These are important issues, but it is also important that you gain an understanding of the social aspects of urban environmental problems. The chapter has focused on two key issues. In Section 2 it addressed the idea that cities are poor or unnatural environments for people to live in and that settlements give rise to a variety of behaviours and problems. Rather than taking you through the empirical evidence for and against the belief, Section 3 concentrated on the writings of some of the early urban theorists who were responding to the new phenomenon of mass urbanisation. Their work is significant because it provided an underpinning for much of the later anti-urban thinking. As with many beliefs, it is important to examine their historical origins if we are to understand them properly. Also examined was the 1970s' argument that modern social behaviour and attitudes are not a product of city size, density or social heterogeneity, but are a result of capitalist urban–industrialism. While it is true that many of the early theorists confused the effects of the urban environment with the effects of contemporary social and economic organisation, the flaw with this view is that it threw the urban baby out with the bathwater and asserted that the only possible causal relationship was between social behaviour and the social and economic system. It also focused entirely on capitalist urbanisation, ignoring the possibility that the causes could lie in urban–industrialism, whether capitalist or socialist.

Section 4 of the chapter shifted the focus from nineteenth-century and early twentieth-century urban theorists to look at the more contemporary question of inner-city problems and their causes. The focus of attention here was on the extent to which these are problems 'of' the inner city or problems which happen to be particularly concentrated in inner cities. It was argued that most so-called 'inner-city' problems were concentrated in the inner cities rather than being unique to them. Economic decline, physical decay and social disadvantage are not found only in the inner cities, though they are particularly concentrated there. This raised questions about the causes of the concentration and the answer outlined pointed to their historical legacy, location and social composition rather than to any direct environmental cause. The inner cities may often look derelict and run-down, but this is a result of their economic and social problems rather than a cause of them. While the concentration of problems in the inner cities can give rise to secondary problems of hopelessness and passivity, it would be a mistake to look for the causes of these problems in the physical environment itself.

As you will realise, the broad thrust of the chapter has been to challenge the idea of physical environmental determinism, and the associated idea that social and economic problems can be solved by physical remedies alone. These may be an integral part of any solution, but they will rarely be a solution in their own right. Rehousing urban slum-dwellers in better houses will improve their housing circumstances, but it will not necessarily improve their economic or social situation. This is not to advocate either a Utopian or a nihilistic position that physical improvements are not worth while because they leave major economic and social problems untouched. Any real improvement is beneficial and should be welcomed, but we must not be seduced into thinking that physical improvements will make any major headway into economic and social problems.

References

DE JOUVENEL, B. (1967) *The Art of Conjecture*, London, Weidenfeld and Nicolson.

DEPARTMENT OF THE ENVIRONMENT (1977) *Inner Area Studies: Summaries of Consultants' Final Reports*, London, HMSO.

DEPARTMENT OF THE ENVIRONMENT (1979) *Policy for the Inner Cities*, London, HMSO.

ENGELS, F. (1969) *The Condition of the Working Class in England in 1844*, St Albans, Granada Publishing.

FISCHER, C. S. (1972) 'Urbanism as a way of life: a review and an agenda', *Sociological Methods and Research*, Vol. 1, pp. 187–242.

GANS, H. J. (1962) 'Urbanism and suburbanism as ways of life', in Rose, A. M. (ed.), *Human Behaviour and Social Processes*, London, Routledge and Kegan Paul, pp. 625–48.

GAULDIE, E. (1974) *Cruel Habitations: a history of working-class housing, 1780–1918*, London, George Allen and Unwin.

GLASS, R. (1968) 'Urban sociology in Great Britain', in Pahl, R. (ed.) *Readings in Urban Sociology*, Oxford, Pergamon, pp. 47–73.

HAWLEY, A. H. (1971) *Urban Sociology: an ecological approach*, New York, Ronald Press.

KERR, C. *et al.* (1962) *Industrialism and Industrial Man*, London, Heinemann.

MILGRAM, S. (1970) 'The experience of living in cities: a psychological analysis', *Science*, Vol. 167, pp. 1461–8.

PARK, R. E. (1925) 'The City: suggestions for the investigation of human behavior in the urban environment', in Park, R. E., Burgess, E. W. and McKenzie, R. D., *The City*, Chicago, The University of Chicago Press.

PICKVANCE, C. (1974) 'On a materialist critique of urban sociology', *The Sociological Review*, Vol. 22, No. 2, pp. 203–20.

ROBSON, B. (1988) *Those Inner Cities*, London, Oxford University Press.

SMITH, L. (1902) 'The influx of population', in Booth, C., *Life and Labour of the People of London* (17 vols), 1st Series, Vol. 3.

STEDMAN JONES, G. (1971) *Outcast London*, London, Oxford University Press.

STUTZ, F. P. AND KARTMAN, A. E. (1982) 'Housing affordability and spatial price variations in the United States', *Economic Geography*, Vol. 58, pp. 221–35.

SZELENYI, I. (1983) *Urban Inequalities Under State Socialism*, London, Oxford University Press.

WILLIAMS, R. (1973) *The Country and the City*, London, Chatto and Windus.

WIRTH, L. (1938) 'Urbanism as a way of life', *The American Journal of Sociology*, Vol. 44, July.

Further reading

HALL, P. (ed.) (1981) *The Inner City in Context*, London, Heinemann.

ROBSON, B. (1988) *Those Inner Cities*, London, Oxford University Press.

SENNETT, R. (ed.) (1969) *Classic Essays on the Culture of Cities*, Harmondsworth, Penguin Books.

Answers to Activities

Activity 1

Q1 They are environmental in that they relate to inadequacies of the city as an environment for its inhabitants. As long as they are imperceptible within London, impacts on the natural environment – such as of rubbish dumped in Bedfordshire or sewage in the Thames estuary – are not Kellner's concern.

Q2 There seem to be four types of problem:
- air and water *pollution* within the city
- decline of the *physical fabric*, such as crumbling sewers, 'sick' buildings
- decline of *public services*, transport, schools, hospitals
- anti-social *behaviour*, such as crime, truancy, aggressive driving.

Q3 The article includes several explicit or implicit explanations:
- 'market forces' resulting in lack of investment and high costs
- out-migration of the better off and more skilled, with consequent reductions in tax income
- government expenditure cuts
- age: the crumbling sewers and many buildings were constructed over a century ago.

Activity 6

Kellner saw the problems of those of physical decay and pollution, declining public services plus anti-social behaviour and the explanations as market forces (leading to lack of investment), government expenditure cuts and selective out-migration. The White Paper saw the problems as job loss, physical decay and social disadvantage, with similar explanations except for any suggestion of a decline in public services being a contributory factor.

When these two views of inner-city problems and their causes are related to the causal structures debated in Section 3, it is also government policies which are least clearly identified. The capitalist economy has built the British inner cities over a century and more, and the restructuring of the capitalist economy has produced the massive loss of manufacturing jobs. But the layout and fabric of the inner cities have become causes of congestion and decay as well as contributors to the way of life which concentrates people with problems in run-down areas. The analyses all seem to agree that the capitalist economy, the physical structure and the way of life all contribute to the inner-city problem – but in themselves they do not indicate how government policy could best be designed to solve the problem.

Activity 7

The concept of the UDCs is entirely consistent with the analysis that the capitalist economy is the root cause of the inner-city problem: it aims to use public funds to pump-prime and to make the inner cities into areas where private investors will want to build offices, factories, shops and housing. It seems a successful strategy for the London Docklands because service employment is growing in London. It may have less potential in areas less attractive to services. However, the means used are largely physical – clearing land, developing transport and communication links and creating a positive image which will attract developers, employers and affluent residents. Little is being done to remedy the social problems of the area. The most likely outcome is what happened in American 'urban renewal' projects of the 1960s – the problem inner-city area was renewed, but the previous inhabitants were squeezed out into other run-down areas. A genuine solution to the inner-city problem would have to tackle the problems of lack of skills, jobs, resources and motivation as well as the physical problems.

1   Introduction

No doubt, you will have read many heart-rending accounts of the poverty in third world cities. You will have seen films about life in the slums of Calcutta or Rio de Janeiro and be familiar with pictures of squalid slum housing, of children living on the streets, of people earning a living on the municipal rubbish dump, of air too polluted to breathe and of water that is poisoned by industrial and domestic waste. From these accounts, you will have gained a picture of the awful physical conditions in which millions of city dwellers lead their everyday lives.

These descriptions are not wrong but neither are they wholly accurate. Often their purpose is to awaken concern among people in developed countries about conditions in the third world. Often they are intended to persuade us to put our hands in our pockets to contribute to some overseas aid project. But, in trying to touch our consciences, they distort reality; they convey a picture of the worst, not of average, living conditions.

The aim of this chapter is to provide a range of information and arguments which will allow you to develop a better understanding both of the environmental problems of third world cities and of the difficulties facing governments which attempt to solve them.

This chapter does not deal only, or even mainly, with the natural environment. Indeed, it will argue that nature is of minor importance. Unlike the countryside, where climate, relief and vegetation have an undoubted influence on human life, the urban environment is largely created by human action. For a start, few jobs have any direct link with climate or relief; the kind of work that people do in different third world cities is not dissimilar – they drive buses, clean shoes or sell newspapers whether it is hot or cold, whether they live in the mountains or on the plains. Equally, there are slums in most cities; the presence of shanty towns seems to have few links with climatic conditions. Of course, nature does intrude on urban lives, sometimes very rudely; earthquakes, floods and other natural disasters all too frequently bring death and destruction. Similarly, the way the natural environment is treated contributes to poor living conditions, particularly the way that humans pollute the air and water. But, unlike the situation in most rural areas, urban conditions are influenced relatively little by nature. What is dominant is the form of economic and social organisation.

Having attempted to define what I mean by the word 'environment', I ought also to explain, or excuse, my use of the term 'third world' (also discussed in Box 1.1). I am using it only as a convenient shorthand for the poor countries in Africa, Asia and Latin America and the Caribbean, the three continents which contain the bulk of the world's poor people. I am using the term interchangeably with equally abused terms, such as less developed countries, and in distinct preference to even more peculiar

◁   *Children scavenging on a rubbish dump in Recife, Brazil.*

phrases such as 'the South' and 'newly emergent countries'. It must be evident that I have little confidence in this popular term. It is clear that the countries contained within the three continents are in no sense a world, for they are in general more closely linked to countries in the first or second world than they are to the rest of the third world. In addition, there is very little in common between many third world countries: China is as different from Chile as Volta is from Venezuela. The only real advantage of my using the phrase is that in general you know what I mean.

Activity 1

Briefly review Chapter 1 of this book and answer the following two questions.

Q   Does the analysis of population change in Chapter 1 support or challenge this view of the heterogeneity of the third world?

A   Chapter 1 supports *both* the pragmatic use of the term third world to distinguish these countries from the different demographic regimes and experiences of economic development in first and second worlds *and* the insistence on the variety within the third world. For example, population growth rates in the third world tend to be higher than in most countries of the first or second worlds, but themselves vary greatly, with much higher rates in Africa and the Near East than in Latin America and Asia.

Q What crucial differences does Chapter 1 identify between urbanisation
    in the third world and that in the first and second worlds?

A First, rates of urbanisation in the third world today are faster than they
    ever were in more developed countries. Secondly, in many countries of
    the third world, high rates of urbanisation occur without significant
    industrialisation.

The wide publicity given to the problems of third world cities raises the
important question: why do millions of people move from country to town if
conditions in the town are so bad? Many commentators have suggested that
these moves are irrational, a pursuit of the bright lights without realisation
of the consequences. This explanation gains little support from the
evidence. Most migrants to the city know what to expect, either from visits
they have made or from relatives who have previously moved. The
explanation is simpler and more brutal: although conditions in the cities are
bad, conditions in the countryside are usually worse.

  If we compare the figures available on most indices of quality of life,
whether it be rates of infant mortality, levels of poverty, or extent of literacy,
there is little doubt that living conditions for the majority are nearly always
better in the cities than in the countryside. In India, for example, rates of
infant mortality in 1981 were twice as high for rural as for urban areas, and in
the Philippines in the mid 1970s they were 50% higher. In Indonesia almost
half of all rural families were living in poverty in 1980 compared to only one
in five in urban areas. In Brazil 42% of rural families were poor in 1974–5
compared with 10% of metropolitan families who were poor and 24% among
other urban families. In the same country there were even greater
differences with respect to ownership of consumer durables. In 1976, for
example, three out of five urban families had a refrigerator compared to only
one in ten in the countryside; two out of three had a television in the city
compared to only one in ten in the rural areas. In Latin America
generally, 62% of rural families are estimated to be undernourished
compared to 26% of urban families.

  The structure of the chapter is as follows. Section 2 describes the
physical fabric of life: the housing, infrastructure, transport and
environment. Section 3 discusses the basic causes of urban problems: the
lack of adequate employment opportunities, the general poverty of these
countries, the uneven distribution of income and wealth, and the nature of
urban segregation. In Section 4 you are asked to consider what it is that
governments should be doing. Should they be stemming the movement of
people from the countryside and slowing migration to the largest cities?
Should they deconcentrate economic activity to smaller urban centres? How
should they go about improving the urban environment? In the process we
shall see that most of the problems are really rather difficult to resolve. We
will also see that many, perhaps most, governments are in practice
surprisingly competent. Although there is far too much corruption and
inefficiency, the real difficulty lies in the scale of the problems they face and
the nature of the political, economic and social systems in which they
operate.

  Finally, Section 5 illustrates the barriers facing one government in its
efforts to tackle major urban problems. The case of Mexico City is used to
explain the principal problems facing the authorities in charge of the world's
largest city and to seek to explain why seemingly obvious steps have not
been taken to resolve those problems.

Activity 2

Although we have included the case study to try to illustrate how a variety of problems occur in one city, the chapter concentrates on analysis rather than what it feels like to live in a third world city. To complement the chapter, go to your local library and find an account of life in such a city. Try to identify what kinds of people live there, what kind of housing they live in, what services they have access to and how they make a living. As you read the chapter, relate the general points it makes to your specific case.

2   The quality of the physical environment

The elements which determine the quality of our physical environment include the structure of the homes we live in, the public services available to us, our ability to get to and from work, the quality of the air we breathe, and the level of physical danger to which we are subjected in our everyday lives. Needless to say, the third world urban poor face a much more hostile physical environment than most of the poor in developed countries. Since there is a much higher proportion of poor people in the third world cities, the implications are clearly serious.

2.1   Housing

Since everyone needs a home and housing occupies by far the largest area of every third world city, the quality of housing is the single greatest influence on our physical environment. And, as the reader well knows, the quality of that housing in third world cities is usually less than adequate. Indeed, low-income housing conditions in most parts of Africa, Asia and Latin America are horrifying to those of us living in developed countries. In India more than three-quarters of all Bombay households lived in one room in 1971 and in Calcutta more than two-thirds. Such a pattern leads to high levels of overcrowding. In Bombay and Madras an average of more than five people occupied every one-room home; the average number of persons per room in India's three largest cities – Calcutta, Bombay and Madras – was well over three per room; in Beijing the average floor space per inhabitant in 1981 was approximately 4.6 square metres. In many cities few homes are provided with adequate infrastructure and services; a majority of homes lack piped water in Ouagadougou (Burkina Faso), Bamako (Mali) and Dar-es-Salaam (Tanzania), a significant minority in many other third world cities. This combination of overcrowding, lack of services and poor-quality construction is a major problem in every third world city.

Overcrowding and poor servicing is in part a consequence of the high cost of accommodation relative to incomes. Most poor families cannot afford to own or rent a decent home. Accommodation in the formal private sector is prohibitively expensive and few governments have been able to build housing on a large enough scale to satisfy more than a small proportion of the urban poor. As a result, most of the poor either crowd into tenement areas, renting rooms with numerous other families, or move into the newly established shanty towns and self-help settlements that surround most third world cities. In practice the proportion renting and owning varies greatly from city to city. As Table 7.1 shows, the great majority of families rent accommodation in Dacca (Bangladesh), whereas the great majority own in Valencia (Venezuela). Even within the same country the proportion of owners can vary considerably. In Mexico four out of five families own homes in Mérida, only one in two in Puebla or Veracruz.

The distinction between owners and tenants is very important but it is becoming of less significance in the sense that all poor families now tend to live in areas of irregular housing. Home ownership among the poor is usually achieved through self-help construction. Increasingly, most tenants also live in consolidated self-help settlements, because there is little room left in the central city areas and because self-help owners are themselves becoming landlords. Indeed, the building of another room for rent is a good way for owners to increase both the value of their home and the family income.

The quality of such self-help accommodation, however, depends crucially upon the conditions in which it is created. For while much of the literature tends to portray self-help housing as being uniformly awful, or in some optimistic cases uniformly adequate, there are huge variations in its quality. The variations depend greatly upon the ease with which owners can obtain land, material and services, something that varies considerably from city to city. (See Plate 13.)

A principal problem is access to land. For while it is often assumed that land is freely available on the fringes of third world cities, this is rarely the case. Certainly there are many examples of poor people organising land invasions on which to build their own homes. In certain Brazilian, Chilean, Peruvian, Turkish and Venezuelan cities, politicians have provided protection for their supporters using land as a source of patronage in exchange for votes and political support. At times such tactics have been used by populist military leaders. However, in many, perhaps most, third world cities, land invasions are not permitted, particularly where peripheral land is held by powerful agricultural families or has a high market value. In such circumstances, the poor have to buy land. The prices are lower than in the higher-income parts of the city: because the settlement lacks planning permission, services are lacking, and the plots also lack title deeds. Even though the transactions are illegal, the plots are sold – and at not insignificant prices. In Bogotá, for example, plots in an illegal subdivision in the late 1970s cost approximately eight dollars per square metre, almost three times the daily minimum salary: a plot of 120 square metres would be equivalent to about fifteen months' earnings. Under such circumstances finding the money to buy a plot was no easy task.

In addition, building materials are often expensive. While it is true that some owners scavenge for discarded material, the sheer numbers of self-help owners mean that most wood, bricks and corrugated iron has to be purchased. Most of the materials are in fact produced by the same companies which supply the formal sector construction industry. Most homes in Latin American 'shanty towns' are not built of cardboard but of bricks and mortar. The materials are obtained from builders' merchants whose prices show an unhealthy tendency to rise relative to incomes. Finally, although much self-help housing is built by the owners themselves, perhaps the majority buy in some kind of help. Many need that help because

Table 7.1
Home ownership in selected third world cities, 1975–85

	Per cent	Year
Ankara (Turkey)	64	1975
Bogotá (Colombia)	57	1985
Brazzaville (Congo)	56	1979
Cairo (Egypt)	31	1981
Caracas (Venezuela)	63	1981
Colombo (Sri Lanka)	56	1981
Dacca (Bangladesh)	22	1973
Islamabad (Pakistan)	38	1980
Istanbul (Turkey)	55	1975
Jakarta (Indonesia)	63	1985
Kabul (Afghanistan)	51	1979
Kumasi (Ghana)	12	1980
La Paz (Bolivia)	43	1976
Lima (Peru)	48	1980
Mexico City (Mexico)	53	1980
Seoul (Korea)	42	1980
Singapore	55	1980
Tehran (Iran)	56	1976
Valencia (Venezuela)	78	1981

Source: United Nations (1985) *Compendium of Human Settlement Statistics, 1982–84*, New York; International Symposium on Housing Organising Committee (1987) *Country Profiles: housing and human settlement conditions*, Yokohama; Abt Associates (1982) *Informal Housing in Egypt* (mimeo); Tipple, A. G. (1988) *The History and Practice of Rent Controls in Kumasi, Ghana*, World Bank, Water Supply and Urban Development Department, Working Paper No. 88-1; Gilbert, A. G. and Varley, A. (1990) *Landlord and Tenant: housing the poor in urban Mexico*, London, Routledge and Kegan Paul; supplemented by the housing censuses of Colombia, Peru and Venezuela.

The data in Table 7.1, like those in the other tables in the chapter, are approximate. One of the problems of working in third world cities is that information is often unreliable and out of date. When comparisons are attempted across countries the problems increase. The availability of data for African countries is generally much worse than that for Latin America. In addition, the definitions used in one country are very different from those in another: the nature of urban areas, slums, unemployment and air pollution are all perceived very differently in different countries.

As a result of these problems the inclusion of cities in the various tables of this chapter has been determined as much by the availability of data as by the appropriateness of the city. Nevertheless, I have attempted to include cities from as wide a range of third world countries as possible. The data have been collected from a wide range of sources, both nationally compiled statistics and those from international organisations such as United Nations agencies, the World Bank and International Labour Organisation, although I have excluded some of the absurd figures that one often sees in official publications. However, for reasons of space these sources are not always referenced.

◀ *Independencia shanty town, Lima, Peru, an area of gradually improving housing: note the drains being laid.*

they lack the skills to do the job themselves. Laying bricks is not a skill that everyone can master, putting in electricity or plumbing systems even less so. And while many households have friends or kin who will do the job for them cheaply, others have to pay the rate for the job – an added drain on already limited budgets.

Despite these barriers, however, there can be no doubt that self-help housing is an architecture that frequently works. What begins as a flimsy hut soon begins to take on the dimensions of a 'proper' house. In Latin American cities, where incomes are generally higher, it is difficult to tell that large areas have been built through self-help. Two-storey dwellings flanking paved streets do not fit most of our perceptions of self-help housing. The bulk of Latin American cities were built in this way. The land may have been occupied through invasion and the process of construction taken several years, but many good-quality houses are the end-result. It is therefore dangerous to assume that self-help housing is always makeshift. Figures on the proportions of housing built in this way are often listed as an indicator of how inadequate housing conditions are. In practice, the fact that 61% of housing in Caracas, 33% in Lima and 46% in Bogotá were built through self-help processes is irrelevant in determining the quality of the housing. It is not who built the house that matters, so much as whether it was built adequately.

2.2 *Infrastructure and services*

Perhaps of greater concern than the poor physical fabric of so many houses is the lack of adequate infrastructure and services. In the poorest and least organised cities, the level of provision for the poor is appallingly low. During the 1970s, 40% of urban households lacked piped water in Egypt, 35% in Morocco, 46% in Mexico, 60% in Jamaica, 62% in Pakistan and 45% in Thailand.

A water seller in Sudan.

Table 7.2   Average time spent per household per day
procuring water in Sango neighbourhood in Ibadan

Time	Per cent
30 minutes	2.0
1 hour	2.0
1.5 hours	4.0
2 hours	7.0
2.5 hours	6.1
3 hours	10.1
over 3 hours	10.2
not applicable	58.6

Source: Egunjobi, L. (1987) 'Disparities in access to urban water
supply: a study of two neighbourhoods in Ibadan', in Makinwa, P. K.
and Ozo, O.A. (eds) The Urban Poor in Nigeria, Evans Brothers,
Ibadan, p. 191.

The effect of poor servicing on living standards is usually serious. First,
the lack of running water means that many families have to spend a
considerable part of their weekly budget on buying water. Such water is
often supplied by tanker trucks which tour the low-income areas.
Sometimes the service is provided cheaply by the local authority, but usually
private companies sell it at a price well in excess of the price charged for
piped water. In Port-au-Prince (Haiti) tankers used to charge poor families
twenty times more per litre than did the water authority. This meant that a
family of five persons without a tap would have to pay around 15% of their
monthly income for water.

    Second, families without piped water or a street tap nearby may have to
spend considerable amounts of time fetching it. In one neighbourhood of
Ibadan (Nigeria), for example, one third of the households spent more than
one and a half hours collecting it: see Table 7.2. The difference between

◀ *Rimac shanty town in Lima, Peru: fetching water from standpipes can be very time-consuming.*

those families with piped water and those without is very marked. This is a particularly serious issue for the women, who are normally responsible for running the home and therefore collecting the water.

Finally, as a result of the cost and the difficulty of obtaining water, per capita consumption tends to be much lower among poorer households. In Pakistan low-income households using water from standposts consume only one-tenth of the amount used by high-income families. Such differentials in use are bound to have major implications in terms of health and cleanliness. In addition, families without piped water are more likely to drink polluted supplies. As a result rates of amoebic dysentery and other forms of water-borne diseases are likely to be much higher.

If the lack of water is a frequent occurrence, the lack of sanitation is still more common. Many cities lack a modern sewerage system or indeed any system at all. Other forms of waste disposal are also a problem and many low-income neighbourhoods simply dispose of their waste in the most convenient place nearby. The modern collection systems which sometimes operate in the high-income areas rarely reach the poor. Low-income areas in Bogotá receive infrequent visits from the rubbish collectors and most settlements suffer from the problems associated with decaying rubbish in the streets. In many cities, and particularly those with many canals and rivers, much of the waste goes straight into the water supply. In the absence of modern systems of sanitation and waste disposal, more traditional methods are sometimes employed. In Cairo the domestic waste of higher-income areas is collected by 40 000 Zabaline households who sell items such as glass, paper and plastic and feed waste food to the pigs that they breed: 'While the system is economically and ecologically sound, it is not without its human cost. Only 40% of all children born to the Zabaline survive the first year' (Khalifa and Moheiddin, 1988; p. 254). Of course, it is not only the disposers of rubbish who suffer; poor health is endemic in poor neighbourhoods lacking adequate services. One study in Porto Alegre, in Brazil, found that the infant-mortality rate was three times higher among the shanty-town dwellers than among the rest of the population.

Fortunately, electricity is less of a problem in most cities and a majority of the population usually has access to supplies. In most Latin American cities, indeed, it is the vast majority who have light in their home. Usually the service is provided legally but many homes are supplied through illegal hook-ups. A local electrician attaches a transformer to the mains system and from there provides his neighbours with illegal supplies. Poles with a tangle of wires attached to them are a very common sight in Latin America. Nevertheless, in cities with very bad electricity supplies, such as most in Africa, even illegal links are difficult to organise as supply lines have to be carried considerable distances.

2.3   *Transportation*

Few reports on the transport situation in third world cities are very positive. Indeed, most commentators seem to take an almost perverse pleasure in arguing that the city where they live or have recently worked has the worst conceivable traffic congestion, the most uncomfortable buses and the highest accident rate in the world. Typical is the comment of one foreign visitor to Calcutta: 'I can say categorically that there is no worse congestion than in Calcutta because speeds could not feasibly go any lower; there is no worse overcrowding of buses and trams because every notch and groove on which to cling is utilized' (Thomson, 1978, p. 247). He may be right but I am sure that travellers in Cairo, Jakarta, Lagos and Mexico City argue that conditions in those cities are just as bad.

If there is a measure of exaggeration in commentaries about third world transport systems, it is clear that the situation in most large cities is deplorable and is often deteriorating. Rising levels of car ownership, the growing numbers of employees trying to get to work, the increasing geographical size of most cities, the lack of adequate investment in transport facilities, and weak controls over private transportation all contribute to a generally worsening situation. As a result, every city faces some form of transport chaos. Admittedly, the causes of the problem often vary: in Caracas, there are too many cars, in Beijing and Shanghai too many bicycles, in Calcutta too few buses, in Lagos too many people walking to work. However, transportation is a real problem everywhere.

The general consequences of poor transport systems are clear in most large cities. First, long journeys to work are a recurrent complaint; in cities such as Calcutta, Lagos, Mexico City and São Paulo journeys of three to four hours per day are not uncommon. As cities grow in size and area, the length of journey and travel time tend to increase.

Second, long journeys are more acceptable if they are at least conducted in comfort. Los Angeles commuters stuck in their stationary cars on the freeways can at least sit and listen to their stereos in comfort. By contrast, the third world traveller is likely to be crushed into a bus standing alongside large numbers of fellow passengers. For example, in Cairo:

> During rush hours (7 am to 8 pm), buses are crammed beyond theoretical capacity, so passengers cling to the outside or sit on the roof or in windows. The city's traffic chaos reduces the speed of the crowded buses, so they never stop. Getting on and off is an art, a sport, and proof of one's spirit. Boarding is to take a running leap and clutch at whatever one can, window or door openings, bumpers, or fellow passengers, who often extend a helping hand. Getting off is the real challenge, requiring what one connoisseur calls the 'flying dismount'.   (Khalifa and Moheiddin, 1988, p. 251)

Travelling is certainly not easy.

▲ *A congested street in Ahredabad, Gujarat, India.*

Third, the discussion of crowded buses assumes that there are buses to board at all. In practice, many cities are desperately short of buses and even shorter of vehicles that actually run. This means that many passengers must walk some distance from their homes to the bus routes and some must walk most of the way. In many cities, the deficiencies of the bus fleet are partially compensated by numerous minibuses or collective taxis. While these are sometimes quicker, that advantage is often negated by higher fares. Elsewhere the bicycle makes up for the lack of buses. In China the bicycle accounts for the bulk of journeys in the smaller cities, up to 60% of journeys in Beijing, and around 30% in Shanghai. While those of us who ride bicycles welcome such figures as a sign of Chinese enlightenment, there is clearly a negative side to the equation – notably the severe bicycle jams that clog Chinese cities and the unpleasantness of cycling during the bad winter smogs in Beijing.

Fourth, the cost of transportation is an important consideration at least for the very poor. Fortunately, transport costs are sometimes subsidised so that long journeys to work are fairly cheap. However, much depends on local circumstances and there are many cities where the government has decided not to subsidise transportation. In such cities, the poor may have to spend a considerable proportion of their income on travel. One survey in São Paulo in 1971 estimated that working-class households devoted 12% of their total budget to transport (Kowarick and Brant, 1978). Such a high proportion is probably atypical. Certainly, in Bogotá, households earning up to three minimum salaries in 1985 spent only about 4% of their income on transport compared with those earning more than 15 minimum salaries who spent 16% (presumably a reflection of the cost of a private car). Similarly, transport was not a major item in the household budget in Colombo, constituting less than 3% of low-income households in the early 1970s.

However, the issue of transportation is still of vital importance to the mass of the population. This is reflected in the fact that so many urban protests have been caused by fare rises. The riots that occurred in January 1989 in Venezuela were ignited by the large rises demanded by privately run bus and minibus drivers. The burning of vehicles was a typical reaction, one that repeated what has happened at some time or another in most third world cities.

2.4   Pollution and environmental degradation

Air pollution is a serious problem in a number of third world cities. In Mexico City pollution levels are supposedly six times higher than acceptable standards and in Manila three to four times higher. However, air pollution is certainly not a problem in every third world city, particularly in those without a great deal of industry. It should also be pointed out that many cities in developed countries suffer seriously from air pollution, largely because they have much higher levels of car ownership and industrial development. As Table 7.3 shows, however, despite high levels of pollution in affluent cities such as Copenhagen, Helsinki, Milan and Zagreb, conditions in third world cities such as Beijing, Delhi, Manila, Santiago, Seoul and Tehran are probably worse.

An important source of air pollution in most cities is the car. In Caracas, vehicles contributed 84% of daily emissions in 1970 and in São Paulo 74%. If the car is massively to blame, however, industry is also a major polluter. In Cairo, the prevailing winds blow either from the north or from the south: 'One brings toxic fumes from the lead and zinc smelters in Shubra al-Khaymah; when the winds shift, they bring poisonous pollutants from the steel and cement factories in the south in Helwan, notable for its myriad of dead trees' (Khalifa and Moheiddin, 1988; p. 253). Elsewhere, the problem is often the source of both industrial and domestic power. In Chinese cities, for example, bad air pollution stems from high levels of coal consumption; coal is the principal generator of industrial energy, it also heats most homes and drives the railway engines. In Shanghai the chronic smog is known locally as the 'Yellow Dragon'. In Seoul air pollution is little better during the winter because coal briquettes are the main source of domestic heating.

Water is also badly polluted in most large third world cities since few possess adequate sewerage and drainage systems, and practically all lack adequate treatment facilities. Most domestic and industrial waste goes straight into the major water courses. For example, in Shanghai:

> The Huangpu may now be the most heavily polluted stream in the world, and it would appear that all aerobic and most other aquatic life had been killed by 1980. Most of the pollution is from industrial wastes, but less than 5 per cent of the city's sewage is treated, and hence something like four million cubic meters of raw sewage enter the Huangpu daily.   (Murphey, 1988, p. 176)

Similarly, in Seoul the Han River is badly polluted by sewage going straight into the river without treatment. In Colombia the Bogotá river receives mostly untreated waste and many of the villages and towns downstream suffer very badly from the pollution. In every city, the cost of waste treatment plants is such that necessary investment is constantly delayed. Some environmental controls have been introduced but most are not strenuously applied.

Table 7.3   Air pollution levels in selected cities (microgrammes/m³), 1982–85

	Peak levels of particulate matter	Peak levels of sulphur dioxide
Developed countries		
Hamilton (Canada)	261	131
New York City (USA)	121	116
Brussels (Belgium)	97	205
Copenhagen (Denmark)	383	135
Helsinki (Finland)	516	103
Athens (Greece)	325	118
Frankfurt (W. Germany)	117	230
Milan (Italy)	n.a.	798
Warsaw (Poland)	248	205
London (UK)	77	171
Zagreb (Yugoslavia)	352	262
Less developed countries		
Rio de Janeiro (Brazil)	230	383
São Paulo (Brazil)	338	173
Santiago (Chile)	402	188
Beijing (China)	1307	625
Shanghai (China)	738	217
Hong Kong	111	143
Bombay (India)	468	85
Calcutta (India)	967	188
Delhi (India)	1062	197
Jakarta (Indonesia)	551	197
Tehran (Iran)	701	467
Seoul (Korea)	n.a.	475
Kuala Lumpur (Malaysia)	353	20
Manila (Philippines)	579	198
Bangkok (Thailand)	741	48

Note: The figures record the highest level registered in the city.

Source: World Resources Institute/International Institute for the Environment and Development/United Nations Environmental Program (1988) *World Resources 1988–89*, New York, Basic Books.

2.5   Natural and other disasters

An important element in the physical environment of many third world cities is the threat posed by natural disasters. Who will easily forget the pictures of the 1985 earthquake tragedy in Mexico City or the floods that engulfed much of Dacca in 1987? When earthquakes, explosions or floods strike urban areas the consequences can clearly be catastrophic. Nevertheless, it is important to remember that far fewer people die in third world cities as a result of major disasters than they do from poor nutrition, lack of decent medical care, or even from road accidents.

It should also be noted that many of the world's greatest natural disasters have hit cities of the developed world. The effects of the earthquakes on Tokyo in 1927 (140 000 dead) and several Armenian cities in 1989 (25 000 dead) were much more costly in terms of life than similar disasters in Agadir (Morocco) in 1960 (12 000 dead), Managua (Nicaragua) (5000 dead) in 1972, and Mexico City in 1985 (10 000 dead). Only the Chinese earthquake in Tangshan in 1976 stands in a class of its own with 242 000 deaths.

If we extend our discussion of urban catastrophes beyond the effects of natural disasters, then the cities of developed countries appear to have been by far the more seriously affected. The simple reason is that these cities have suffered much more seriously from the effects of war. Several major cities in Europe, including Berlin, Coventry, Hamburg, Leningrad, Moscow and Rotterdam, were terribly damaged, and in Japan Hiroshima and Nagasaki were almost completely destroyed. In the third world only Hanoi and Seoul have suffered destruction on a similar scale to the European cities.

It is only when we turn to major industrial disasters that cities in poorer countries seem to suffer more. Major explosions have killed hundreds of people in recent years in Cubatão (Brazil) and Mexico City. And the Bhopal disaster, where the official death toll was 3150 and another 50 000 were totally or partially disabled by the escape of gas from the Union Carbide pesticide plant, stands out in terms of its devastation. Nevertheless, we still need to remember that terrible industrial disasters also afflict cities in developed countries, as the recent experience of the Chernobyl nuclear disaster testifies.

2.6   Summary

Physical conditions in third world cities are often very poor. Housing is often flimsy and services and infrastructure rudimentary. These conditions have a direct impact on health and on living standards generally. Transportation is a further complication, making the journey to work slow, uncomfortable and even dangerous. Air and water pollution worsen the urban environment and natural and industrial disasters constitute a major, if occasional, hazard.

Nevertheless, we should not assume that all cities suffer equally. Living conditions are better in some cities than in others. Urban housing is generally better in Latin America than in Africa or Asia, so too is transportation. Not every city is liable to be hit by earthquakes or floods, not every city suffers from air pollution. Nor should we automatically assume that urban life in developed countries is invariably better. Air pollution in certain rich cities is a major problem and over the years major disasters have affected cities in the developed world much more seriously than those elsewhere.

Activity 3

Review the environmental problems described here and consider whether economic and technological development are causes or cures.

Then compare your answer with the one given at the end of the chapter.

3 *The causes of a poor urban environment*

3.1 *Employment and unemployment*

Probably the greatest source of problems in the third world city is the lack of sufficient well-paid, safe and personally rewarding work. While conditions vary a great deal between cities, it is generally true that the majority of workers are engaged in low-productivity work, many of their occupations are conducted in dangerous environments, and few jobs give the kind of job satisfaction that most people would wish for.

The lack of adequate jobs stems from the nature of the urban economy. Such economies are inserted into the world system in such a way that relatively few third world cities have managed to develop major industrial sectors. Apart from a limited number of newly industrialised countries, notably South Korea, Taiwan, Singapore, Hong Kong, Brazil and Mexico, and a number of giant countries with large manufacturing sectors, such as India and China, few third world countries have developed much industrial employment. More countries have been successful in creating large numbers of adequately paid jobs in the service sector, particularly in the more affluent cities of Latin America and the Middle East. Indeed, in a few countries large numbers of industrial and office jobs have been created in a relatively short period. In Venezuela, for example, half-a-million office jobs were created in the 1970s during the petroleum boom. The pace of **formal sector** job creation, however, has rarely kept up with the rapid growth of the labour force. With large numbers of young migrants moving to the cities, the rate of natural increase in the cities has tended to rise. Today, many African cities are experiencing rises in their populations of around 6% or 7% per annum.

The fact that there are insufficient numbers of formal sector jobs, however, does not mean that the rest of the population is without work. In practice, it is not easy to be unemployed in a third world city. Since few countries have comprehensive social security systems, an unemployed worker is simply not paid. As a result, it is only those with some savings, or with a family who can support them, or those with sufficient qualifications to acquire a well-paid job in the future who can remain without work for long. This is why workers with secondary school education are more likely to be unemployed than those with less education, although workers with advanced education are most likely to have jobs (Squire, 1981). In urban Colombia in 1986, for example, those with no education had an unemployment rate of 9% compared to those with primary education of 11% and those with secondary education 17%; those with tertiary education had a lower unemployment rate of 7%.

As a result, the rates of recorded unemployment in third world cities are much lower than we might expect. In Latin America the severe recession of the 1980s did raise unemployment levels; nevertheless, in few cities are they higher than they were in British cities in 1981: see Table 7.4.

The otherwise unemployed take up other kinds of work. This work is often crudely categorised as forming part of the **informal sector**. This is an inadequate term if only because the sector is so diverse and heterogeneous that any kind of classification is bound to be inaccurate. However, since some shorthand is needed and there is no less misleading term, we will

Table 7.4   Unemployment in selected Latin American and British cities

	Year	Per cent
Bogotá (Colombia)	1988	10.9
Buenos Aires (Argentina)	1987	5.4
Lima (Peru)	1987	4.8
Mexico City (Mexico)	1987	4.5
Montevideo (Uruguay)	1988	9.2
Santiago (Chile)	1988	11.2
London (UK)	1981	9.7
Tilbury (UK)	1981	21.9
Portsmouth (UK)	1981	9.1
Southend (UK)	1981	10.5

Source: United Nations Economic Commission for Latin America (1988) Preliminary Overview of the Latin American Economy 1988, *Notas sobre la Economia y el Desarrollo No. 470/1*; Colombia DANE (1988) *Colombia Estadistica 1988, Bogotá.*

continue to use it. What can be said is that few workers in this 'sector' have secure employment, few have formal contracts, few have social security benefits or health care, and few are covered by government safety or environmental regulations (Bromley, 1979; Moser, 1978).

The informal sector contains most of the badly paid jobs in the third world city. The jobs exist because the poor are forced to work for little reward and because at that low price there is a demand for the product. Many jobs that used to exist in Victorian England, but which most people now generally refuse to undertake, continue to proliferate in most third

▲ *The informal economy: a small 'big wheel' in Madras, India, and children selling souvenirs to tourists in Manila, the Philippines.*

world cities. Occupations such as domestic service, cleaning shoes in the streets, hawking at street corners, prostitution and sorting rubbish are all very common in most less developed countries. There may be few chimney sweeps, but children are very active doing a number of other awful, poorly paid jobs.

It is important to remember, however, that some jobs in the informal sector are well paid: lottery-ticket sellers with a good clientèle, some self-employed taxi-drivers, newspaper sellers occupying a busy site, even successful cocaine dealers. As a result, some informal sector workers have chosen to leave stable jobs in the formal sector. Indeed, this tendency has probably increased during the recession of the 1980s for in cities where the economy has been in severe decline, wage rates in the formal sector have fallen considerably. In countries such as Bolivia, Brazil, Nicaragua and Peru, which have been suffering from hyperinflation, formal sector workers have suffered badly as governments have held back rises in the minimum salary in an effort to control escalating prices. In Nicaragua many government workers are now forced to supplement their badly eroded incomes with informal sector employment. The black market currently generates much higher incomes than office work.

Working conditions are rather bad in both the formal and the informal sectors. Certainly, many managers of large corporations expect their employees to work in dangerous and insalubrious conditions. A Trades Union Congress mission to South Korea some years ago returned very shocked at working conditions in the factories of that country. Certainly, working hours in many third world factories are very long, safety standards are low, and governments do not check working conditions in the way that is customary in most developed countries. But, if conditions in the formal sector are often bad, they are certainly worse in many parts of the informal sector. Watching ten- to fourteen-year-old children selling sweets or oranges at the traffic lights in Latin American cities is a revelation. They hop in and out of the traffic, constantly courting danger in order to sell more. Picking rubbish off the waste tips of third world cities is probably less physically dangerous but obviously constitutes an uncongenial and unhealthy working environment.

In sum, far too much work in third world cities is badly paid, involves long hours and is conducted in a bad working environment. The overall effects on social welfare are obvious. Low wages have knock-on effects in the rest of the city. Long hours affect family life and the ability to improve housing conditions. Poor working conditions lead to a high incidence of accident and disease. The work situation is undoubtedly at the core of most problems of the third world city.

These generalisations, of course, have to be heavily qualified. General working conditions are not the same throughout Africa, Asia and Latin America. The great poverty of Bangladesh, India and Ethiopia is bound to create more awful jobs than is the case in most parts of Latin America. In the latter, for example, most transport is motorised, and therefore most drivers are at the wheel of a bus or a taxi. By contrast, the transport workers of many Indian cities are pedalling their passengers around town; in some cities the rickshaw has still not disappeared. Similarly, in most Latin American cities, construction sites have cranes or at least pulleys; in India, labour is so cheap that even these work aids are often absent: construction sites in Bangalore, for example, may use twenty-five workers to pass cement up to the fifth floor of the building. (See Plate 14.) In Indian cities, men will sit all day in the market offering to change notes into small change, taking a commission of 5% on the exchange.

3.2   Poverty, the distribution of income and urban segregation

The quality of the physical environment is so poor in so many third world cities due in part to the general poverty of the society. In most African and Asian cities a majority of the population are poor and even in the more affluent cities of Latin America, a considerable proportion of the population are living in poverty. In Brazil, for example, immediately after the 'economic miracle' of the early 1970s, 5% of families in Rio de Janeiro and 9% of those in São Paulo were classified by the World Bank as poor – a total of 264 000 families. Today, as a result of the recession the situation is at least twice as bad. If the conditions in affluent Brazilian cities are so bad, they are infinitely worse in poor cities such as Calcutta, Dacca or Ouagadougou.

The Brazilian example should remind us, however, that it is not only the level of income that is important but also how it is distributed that is important. Unfortunately, most third world cities have a highly unequal distribution of income. In Manila, for example, the top 10% of income-earners in 1975 received 22 times the average income of the poorest 10%. In Bogotá the top 5% of income-earners in 1978 received twenty-five times the average of the poorest 20%; in Bangkok the top 5% in 1985 received at least ten times more than the poorest 50%.

The unequal distribution of income in turn fosters social segregation and most third world cities have very obviously rich and poor areas of town. The rich tend to live in affluent surroundings with the best infrastructure and services while the poor are condemned to living in a much less salubrious environment. Table 7.5 provides a not untypical example, showing the variations in living standards between neighbourhoods in Khartoum.

Activity 4

Consider the figures in Table 7.5 and then provide an explanation of the likely causal links between the variables.

Table 7.5   Variations in living standards in selected areas of Khartoum, Sudan

	Manual workers	Literate	Earth floor	Pit latrine	Tuberculosis
First-class extension	0.0	100.0	0.0	0.0	0.0
Shagara	5.6	86.1	27.6	68.0	2.4
Hai Mekki	4.8	89.3	18.2	78.0	0.0
Mahdia	5.8	96.8	2.4	84.0	0.0
Gamaire	44.0	16.8	95.2	0.0	13.2
Jartoum Deims	16.8	67.2	46.4	20.6	7.2
Hillat Khogali	2.0	95.0	25.4	62.0	0.0

Source: Herbert, D. and Hijazi, N.B. (1984) 'Urban deprivation in the developing world: the case of Khartoum/Omdurman', Third World Planning Review, No. 6, pp. 269–71.

It is difficult to establish whether such social segregation has become more or less marked through time. Certainly, it is not a recent phenomenon, for in many African and Asian cities a person's residential area has long been determined by race or tribal affiliation. In Kuala Lumpur the Chinese tend to live in different areas from Malays. Similarly, in racially heterogeneous Indian cities, such as Hyderabad, Muslims, Hindus and Christians tend to live in different areas. In Africa, while racial and ethnic segregation is most obvious in South Africa, it is also apparent in Addis Ababa and certain Nigerian cities such as Kano, Ibadan and Benin. Ethnic segregation became much more marked during the colonial period when separate quarters were established for expatriate staff; the British, the Dutch and, to a less extent, the French had little intention of living with the natives. Of course, such marked European/native segregation disappeared after independence, although it was immediately replaced by another form of differentiation: as the Europeans left, new local élites moved into the exclusive residential areas.

Indeed, throughout the third world, income and social class have tended to become the main determinant of **residential segregation**. Those who cannot afford the large suburban homes, or the cars required to live there, must live in a different part of town. Third world cities are increasingly divided in terms of income. Well-planned and serviced élite and middle-class areas occupy one zone of a city, areas of self-help housing cover most of the rest. With the exception of domestic servants, few poor people live in the same areas as the rich.

Class segregation is one outcome of the development of a capitalist housing and land market. It is also a result of town planning. Planning norms have been established which prevent the poor from moving into high-income areas. Most cities are zoned by class, as well as by land use. Some would argue that segregation of this kind has little to do with good planning practice and everything to do with keeping the poor away from the rich. Support for such a belief is provided by the tendency for planning

▲   *The other face of third world housing: a house in an élite area of Bolivia.*

regulations to be well policed in the high-income areas and largely ignored in the low-income areas. The erection of a hut in a high-income residential suburb is likely to bring instant police action. By contrast, although most low-income settlements are built in areas without planning permission and without the legally required services and infrastructure, the authorities rarely intervene.

3.3   The quality of urban management

Few governments do their job very well; some government agencies are simply incompetent. As a result, holes in the road are not repaired, water systems leak, electricity systems are susceptible to black-outs, buses do not run, and there is a general lack of good policing. City life would be vastly improved if urban management were made more effective.

Unfortunately, that is easier said than done. Many cities, for example, do not even have a single administration to govern them. National and local governments often have overlapping functions and frequently compete with each other for political reasons. Some major cities also lack a single municipal government because they cross local boundaries (see Section 5). Thus responsibility for Caracas, Mexico City and Lima is divided between two local administrations, Guadalajara between three and Lagos between six.

There are numerous other reasons why urban administrations do not work properly. The most common is that they are all very short of money. In part, this is because of the reluctance to levy sufficiently high taxes on industry and the better-off, in part because the tax base is simply too small to provide for the needs of the city. The quality of public officials also leaves much to be desired, often because it is difficult to recruit well-trained people to badly paid jobs.

Poor administration is also due to the fact that few third world cities are democratically governed. In places this is because the national administration is autocratic; elsewhere – and particularly in capital cities such as Brasilia, Delhi, Caracas and Mexico City – it is because the head of the city administration is appointed by the President rather than being elected. Even where both local and national leaders are democratically elected, few systems are entirely fair. Certainly democracy in the sense of allowing people to complain about their living conditions is not common and social protest is strongly discouraged. Throughout the third world many protestors have been tear-gassed, many a head banged by the police. Even where physical means of repression are not used, more subtle means of control, such as co-option and patronage, are employed.

Certainly the exercise of power is rarely dispensed fairly: some are favoured, others ignored. Residential zoning decrees, for example, are likely to be implemented in high-income areas and ignored in poorer districts. Important companies are permitted to pollute air and water close to low-income areas, but not near to the homes of the élite. Élite homes receive planning permission even where they are located in the green belt or occupy land that should not have been sold.

Such abuses often result from corruption. Many building licences are awarded improperly because money is surreptitiously given to the officials. The police in many cities spend more time extracting bribes than trying to catch criminals. But corruption can also occur on a much more spectacular scale. When the centre of Managua was flattened by an earthquake in 1972, the dictator of Nicaragua himself kept most of the foreign aid that was given for rebuilding. Less blatant, but often as damaging to urban interests, is the manipulation of urban contracts. Urban politicians reward their friends in the construction industry, overpriced contracts are agreed, projects are approved that are simply inappropriate to the needs and budget of the city. Many cities are particularly well provided with roads and infrastructure because this has proved to be a rewarding approach for politicians and allies alike.

Indeed, this general line of argument suggests that many of the problems that face major cities are less the fault of bad planning and administration than the outcome of vested interest politics. The failure to act against speculative land-holding, the construction of public housing estates which are inappropriate to the needs of the inhabitants, and the persistence of bureaucratic procedures that waste everyone's time: all can be explained in terms of their income-generating effects for particular officials and their friends. As Kowarick and Brant (1977) have described the situation in São Paulo, there is a 'logic of disorder'. Maladministration is not only the inevitable outcome of the poverty and poor levels of education endemic in such societies, it is part of the way the whole society operates (see Section 5).

3.4   Summary

Perhaps the greatest problem confronting third world cities is the lack of well-paid and secure employment. Far too many people are working long hours to produce little, struggling to earn sufficient to keep the family adequately fed. Unemployment is not generally the problem, for most people have jobs of a kind. In the absence of unemployment benefits the urban poor are too poor not to work; the difficulty is that the only jobs available pay them so little.

Most of these poorly paid jobs are located in the so-called 'informal sector'. Admittedly, many occupations are included within that rather unsatisfactory category which are quite well paid. But, in general, most poor people labour without receiving contracts, social security, or even the legally defined minimum wage. The numbers of such people have undoubtedly increased as a result of the economic recession of the 1980s. Today, the numbers of beggars, street traders and prostitutes have grown noticeably in most third world cities.

Poverty results from poor employment prospects but, of course, not everyone has a low income. Many professional people earn high salaries and live very well. Indeed, the uneven distribution of income is a major cause of further urban problems. It leads to residential segregation, the creation of a poor social environment in many low-income poor neighbourhoods and, possibly, even increases the level of crime.

Better urban management is undoubtedly required. Unfortunately, inappropriately drawn administrative boundaries, poor-quality personnel, inefficient administration and corruption all combine to undermine good government. Perhaps the fundamental problem is that poor government is part and parcel of underdevelopment. Indeed, how can good government be established when the urban tax base is so low, when politics are so unstable, when so many government administrators are so poorly paid? Poor urban management is not due to third world people being incompetent; it is principally a structural outcome of poverty.

4   Approaches to improving the urban environment

4.1   Too many people in the city: stem the tide of migration?

Many of the problems of urban areas are aggravated by the flood of migrants from the rural areas. For this reason many city governments have argued that the pace of urban growth should be slowed. Some slowing would obviously help the authorities accommodate the newcomers and give them time to provide the necessary infrastructure and services. On the other hand, it is clear that rural conditions are often so bad, and the pace of rural population growth so rapid, that potential migrants are difficult to discourage. Certainly, few governments in the third world have had any real success in keeping people in the countryside. In fact, the only effective policies have been implemented in countries with totalitarian governments. China and Cuba have both made migration difficult by controlling access to food, jobs and housing in the cities, Kampuchea under Pol Pot simply closed down the country's capital city, and in South Africa governments have restricted migration through strict application of the pass laws. None of these policies is wholly desirable and even in these countries there are clear signs that governments have recently been forced to ease controls. It is thought that up to 200 million Chinese may move to the cities over the next twenty years.

Clearly, if migration to the cities cannot be controlled, a good case can be made for improving conditions in the countryside. If more investment were to be directed to the rural areas and less to inefficient forms of urban development, many third world societies would benefit. Such an argument is, of course, made by Michael Lipton (1977) who suggests that a process of 'urban bias' is operating in most third world countries. Such bias is not only inequitable but it is also inefficient. Rather than accelerating economic growth at the expense of the poor, it is slowing growth and harming the interests of the majority. More investment in the countryside would be equitable because it would benefit poor people, most of whom live in the countryside. Such a change in strategy would accelerate national economic growth by directing investment into more productive forms of economic activity.

In practice, the argument is less clear-cut. Countries such as South Korea which have a high population/land density, would certainly have problems implementing such a policy and in parts of Latin America rural bias would only be equitable if a major process of land redistribution were introduced first. In any case, it is less than certain that all urban investments are inefficient: would South Korea or Taiwan with their successful export-led industrial policies really benefit from a policy of rural bias?

4.2   Too many people in the big city?

Besides the argument that too many people live in urban areas, many authorities suggest that the cities they live in are too large (see Figure 7.1). Indeed, the case for controls on metropolitan growth is normally linked to the argument that living in these giant cities is very unpleasant. In Mexico City or São Paulo the combination of air pollution, severe traffic congestion,

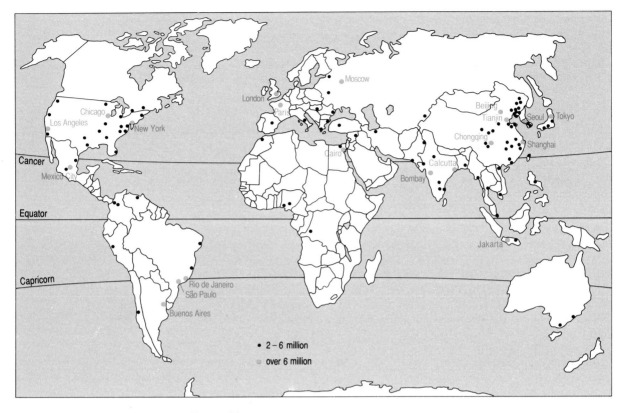

▲   *Figure 7.1   The distribution of large cities.*

long journeys to work, and rising housing deficits make everyday life almost impossible (see Section 6). Some experts argue that the growth of these giant cities should be slowed by redirecting investment towards secondary cities in other parts of the country (Richardson, 1981; Rondinelli, 1983). Sensibly managed growth in these intermediate centres would benefit the whole country.

Unfortunately, the case is easier to make in theory than to apply in practice (see Section 6). Where **urban deconcentration** policies have been applied around the globe, and few governments have failed to do something in this regard, they have rarely been very successful. First, the new cities have not always been very sensibly managed. The large new industrial city of Ciudad Guayana, for example, arguably suffers from most of the evils of Caracas. Despite a major effort at planning, 70% of the population live in self-help housing, many still lack adequate services, and the journey to work is both long and slow. Second, most people living in the metropolitan centres are reluctant to move from their existing homes and jobs. Nor are people in the secondary centres especially keen to receive the metropolitan overspill. Third, decentralisation policies are often very expensive. Not only does a new set of infrastructure have to be created but industrialists have to be tempted to the new locations by generous incentives. Finally, even when industry does move, the new plants have often created few jobs and have accentuated rather than reduced local income inequalities.

Urban deconcentration policies are certainly appropriate in some places, but they are clearly no panacea for the difficulties of metropolitan expansion. Some encouragement should be given to employers to consider alternative locations and, at times, some measure of compulsion should be applied. On the other hand, it is by no means certain that secondary cities always provide better living conditions than metropolitan areas. In Brazil in the mid 1970s, for example, 10% of families in metropolitan cities were poor compared to 24% of families living in other urban centres.

Fortunately, there is some evidence that a process of urban deconcentration has begun to affect the largest third world cities. Industries have begun to move out of Buenos Aires, Mexico City, São Paulo and Seoul, locating in smaller cities within easy reach of their existing markets. Such movement has sometimes been prompted by government action (particularly in São Paulo and Seoul) but it is also a response to the problems that particular companies face in operating in those cities. Perhaps the lesson is that the national settlement system is to some extent self-regulating. Once life in metropolitan centres really becomes insupportable, people begin to move out.

4.3   Improving the urban fabric

Whatever the rights and wrongs of urban deconcentration, the urban fabric needs to be improved. But what specifically should be done to improve housing, transportation and services? How might levels of air and water pollution be reduced?

Housing

The classical remedy for bad housing conditions has always been for governments to build homes for the poor. Such a recipe has been practised in most advanced capitalist and socialist countries. And, while it has increased the availability of housing it has come under sustained criticism in recent years because too much public housing has deteriorated into high-rise slums.

In less developed countries the construction of public housing has long been thought to be inappropriate for a different reason: it is too expensive. If governments build good-quality homes, few families can afford them. If a government reduces the cost through subsidies, then it cannot afford to build many homes. Despite this problem, most governments have invested in public housing, if only as a way of rewarding political supporters and civil servants.

Instead of governments building new homes, the conventional wisdom is now that they should encourage the poor to build their own. The state should confine itself to those problems that the poor cannot resolve for themselves. In short, governments should make land available, build infrastructure and provide services; the poor have shown themselves very capable of building their own homes.

The main problem with this strategy is that few governments have been prepared to confront the critical issue of land supply. Since land prices rise as the urban economy grows, peripheral land often becomes too expensive for poor people. The situation is usually made worse by speculators buying up land close to the urban perimeter. As a result, the cost of land on the periphery has become too expensive even for sites-and-services schemes. If governments buy land at the market price, the poor cannot afford even semi-serviced plots. This is one reason why despite the unanimity about the

*◁ Government-built
housing in São Paulo,
Brazil.*

principle, very few third world cities have invested in sites-and-services
schemes on a large scale.

In practice, most governments adopt an eclectic, ad hoc response to the
housing problem. Governments do upgrade low-income housing areas and
extend infrastructure networks, but they also demolish squatter settlements
and build expensive houses. Their policies are determined by political
realities and by their limited budgets. Providing that the poor are not
making too much fuss, little is done. Only if a political problem arises will
some action be taken to confront it; given sufficient political agitation,
improvements will be made to the water system, notorious land developers
may be arrested, rent controls may be reactivated.

Of course, none of these policies can really touch the core of the housing
problem: low incomes combined with high prices of land and materials.
Sometimes, indeed, government policy merely aggravates the housing
situation. Rent controls, for example, may encourage existing landlords to
sell their property or to adapt it for uses not covered by rent controls.
Perhaps, the lesson to be learned from this experience is that policy is rarely
determined objectively; more often than not housing policy stems from a
political compromise.

Infrastructure and services

For cities to grow efficiently and equitably, the urban authorities need to
establish effective utility companies. Whether these are publicly or privately
run is less important than that such agencies should operate efficiently
(Roth, 1987).

In order to operate effectively, the World Bank argues that companies
need to charge the marginal cost of providing the service. If they do not
generate a surplus, they will be unable to expand capacity, a necessity given
the pace of urban growth. In practice, service charges are rarely raised
sufficiently, investment is cut back to reduce losses, the quality of service
deteriorates, and the government has to provide a subsidy to keep the
company operating. The main problem is that it is the poor who suffer most

from the failure to increase capacity; whereas the rich receive water, telephones and electricity, the poor do not. Government subsidies, therefore, provide services which benefit the rich proportionally more than the poor. That would matter less were it not for the fact that taxation systems in most third world cities are highly regressive. The paradox, therefore, is that the poor pay taxes to subsidise services which they often do not receive (Linn, 1983). Ideally, therefore, companies should cover their costs, be free of general subsidies, but have the ability to increase their capacity to cover the service deficit. They should charge the rich more for the service than the poor, with heavy users of the service being charged premium rates.

Logical though this argument is, it is not always good politics. Most voters are very sensitive to rises in service charges. As a result, few politicians like to raise bus fares or the cost of water or electricity. In the short term this need pose no problem, but in practice one government after another fails to raise the rates. In the longer run, therefore, company losses increase, efficiency declines, and services deteriorate. Large subsidies help produce a government budget deficit which can fuel inflation. Under such circumstances, politicians are then voted out of power because they have provided inadequate services and have failed to control inflation. Short-term political goals have a nasty habit of catching up with society at large.

Improving transportation

Transportation is a critical ingredient in the quality of life. Improving the transport system opens up a wider range of housing and job choices: a family may live in areas distant from where they work; individuals may seek work in places where they do not live. Without such a good transport system, the choice of both jobs and homes is severely limited. Unfortunately, it is very difficult to handle transport problems without adequate controls over the private sector and without reorganising the spatial structure of the city.

Clearly, the pattern of urban land use is critical. As cities grow, more jobs are created in the central city area and increasing numbers of people are forced to travel there each day. Although there are signs that companies begin to move jobs out of the central city as cities grow in size, this decentralisation occurs too slowly to prevent a massive increase in the number of daily commuters. Ideally, government would encourage more jobs to be created in the periphery of the city, allowing people to work closer to home.

Something also needs to be done to control car use. Such a policy is complicated, of course, by the fact that many governments have encouraged car ownership as a means of accelerating industrial growth; the numbers of cars on the road has often risen very rapidly. In Brazil, for example, the number of road vehicles increased from 640 000 in 1960 to 2.5 million in 1970 and 8.2 million in 1980. In Mexico the numbers increased from 1.2 million in 1970 to 4.3 million ten years later. Clearly, most of these vehicles are concentrated in the major cities and contribute massively to traffic congestion. Despite this kind of expansion, few governments have been prepared to limit the use of private cars. Only Hong Kong and Singapore have taken serious measures to tax cars using the central area or to restrict town-centre parking spaces. Even where traffic congestion has reached extreme levels, few governments have done more than order owners of cars with certain number plates to leave their vehicles at home one day per week (for example in Bogotá, Caracas, Lagos and Mexico City).

Clearly, far more investment is needed in mass-transit systems. Unfortunately, when governments have supported transport programmes, they have usually favoured grandiose projects. Huge urban motorway systems have been constructed in Caracas, Rio de Janeiro and São Paulo and since 1954 new metro systems have been built in Cairo, Calcutta, Caracas, Hong Kong, Mexico City, Rio de Janeiro, Santiago and São Paulo. It is highly debatable how successful these schemes have been; what is beyond doubt is that they are fearfully expensive. Arguably, greater controls over private transport and adequate investment in an extensive bus fleet would have been a far more effective approach.

Pollution controls and the prevention of disasters

Most governments would like to take action against pollution, traffic congestion and potential disasters but feel that such action would be too expensive or have undesirable side-effects. Pollution controls, for example, may increase the cost of manufacturing, increasing prices at home and making exports uncompetitive on the world market.

Of course, some governments have taken action: major air polluters have been encouraged to move out of São Paulo and sewage treatment plants have been built in several cities. But, for every success, there have been many failures. Even when legislation is approved, it does not guarantee success. In 1974, for example, the Venezuelan government decreed that contaminating industry should leave Caracas or be closed down. The La Vega cement plant, located in a poor neighbourhood in the south-west of Caracas, was clearly required to leave under this legislation. Despite the law and severe criticism from the national president in 1981, the plant continues to pour smoke over the homes of 300 000 people. The company argues that it has greatly improved the quality of its filtration procedures and that relocation would lead to closure and the loss of one thousand jobs. Its continued presence in Caracas is a classic example of the weight given to economic arguments over those in defence of the environment.

Activity 5

The Secretariat for Urban Development and Ecology (SEDUE) is the ministry in charge of pollution controls in Mexico. This cartoon appeared in 1987 after the SEDUE announced its one-hundred-point plan. Consider the following questions:

Q   Should polluting plants be closed even if this would lead to workers being laid off?

Q   What is the best way of tackling industrial pollution: the threat of closure, required relocation, a tax according to the level of pollution, or what?

Verde Será

('Let everything be green' – or 'Let everything die')

If it is difficult to control everyday problems such as pollution, it is even more difficult to take effective action against irregular hazards such as natural disasters. Given that earthquakes, volcanoes, hurricanes and floods occur infrequently, the danger is all too easily put to the back of the collective mind. As a result, little is done to guard against potential disaster. Low-income housing is not adequately protected against earthquakes and even skyscrapers are not always built properly; in Mexico City the effects of shoddy construction were revealed when many modern hotels and public buildings collapsed during the 1985 earthquake. Shanty towns built on the hillsides in Caracas regularly suffer from landslides during the rainy season. Similarly, despite the rules and regulations, illegal housing areas develop around factories in most third world cities. With luck, no serious consequences arise. The occupants suffer from noise and pollution but otherwise life carries on as usual. Unfortunately, not every settlement has such luck and in recent years there have been several terrible industrial accidents. In Bhopal slums housing many thousands of people were devastated when methyl isocyanate gas escaped from the Union Carbide pesticide plant in December 1984. Were land-use controls more effectively policed, there would be far fewer major disasters. On the other hand, there would also be far fewer families with a roof over their head.

Perhaps the lesson is that the very structure of third world cities makes the prevention of natural disasters very difficult. Given the cost of introducing adequate measures and the inefficiency, and even corruption, of most state machines, most people are always going to be susceptible to danger. If people continue to suffer from malnutrition and disease on a daily basis, what hope can there be that they will be protected from occasional floods and tempests?

4.4   Summary

Perhaps there are too many people moving to the cities. But, action to stem the tide will not be popular – and has rarely proved effective. The alternatives are to improve rural conditions but even this may be ineffective if rapid population growth continues. Urban growth seems to be inevitable.

If urban growth is inevitable, then should action be taken to direct migrants into cities of manageable size? Certainly, many governments have introduced policies to this effect, although few seem to have managed it very successfully. While there have been numerous attempts at regional development, and even the construction of new capitals, few have been an outstanding success.

It is obvious, though, that all cities should be managed more efficiently and equipped with better services and infrastructure. Transportation systems should be dramatically improved and local authorities should take action against pollution and the danger of industrial accidents or natural hazards. But such action is expensive or has unpopular side-effects: closing polluting industries may lead to local workers losing their jobs. Installing services may require the raising of tariffs and the removal of subsidies. Not surprisingly, politicians are wont to take the easy or the short-term option.

5   Mexico City: how on Earth can such a monster be managed?

5.1   The problems facing the city

Some 19 million people live in Mexico City today compared to 'only' 14 million in 1980. And, if the pace of demographic growth has slowed a little, continued migration and a high rate of natural increase still promise to add many millions more during the 1990s. Needless to say, a city so large, and located in what is still a relatively poor country, faces many seemingly insurmountable problems. (See Plate 15.)

Housing conditions for many are difficult: 40% of families live at densities of more than two persons in a room; 25% live in a house with only one room. Service provision is inadequate although by third world standards certainly not disastrous. Virtually every home has electricity and most homes are supplied with drinking-water, even if some are served by water tankers rather than by taps. Sanitation is much less satisfactory, with the homes of nearly two million people lacking mains drainage in 1980. Poor sanitation, linked with a deficient garbage disposal system, poses a major health and pollution problem.

The transport situation is also very serious in part because of the dramatic increase in the number of road vehicles, a legacy of the petroleum boom of the 1970s. Today, there are 2.7 million road vehicles in the city compared to only 248 000 in 1960. While road projects were given high priority during the 1970s, they could not absorb such a huge expansion in traffic. As a result, the congestion is awful: it is estimated that during the much extended rush hour the average vehicle speed is only 16 km per hour. Admittedly Mexico City has had a well-run metro since 1969, a system which accounted for 29% of all the city's vehicular journeys in 1983. Nevertheless, the trains are bulging at rush hour and long queues form outside the principal stations. While major extensions are being planned, those areas of the city which lie outside the Federal District are currently not

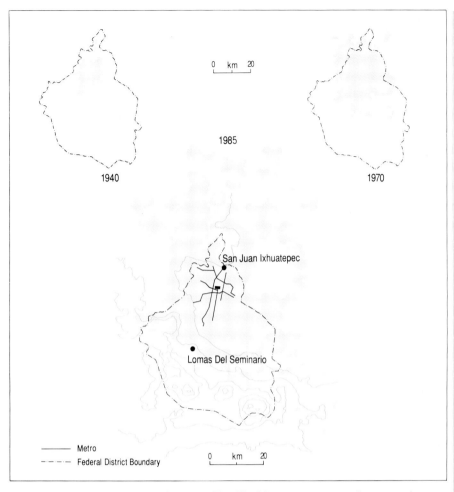

San Juan Ixhuatepec

Lomas Del Seminario

0   km   20

1985

1940

1970

——— Metro
–––– Federal District Boundary

0   km   20

▲ *Figure 7.2   The growth of Mexico City. The Metro system stretches more than 100 km and serves about 4 million commuters every day.*

linked into the network (see Figure 7.2). Many poor families living in those areas are forced to travel to the metro stations on heavily congested buses and minibuses. In a major survey of 76 500 households in 1983, it was found that every individual was travelling, on average, 52 minutes per day.

Huge numbers of road vehicles also contribute to another of Mexico City's major problems: air pollution. The density of suspended particles in the air is over 5½ times that permitted in Canada, the quantity of sulphur dioxide over 4 times higher, and levels of carbon monoxide almost 3 times higher. The subsequent smog is particularly noticeable during the dry half of the year when a deep temperature inversion combines with major duststorms to reduce visibility and make walking in many parts of the city both unpleasant and dangerous. (See Plate 16.)

Mexico City's air also suffers from the pollution produced by oil refineries, power stations and cement plants located within the metropolitan area. Such plants are not only a major inconvenience for the local communities, they also represent a real source of danger. This was demonstrated in November 1984 when the nationalised petrol company's liquified gas storage plant exploded. Situated in the northern neighbourhood of San Juan Ixhuatepec (see Figure 7.2), the plant was located close to a populous area of self-help housing. When the gas exploded, 452 people were killed and approximately 1000 homes destroyed.

If the human contribution to Mexico City's physical dangers were not sufficient, nature occasionally gives a further hand. Floods are a recurrent threat but the major problem is earthquakes: the city has been struck 122 times since 1460. In 1985, of course, a serious tremor reduced parts of the city to ruins. Even though only 5% of the urban area was affected, the result was disastrous. The authorities have never produced a satisfactory estimate of the number of victims, but a total of 10 000 deaths is sometimes cited and one estimate suggested that as many as 60 000 may have died. At least 45 000 homes were destroyed or damaged beyond repair, schools accommodating 40 000 pupils were devastated and several major hotels and public buildings were destroyed; it is estimated that 40% of the city's hospital beds were put out of action.

Another factor which has to be borne in mind when considering the City's problems, is the background of Mexico's economic situation. Like most third world countries it has chronic debt problems, actually defaulting in 1982. In fact it is the second-largest debtor (after Brazil) with $102.6 billion outstanding, with interest payments representing 27.3% of the value of its exports. Like most countries, it is not always clear where the massive loans taken out by successive governments actually went, but the result is a huge debt liability which hampers economic recovery. In order to service the debts, which have to be paid in foreign currency, either imports have to be cut back or goods diverted from the home market into exports. Spending at home has to be depressed through high interest rates and taxes. The result has been a reduction in output, and living standards which have fallen sharply below their level at the beginning of the 1980s. Thus, although Mexico renegotiated its debts and new loans at the beginning of 1990, it remains in a financially difficult situation, particularly given its increasing population.

▲   *After the earthquake in Mexico City in 1985.*

5.2   Managing the city

Most articles written about Mexico City berate the incompetence of the government. Certainly, there is no lack of evidence to support the claim that the administration is less than efficient and is sometimes positively corrupt. Competent government is made more difficult by the way the city is divided into two separate administrative areas. Ten million people live within the Federal District while a further nine million are spread over seventeen municipalities in the neighbouring State of Mexico. Ideally, the metropolitan area would be run by a single authority but any kind of merger would be fraught with political difficulty. In any case, how can we British criticise Mexico City for lacking an integrated urban administration when we have recently abolished the Greater London Council and the major metropolitan authorities?

Most criticism of the Mexican authorities also ignores the facts that over the years they have actually accomplished a great deal. It should not be forgotten that during the 1970s five million people were added to the city's population and somewhat more than that during the 1980s. Any city in the world would have difficulty in managing such a huge addition to its population. How would London, say, have managed had it been obliged to cope with even an extra couple of million inhabitants in a ten-year period?

Despite its rapid growth the quality of service provision was generally maintained and, in some respects, actually improved. The proportion of homes with piped water increased from 60% in 1970 to 69% in 1980 and the proportion of homes without mains drainage fell from 25% in 1970 to 14% in 1980. Transport provision improved with metro extensions, important new road programmes and major expansions to the bus fleet. While these efforts could clearly not resolve the problems, the pace of population growth was such that it would have defeated most governments.

Nevertheless, the city's response to two major problems – water supply and air pollution – has clearly been inadequate. In both cases the situation is now very serious. However, it must be stressed that the inadequacy of the response lies less in the nature of the government's policies than in the conflicts that the resolution of those problems would engender. Indeed, the following paragraphs will seek to demonstrate that the problems are well-nigh insoluble given the existing political and economic circumstances.

Water supplies

Most of the city's water is pumped out of the subsoil. Unfortunately, too much water is extracted and in consequence parts of the city are sinking: the famous Palace of Fine Arts in the city centre is sinking several centimetres each year. Everyone in the city knows that this situation cannot continue for ever and yet little has been done to control the rate of extraction. Admittedly, water is brought from outside the Valley of Mexico, with 24% of the city's water coming from the Lerma valley to the west and a further 5% from the Cutzamala basin to the south-west. The problem with this alternative source is that it is expensive to pump water up to Mexico City and currently requires the operation of 102 pumping stations. While the present supply is adequate, the head of public works for the Federal District was recently quoted as saying the future situation is 'terrible': there are simply no projects under way to increase the supply.

One seemingly obvious alternative is to save some of the water that is currently lost within the city. At present, losses through leaks, poor accounting and illicit tapping accounts for about 30% of the total supply.

Certainly, this strategy is current policy, the President having announced it
in July 1989. Unfortunately, such an approach will have been made more
difficult by the authorities' recent efforts to charge users the full cost of
supplying the water. However sensible such a policy, it encourages major
users to falsify their accounts; it is estimated that 45% of industrial and
commercial users currently pay the lower domestic supply tariff. Should the
savings strategy fail, as indeed it has in the past, the only real alternative is to
tap other more distant sources of supply. However, this is not a desirable
alternative for two reasons. First, the most obvious sources are the
Temascaltepec well, over 100 kilometres to the south-west, or to pump
water up 1000 to 1200 metres from the Aracuzac, which would be an
expensive solution. Second, any water diverted to the capital will reduce the
possibilities for irrigation in the surrounding valleys. Since agricultural
self-sufficiency is also one of the government's objectives, providing Mexico
City with water may also cut the capital's supply of food.

Air pollution

Air pollution appears to be a still more intractable problem. Perhaps this was
why the authorities took so little action for so many years. It was not until
1987 that the Ministry of Urban Development and Ecology introduced a
one-hundred-point plan to help reduce pollution. Towards the end of the
year, the Minister was already claiming reductions in the amount of sulphur
dioxide, lead, and suspended particles found in the air. He also claimed that
the government was spending much more on environmental protection.

In fact, it is difficult to control the main sources of air pollution without
setting in train a series of problematic side-effects. Attempts to control the
pollution caused by motor vehicles would be vigorously opposed by the
motor industry and indeed by those in government concerned with
stimulating economic growth. The rapid growth of the motor vehicle
industry has contributed considerably to Mexico's manufacturing
production during the last twenty years. Now that vehicle production has
been cut by the recession, both management and unions would react
vigorously against any suggestion of controls on production.

Admittedly some action has been taken to control vehicle use and to
improve the quality of exhaust emissions. In November 1989 all private
car-owners in the city were prohibited from driving their cars on one day
each week. While this has cut the number of cars on the roads every day, it is
already clear that total journeys have declined far less; people drive more
during the other days of the week. In addition, during 1990 a programme
was introduced requiring every vehicle to be checked twice annually for the
quality of its exhaust.

Stronger measures might be taken against the principal industrial
polluters, which now contribute around 30% of the total air pollution.
Efforts to impose controls on the pollution caused by these plants are clearly
required but they will be bitterly contested. If production costs rise, and are
passed on to the consumer, this will add to inflation. Since Mexico
experienced very serious inflation during the 1980s – the annual rate reached
159% in 1987 – the last thing that the government wants is further
inflationary pressure. If the plants are encouraged to move, both unions and
companies will object. If they are encouraged to move through the offer of
incentives, it will work against the aim to cut public expenditure.

A further source of pollution is the dust which blows across the city
during the dry season. This problem has been accentuated in recent years by
the amount of soil erosion and deforestation occurring on the edge of the
city. Unfortunately, it is difficult to control the rate of deforestation without

slowing the pace of suburban development, the principal way in which the majority of the population has been housed during the past three decades. Affluent suburbs and areas of self-help housing have both spread inexorably outwards from the city centre (see Plate 16). While everyone recognises that urban sprawl brings problems, to stop this process will slow the shift to home ownership that so many Mexicans expect and desire. Admittedly, the government has begun to take action. Between 1982 and 1988, 3202 hectares were designated as territorial reserves to be used for future urban development in the State of Mexico. Of this total, about two-thirds had actually been acquired. Within the Federal District, the main policy was to increase housing densities by preventing extensions to the built-up area. The obvious corollary of this policy has been to control the illicit occupation of land and in November 1988, a large settlement in Lomas del Seminario (see Figure 7.2) was removed by the police. Officially 1000 families were removed although community leaders claim that up to 5000 families were living there. However necessary such controls may be, there is a high social cost to be paid.

In sum, therefore, however necessary it is to control air pollution, it will not be easy to improve the situation without a great deal of political conflict.

5.3   The case for deconcentration

Given Mexico City's rapid growth and its seemingly insoluble problems, it is not surprising that recent Mexican governments have all espoused the goal of urban deconcentration. During the 1950s and 1960s they established river basin commissions to stimulate agricultural development in the regions. They have also tried to encourage industrial deconcentration, offering tax incentives to companies wishing to locate outside the metropolitan area and established 131 new industrial estates throughout the country. In practice, such schemes have had only limited success; more and more activity has continued to locate in the greater Mexico City area.

When the earthquake struck in 1985, however, it seemed to give renewed strength to the decentralisation campaign. The President and his ministers began to speak of the opportunities that the earthquake had given to the country. Meetings were held to discuss how decentralisation could be encouraged. The government announced that many of its own officials would be moved out to cities such as Aguascalientes, Cuernavaca, Toluca and Veracruz (Figure 7.3).

In practice, rather little has happened. Although the government has claimed that 62 000 federal employees were moved during the 1982–88 sexenio, it is probably less than that. The only major government office to have been substantially decentralised is the census authority, to Aguascalientes. Other expected moves, such as the Navy Ministry to Veracruz and the Agrarian Reform Ministry to Cuernavaca, seem to be proceeding rather leisurely.

One reason why deconcentration has proceeded so slowly is the cost. Moving government offices is an expensive business at least in the short run. New offices have to be built in the provinces, workers have to be helped to move to the new locations, and there is the cost of physically moving the files and equipment. While, in the longer term, government buildings in the capital can be sold, during the current recession this is less easy. Indeed, the recession is a major barrier facing the deconcentration programme. With the government cutting back its expenditure, there is little money for moving offices and employees.

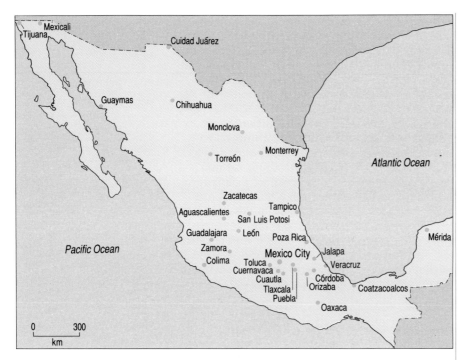

▲ Figure 7.3   Mexico: major cities. Mexico City is by far the largest city in Mexico, with over 9 million in the Federal District, and about 19 million overall, with the next largest cities being Guadalajara at 3.2 million, Monterrey at 3 million and Puebla at 1.7 million; other Mexican cities are less than 1 million.

Second, in so far as decentralisation has been attempted, it has proved less than popular among the employees involved. Officials complain that adequate housing is difficult to obtain in the provinces. They also point out that many employees have working husbands or wives who will be unable to obtain jobs in provincial cities. Government workers thinking about moving are also deterred by the hostile reaction given to the first 'evacuees'. In Guadalajara graffiti appeared on the walls, enjoining true citizens to do their duty, the approximate translation of which would be 'Kill a Cockney a day'.

Third, the damage inflicted by the earthquake meant that considerable sums of money had to be spent in Mexico City. Although the government might have decided not to rebuild housing and offices in the devastated areas, they soon came under pressure to take immediate action. Tenants' organisations mobilised large protests in the city's main square, marches were directed towards the Presidential palace. As a result, the government agreed to rebuild 45 000 homes in the centre of the city. The cost of this programme, however successful it may have been, reduced the budget available for decentralisation.

Fourth, the political circumstances have certainly not been propitious. Since 1985 the government has certainly not been very popular with the electorate and lost heavily to the opposition parties in the 1988 elections. The state of disaffection was also reflected in the way that President de la Madrid was booed at the opening ceremony of the World Cup in 1986. As a result, there was great concern among members of the President's party, the PRI, that they might soon lose control of a number of state governorships.

Normally, their reaction would have been to spend money in those states convincing the electorate to vote for them. But the ability to spread government patronage was already being cut by the recession.

Even if there had been total support for decentralisation, such a huge programme would have had cataclysmic effects on the provinces. Most of the provincial cities face service and housing deficits at least as serious as that of Mexico City. If large numbers of government workers had been added to their existing populations, their situation would have become very difficult. Indeed, the numbers of people involved would have completely swamped most provincial cities.

6   Conclusion

Physical conditions in third world cities are not good, and in the poorest cities the majority live in a generally unhealthy physical environment. These poor conditions are not primarily the consequence of nature but of the way in which cities have been developed. For the third world, urban environment is an outcome of an unequal world. Poor urban conditions merely reflect the poverty that is manifest throughout these countries; social inequalities are a reflection of the general unfairness found throughout their societies. Rural poverty leads to urban poverty as migrants move to the cities to escape from still worse conditions in the countryside. A shortage of decently paid jobs brings urban poverty. Urban poverty leads to bad housing, deficient services and a polluted environment.

As a consequence, there is no simple way to improve the urban environment. Poor countries do not have a great deal of money to spend on improvements and building new dams to provide water and electricity, buying more buses to carry people to work and introducing new technology to cut pollution levels are expensive. Nor is it easy to slow the pace of urban growth or to reduce the rate of metropolitan expansion; to take either path will require major changes in society.

Improvements would be easier to achieve if governments were fair and competent. Unfortunately we cannot assume that third world governments are greatly concerned with the living conditions of the majority. After all, many are not democratically elected and many others follow policies which favour vested interest groups. Not only are governments partial, they are sometimes inefficient. But, while it is obvious that a better urban environment cannot be produced without better government, that is not an easy task. Corruption, favouritism and bureaucracy are a way of life in many third world societies, they continue not because people do not realise the negative consequences but because that is the way in which government traditionally operates. Without such methods nothing would get done at all.

Of course, such an argument is not very optimistic. Perhaps the only hope is that there are a few cities, particularly in the Far East, which are beginning to confound this interpretation. These may, however, be exceptions, born of a strange combination of rapid economic growth, efficient state control, lively private enterprise, and societies imbued with

Confucian values. Elsewhere, the signs are that conditions will deteriorate further before they will get better; a glance at economic growth rates in Africa and Latin America is testimony to that. If that interpretation is correct, then we must be patient and must ponder the idea that the only long-term method of improving third world urban environments is to re-think the nature of technological and economic development so that they provide better living standards without adverse environmental impacts. These changes are the concern of Books Three and Four of this series.

References

BROMLEY, R. (ed.) (1979) *The Urban Informal Sector*, Oxford, Pergamon.

DOGAN, M. and KASARDA, J. D. (eds) (1988) *The Metropolis Era*, Vol. 2, *Mega-cities*, London, Sage.

KHALIFA, A. M. and MOHEIDDIN, M. M. (1988) 'Cairo', in Dogan, M. and Kasarda, J. D. (eds), pp. 235–67.

KOWARICK, L. and BRANT, V. C. (eds) (1978) *São Paulo 1975: growth and poverty*, London, The Bowerdean Press.

LINN, J. (1983) *Policies for Efficient and Equitable Growth of Cities in Developing Countries*, London, Oxford University Press.

LIPTON, M. (1977) *Why Poor People Stay Poor*, London, Temple Smith.

MOSER, C. (1979) 'Informal sector or petty commodity production: dualism or dependence in urban development', *World Development*, No. 6, pp. 1041–64.

MURPHEY, R. (1988) 'Shanghai', in Dogan, M. and Kasarda, J. D. (eds), pp. 157–83.

RICHARDSON, H. W. (1981) 'National urban development strategies in developing countries', *Urban Studies*, Vol. 18, pp. 267–83.

RONDINELLI, D. (1983) *Secondary Cities in Developing Countries: policies for diffusing urbanization*, London, Sage.

ROTH, G. (1987) *The Private Provision of Public Services in Developing Countries*, London, Oxford University Press.

SQUIRE, L. (1981) *Employment Policy in Developing Countries: a survey of issues and evidence*, London, Oxford University Press.

THOMSON, J. M. (1978) *Great Cities and their Traffic*, Harmondsworth, Penguin Books.

Further reading

DOGAN, M. and KASARDA, J. D. (eds) (1988) *The Metropolis Era*, Vol. 2, *Mega-cities*, London, Sage.

GILBERT, A. G. and GUGLER, J. (1989) *Cities, Poverty and Development* (2nd edn), London, Oxford University Press.

GILBERT, A. G. and WARD, P. M. (1985) *Housing, the State and the Poor: policy and practice in Latin American cities*, Cambridge, Cambridge University Press.

GUPTA, A. (1981) *Ecology and Development in the Third World*, London, Routledge and Kegan Paul.

UNITED NATIONS CENTRE FOR HUMAN SETTLEMENTS (HABITAT) (1987) *Global Report on Human Settlements 1986*, London, Oxford University Press.

WARD, P. M. (1990) *Mexico City*, London, Belhaven.

Answer to Activity

Activity 3

As suggested in the book introduction, economic and technological development seem on the one hand to offer cures for problems of housing, services and pollution (because higher living standards would allow provision of piped water, sewage treatment and sounder buildings) but on the other hand are the causes of some of the worst problems, from air pollution by car traffic to accidents and polluting industry. Development is too general a term to be helpful. What matters is the form of development.

Acknowledgements

Grateful acknowledgement is made to the following sources for permission to reproduce material in this book:

Covers

Front cover, clockwise from top right: Stephen Best; Dr. David Snashall; Ed Buziak/Farming Information Centre, NFU; Farming Information Centre, NFU; Ed Buziak/Farming Information Centre, NFU; David Sims/ICCE; Roy Lawrance; Martin Bond/Environmental Picture Library; Alan Gilbert; *centre:* J.Goodman/Farming Information Centre, NFU; *back cover:* Information Service of the European Community.

Colour plate section

Plate 1: Patrick McClay/OXFAM; *Plate 2:* Sally and Richard Greenhill; *Plate 3a:* Steven C.Wilson/ENTHEOS; *Plates 3b and 4:* Mark Boulton/ICCE; *Plates 5 and 6:* Sally and Richard Greenhill; *Plates 7 and 8:* Tony Stone Photolibrary, London; *Plate 9:* Copyright © Geoffrey Sinclair/Environment Information Services; *Plates 10 and 11:* Peak District National Park; *Plate 12:* Aerial Photography by Chorley and Handford; *Plate 13:* Rio Branco/Magnum Photos; *Plate 14:* Alan Gilbert; *Plate 15:* Copyright © John Goldblatt/Mexicolore; *Plate 14:* Copyright © Alicia Sanchez/Mexicolore.

Figures

Figure 1.2: R. G. Barry and R. J. Chorley (1968) *Atmosphere, Weather and Climate,* Methuen & Co; *Figure 1.6:* A. Wood and J. Clarke *et al.* (eds.) (1984) *Population and Development Projects in Africa,* Cambridge University Press; *Figure 1.7(a):* A. Findlay and A. Findlay (1987) *Population and Development in the Third World,* Methuen & Co.; *Figure 1.7(b):* R. Woods (1987) *Theoretical Geography,* Methuen & Co.; *Figure 1.8:* from *New Internationalist Calendar 1987.* Copyright © 1982 The Population Division of the Department of International Economic and Social Affairs of the United Nations Secretariat; *Figure 1.9:* A. Findlay and P. White (1986) *West European Population Change,* Croom Helm; *Figure 1.10:* A. Gibb (1988) 'The demographic consequences of rapid industrial growth', *Occasional Papers,* 24, Department of Geography, University of Glasgow; *Figure 1.11:* A. Findlay and A. Findlay (1987) *Population and Development in the Third World,* Methuen & Co; *Figure 2.1:* Reproduced with permission from Professor P. D. Harvey, Literary executor of the late Professor C. D. Darlington; *Figure 2.3:* from *Physical-Geographical Atlas of the World; Figure 2.4:* P. E. Lydolph (1985) *The Climate of the Earth,* Rowman and Littlefield; *Figure 2.5: The Times Atlas of the World,* copyright © 1968, Bartholomew; *Figure 3.3:* Illustrations by Patricia J. Wynne from M. S. Swaminathan, 'Rice', in *Scientific American,* January 1984, International Edition; *Figure 3.5:* Illustration by Andrew Tomko from M. S. Swaminathan, 'Rice', in *Scientific American,* January 1984, International Edition; *Figure 4.1:* Erlichman, J., Consumer Affairs Correspondent, *The Guardian,* © James Erlichman, 1989; *Figure 4.4: Countryside Commission News,* Part 23 (1986) and Part 29 (1987), Countryside Commission; *Figure 4.6:* CAB International, Wallingford, Oxon; *Figure 4.12:* 'Countryside Conflicts' from 'In', 1986, Gower Publishing Ltd; *Figure 4.13:* Institute of Terrestrial Ecology, © NERC, 1987; *Figures 4.14 and 4.15:* Guardian News Services Ltd; *Figure 5.1:* Based upon the 1975 Ordnance Survey 1:1250 000 with the permission of the Controller of Her Majesty's Stationery Office © Crown Copyright; *Figure 5.3:* UK Centre for Economic and Environmental Development; *Figure 5.4:* based on information supplied by Chris Amos, New Settlements Research Group, University of Loughborough; *Figure 5.5:* Nigel Moor & Associates, Stone Hall, Wallingford, Oxon; *Figure 5.6:* Countryside Commission; *Figure 5.7: The Sunday Times* © Times Newspapers Ltd; *Figures 6.3 and 6.4:* from Inner Cities Directorate, DoE, *Information Note No. 3 on the Comparative Position of Inner-city Partnership Areas,* 1983, reproduced with the permission of the Controller of Her Majesty's Stationery Office; *Figure 6.6:* from the book *Those Inner Cities* by Brian Robson, Clarendon Press, 1988, by permission of the Oxford University Press; *Figure 7.1:* mapped from material compiled by The Economist, 1987; *Figure 7.2:* adapted from *Mexico City: The Production and Reproduction of an Urban Environment* by Peter Ward (1990) by permission of Pinter Publishers Ltd. All rights reserved.

Photographs and cartoons

p.9: (left) Courtesy of the Royal Danish Ministry for Foreign Affairs/Foto: Lars-Kristian Crane, *(right)* Maggie Murray/Format; *p.19:* © D.Ross/OXFAM 1984; *p.21:* Punchline by Christian *New Internationalist*, © Christian 1988; *p.25: (both)* Maggie Murray/Format; *p.27:* © Andes Press Agency/Carlos Reyes; *p.30:* The Glasgow Room, The Mitchell Library, Glasgow; *p.31: The Independent/*Brian Harris; *p.32:* Alan Gilbert; *p.44:* Maggie Murray/Format; *p.47: (top)* Institute of Agricultural History and Museum of English Rural Life, University of Reading, *(bottom) Farmers' Weekly* Photo Library; *p.48: Farmers' Weekly* Photo Library/Peter Allen; *p.58:* Sharma Studios; *p.69:* © Andes Press Agency/Carlos Reyes; *p.73:* Courtesy of Professor R.B. Bryan, Soil Erosion Laboratory, Scarborough College, University of Toronto; *p.74:* Jeremy Hartley/ OXFAM; *p.76:* Christian Aid; *p.77:* Jeremy Hartley/OXFAM; *p.80:* © Patrick Sutherland; *p. 81:* Punchline by Christian *New Internationalist*, © Christian 1989; *p.100:* © Andes Press Agency/Julian Filokowski; *pp.102, 112, 119 (left):* Sally and Richard Greenhill; *p.119 (right):* Sally and Richard Greenhill/Society for Anglo-Chinese Understanding; *p.129:* Sheila Gray/Format; *p.133: Farmers' Weekly* Photo Library; *p.144:* Czech Embassy; *p.145:* Steven C. Wilson/ENTHEOS; *p.149: (both)* © Patrick Sutherland; *p.154: (top) Farmers' Weekly/*Keith Huggett; *(bottom) and p. 155 : Farmers' Weekly/*Charles Topham; *p.156:* Colin Molyneux/ Farming Information Centre, NFU; *p.157:* © Thelwell; *p.163:* © Patrick Sutherland; *p. 165: (both)* © Richard Denyer; *p.152:* © Thelwell; *p.178:* S. & O. Mathews Photography; *p.182:* Ramblers' Association; *p.185: (top)* Forestry Commission, *(bottom)* © Fay Godwin; *p.186:* Forestry Commission; *p.191: (bottom)* CEGB Photo Library/Nuclear Electric plc; *p.194:* © Thelwell; *p.195: (both)* Peak National Park; *p.199:* S. & O. Mathews Photography; *p.203:* The Rural Development Commission; *p.207: (both)* Peak National Park; *p.212:* © Richard Denyer; *p.220:* The Glasgow Room, The Mitchell Library, Glasgow; *pp.221, 224, 225:* Gustave Doré and Blanchard Jerrold, *London: a pilgrimage*, Grant & Co., 1872; *p.241:* Gavin Robertson; *p.251: (top left and right)* Maggie Murray/Format, *(bottom)* Jenny Matthews/Format; *pp.257, 262, 263, 264:* © Andes Press Agency/Carlos Reyes; *p.266:* Robert Harding Picture Library; *p.271: (top)* Alan Gilbert; *(bottom) and pp. 274, 280, 282:* © Andes Press Agency/Carlos Reyes; *p.283:* reproduced from *Proceso*, No. 576, 16 November 1987, p. 5; *p.286:* Foto Marco A. Cruiz/IMAGEN-LATINA/Mexicolore.

Tables

Table 1.2: J. Coward (1986) 'Fertility patterns in the modern world', in M. Pacione (ed.) *Population Geography: progress and prospects*, Croom Helm; *Table 1.4*: from *Population Change and Economic Development 1985*. Copyright © 1984 by The International Bank for Reconstruction & Development/The World Bank. Reprinted by permission of Oxford University Press, Inc; *Table 1.5*: from *World Resources 1986*, A Report by The World Resources Institute and The International Institute for Environment and Development. Copyright © 1986 by The World Resources Institute and The International Institute for Environment and Development. Reprinted by permission of Basic Books, Inc., Publishers, New York; *Tables 2.1 and 2.2*: FAO (1986) *Production Yearbook*, Vol. 40, Food and Agriculture Organisation of the United Nations; *Table 2.3*: D. B. Grigg (1986) 'World patterns of agricultural output', *Geography*, Vol. 71, The Geographical Association; *Table 2.6*: FAO (1977) *The State of Food and Agriculture*, 1976, Food and Agriculture Organisation of the United Nations; *Table 4.1*: Duckham, A.N. and Masefield, G.B., *Farming Systems of the World*, Chatto & Windus, 1971; *Tables 4.5, 4.6, 4.7*: Spath H.J. in Turner, B.L. and Brush, S.B (eds) *Comparative Farming Systems*, New York Guildford Press, 1987; *Table 7.2*: Makina, P.K. and Ozo O.A. from *The Urban Poor in Nigeria*, Evans Brothers (Nigeria Publishers) Ltd, 1987; *Table 7.3*: from *World Resources, 198/89* by The World Resources Institute, The International Institute for Environment and Development, in collaboration with the United Nations Environment Programme. Copyright © 1988 by The World Resources Institute, The International Institute for Environment and Development and United Nations Environment Programme. Reprinted by permission of Basic Books, Inc., Publishers New York.

Text

Box 6.1: Kellner, P., 'A capital example of British rot', *The Independent*, 1989.

Index

(Page numbers in *italics* refer to figures, tables and photographs.)